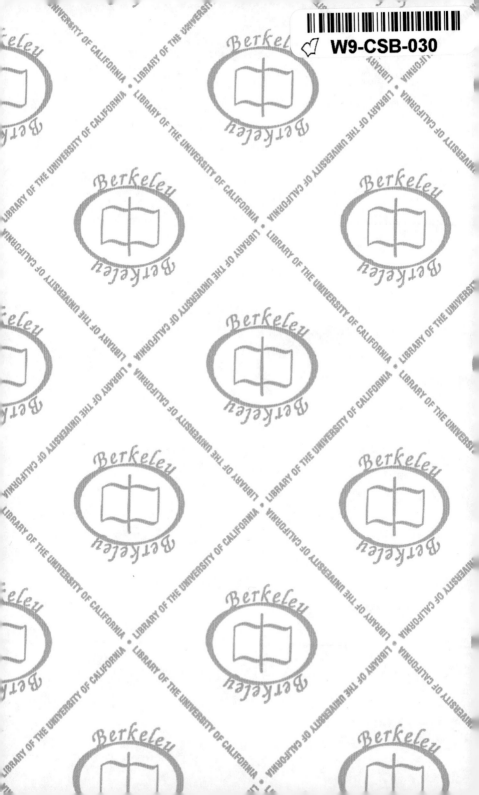

MODERN DEVELOPMENTS IN
FLUID DYNAMICS

MODERN DEVELOPMENTS IN
FLUID DYNAMICS

AN ACCOUNT OF THEORY AND EXPERIMENT
RELATING TO
BOUNDARY LAYERS, TURBULENT MOTION
AND WAKES

Composed by the

FLUID MOTION PANEL OF THE
AERONAUTICAL RESEARCH COMMITTEE
AND OTHERS

and edited by

S. GOLDSTEIN

in two volumes

VOLUME I

NEW YORK
DOVER PUBLICATIONS, INC.

TO

THE MEMORY OF

HORACE LAMB

*This book has been composed by the Fluid Motion
Panel of the Aeronautical Research Committee
with the collaboration of*

V. M. FALKNER, B.Sc., A.M.I.Mech.E.

L. HOWARTH, B.Sc., M.A., Ph.D.

L. ROSENHEAD, Ph.D., D.Sc.

H. C. H. TOWNEND, D.Sc., F.R.Ae.S.

The Members of the Fluid Motion Panel are

L. BAIRSTOW, C.B.E., D.Sc., A.R.C.S., F.R.S., F.R.Ae.S.

A. FAGE, A.R.C.S., D.I.C., F.R.Ae.S.

S. GOLDSTEIN, M.A., Ph.D., F.R.S.

B. M. JONES, C.B.E., A.F.C., M.A., F.R.Ae.S.

A. R. LOW, M.A., A.M.I.E.E., F.R.Ae.S.

E. OWER, B.Sc., A.C.G.I., F.R.Ae.S.

E. F. RELF, A.R.C.S., F.R.S., F.R.Ae.S.

L. F. G. SIMMONS, M.A., A.R.C.S., A.F.R.Ae.S.

R. V. SOUTHWELL, M.A., F.R.S., M.I.Mech.E., F.R.Ae.S.

H. B. SQUIRE, M.A., A.F.R.Ae.S.

G. I. TAYLOR, M.A., F.R.S.

For when propositions are denied, there is an end of them, but if they bee allowed, it requireth a new worke.

The Essaies of S^r. Francis Bacon
London, 1612

PREFACE TO THE DOVER EDITION

It is both a pleasure and a privilege to write a prefatory note to the Dover edition of *Modern Developments in Fluid Dynamics*: a privilege, since the work is already a classic, and a pleasure, because the new edition will make it more readily available for students. When a new edition was contemplated, many instructors and other workers in fluid mechanics were approached, and the general opinion was that there is still a steady and continuing demand for the work, and that a cheaper edition was particularly desirable. It is clear that the work, which was dedicated to the memory of Horace Lamb, does indeed provide an enduring memorial.

It is nearly thirty years since the material for these two volumes was compiled and the authors and editor began to write the chapters. In the intervening period, considerable and significant advances have been made in many aspects of knowledge of fluid mechanics. In particular, mention may be made of the remarkable advances in the theory of isotropic turbulence and in the applications of singular perturbation methods which have extended the mathematical theory of laminar boundary layers. Inevitably, certain sections of the work have been overtaken by subsequent developments, and if they were written today, these sections would be very different and much longer: an example is Chapter V, which was written very near the time of the birth of the ideas leading to the theory of isotropic turbulence mentioned above. However, it seemed best to leave the text largely in its original form, since any attempt to bring it really up to date would have changed its character and bulk, robbed it of its simplicity, and delayed the appearance of the new edition. A few changes have been made in Chapter V, where statements appeared which later developments have shown need emendation; the only other changes made in the text are corrections of minor errors and misprints. Substantially, therefore, the work is upwards of a quarter of a century old; but in view of the fundamental nature of its contents, the title *Modern Developments* is still appropriate.

The two volumes of *Modern Developments* were among the first essays of the Aeronautical Research Committee (later the Aeronautical Research Council) in sponsorship of textbooks as distinct from original research papers. Since few books dealing with the behaviour of real fluids were then available, the time chosen was most appropriate; so also was the editor. Besides contributing as an author, Professor Goldstein spared no effort to make the work as a whole homogeneous, accurate, and lucid; his success is evidenced by the continuing demand for the work which has led to the appearance of this new edition. It gives very great pleasure to his many friends that he has himself supervised the preparation of the new edition.

A. R. COLLAR,
Chairman, Aeronautical Research Council.

November, 1964

PREFACE TO THE FIRST EDITION

PROBLEMS of the flow of fluids are of great interest and complexity, and the practical importance of their solution is very wide. The study of the flow of fluids in pipes and channels, and of the transfer of heat from solids to fluids, for example, is of importance in nearly every branch of engineering. The study of turbulence is not only of direct interest to aeronautics, but is indispensable for the advance of the sciences of meteorology and oceanography. But the chief incentive to explore such problems in recent years has been provided by the study of the practical problems of flight.

In May 1930 the Aeronautical Research Committee appointed a Fluid Motion Panel, and gave it the responsibility of encouraging and initiating general researches in hydrodynamics of direct or indirect interest to aeronautics. The Committee has had the advantage of the help of many distinguished men of science in the course of this work, among whom must be specially mentioned the late Sir Horace Lamb, who will always be remembered gratefully by those who knew and worked with him. The present book was started at his suggestion. It makes no pretence to provide an exhaustive account of all modern advances in hydrodynamics, but only to present and summarize methods of experiment and development of theory in certain branches of hydrodynamics of special interest to aeronautical science. The book does not deal with the potential flow of inviscid fluids or with the trailing vortex theory of aerofoils, except to summarize the results of work recorded in other books, nor does it discuss problems of compressibility, which have recently become of practical interest to aeronautics. On the other hand, the book is concerned with the laminar and turbulent flow of viscous fluids, particularly near and at the surfaces of solids and in wakes, and with transfer of heat in laminar and turbulent flow. Modern theories of such flow are fully discussed; exact mathematical solutions of particular types of flow are given, when possible, and approximate methods for the solution of more general cases are developed. The experimental results and illustrations of theory are naturally mainly of aerodynamic interest, but technical applications are avoided.

The book has been written by many authors, but an attempt has been made to make the account connected. The name of Dr. Hermann Glauert does not appear in the list of collaborators; his premature death in August 1934 deprived the Panel of a colleague whose ability was outstanding. Sir Horace Lamb originally undertook the general Editorship, but when he was compelled to relinquish this task it was entrusted to Dr. Sydney Goldstein. If the book fulfils its object of meeting the needs of those who are primarily interested in the physical and engineering aspects of fluid flow, as well as those who are engaged on its mathematical study, this will be largely due to the work of Dr. Goldstein.

H. T. TIZARD.

Chairman, Aeronautical Research Committee.

EDITOR'S NOTE TO THE DOVER EDITION

It has been suggested that some later texts might be mentioned for the benefit of newcomers to the subject working alone. A complete list is not possible here, and the task of selection is an invidious one. The following list is not intended to bring the reader to the boundaries of published knowledge of fluid mechanics in all directions.

Modern Developments in Fluid Dynamics: High Speed Flow. Edited by L. Howarth. Clarendon Press, Oxford, 1953. (Two volumes.)

Incompressible Aerodynamics. Edited by B. Thwaites. Clarendon Press, Oxford, 1960.

Laminar Boundary Layers. Edited by L. Rosenhead. Clarendon Press, Oxford, 1963.

These three works were sponsored by the British Aeronautical Research Council, which sponsored the original edition of the volumes here republished.

L. D. Landau and E. M. Lifshitz. *Fluid Mechanics* (translated by J. B. Sykes and W. H. Reid). Pergamon Press and Addison-Wesley, 1959. (Vol. 6 of Course of Theoretical Physics.)

S. Goldstein. *Lectures in Fluid Mechanics.* Interscience, 1960.

H. Schlichting. *Boundary Layer Theory* (translated by J. Kestin). McGraw-Hill, 1955.

M. Van Dyke. *Perturbation Methods in Fluid Mechanics.* Academic Press, 1964.

C. C. Lin. *The Theory of Hydrodynamic Stability.* Cambridge University Press, 1955.

G. K. Batchelor. *The Theory of Homogeneous Turbulence.* Cambridge University Press, 1953.

J. O. Hinze. *Turbulence.* McGraw-Hill, 1959.

SYDNEY GOLDSTEIN.

November, 1964

EDITOR'S NOTE TO THE FIRST EDITION

My thanks are due to all collaborators for their co-operation, to Mr. Ower, Dr. Howarth, and Mr. Squire for assistance to myself and the authors in reading proofs, to Mr. Ower and to Mr. W. S. Brown for assistance in making the indexes, to Mr. Ower for the checking of references, and to the staff of the Clarendon Press for their assistance and courtesy in the very difficult task of getting the book into print.

S. GOLDSTEIN.

CONTENTS

VOLUME I

I. INTRODUCTION. REAL AND IDEAL FLUIDS.

II. INTRODUCTION. BOUNDARY LAYER THEORY.

III. THE EQUATIONS OF VISCOUS FLUID FLOW.

IV. THE MATHEMATICAL THEORY OF MOTION IN A BOUNDARY LAYER.

V. TURBULENCE.

VI. EXPERIMENTAL APPARATUS AND METHODS OF MEASUREMENT.

Section I. Wind Tunnels, Water Tanks, and Whirling Arms.

Section II. Velocity and Pressure Measurements.

VOLUME II

VIII. FLOW IN PIPES AND CHANNELS AND ALONG FLAT PLATES (continued).

SECTION III. TURBULENT FLOW.

IX. FLOW ROUND SYMMETRICAL CYLINDERS. DRAG.

X. FLOW PAST ASYMMETRICAL CYLINDERS. AEROFOILS. LIFT.

XI. FLOW PAST SOLID BODIES OF REVOLUTION.

Section I. Spheres.

Section II. Airship Shapes.

XII. BOUNDARY LAYER CONTROL.

XIII. WAKES.

XIV. HEAT TRANSFER (LAMINAR FLOW).

PLATES

ACKNOWLEDGEMENTS

THE FLUID MOTION PANEL wishes to record its indebtedness for the assistance it has had from a number of sources in obtaining material for many of the illustrations in this book. The Panel wishes particularly to express its thanks to Professor Prandtl for the trouble he has taken in providing photographic prints from which Plates 7–8 (from a dissertation by Dr. H. L. Rubach (see footnote † on page 63)), 10*a*, 12, 19*a* and 31–2 (from a dissertation by Dr. F. Homann (see footnotes ‡ and † on pages 551–2 respectively)) and 33–4 (from a paper by Professor O. Flachsbart (see footnote † on page 553)) have been prepared. Acknowledgements for a large number of other illustrations which have appeared in Professor Prandtl's works are given in footnotes, as are also the sources of, and acknowledgements for, many of the other illustrations. The Panel is also greatly obliged to the following for the provision of prints and negatives, and for permission to reproduce them: Mr. W. S. Farren for Plates 5*b* and *c*, 13, 14*c*, 19*b* and 21*b*; The Royal Aeronautical Society for Plates 5*a*, 10*b*, 14*a* and *b*, and 15–16. Thanks are also due to the Controller of H.M. Stationery Office for permission to reproduce a number of plates and diagrams from Stationery Office publications; the source of each such reproduction is acknowledged in the text.

ABBREVIATIONS

THE following abbreviations are used throughout the book:

A.R.C.: Aeronautical Research Committee.

D.V.L.: Deutsche Versuchsanstalt für Luftfahrt.

N.A.C.A.: National Advisory Committee for Aeronautics (U.S.A.).

N.P.L.: National Physical Laboratory.

R.A.E.: Royal Aircraft Establishment.

INTRODUCTION. REAL AND IDEAL FLUIDS

1. Real and ideal fluids.

IF we imagine a surface S drawn in a fluid, then forces are exerted between the portions of the fluid close to S on its two sides, these sets of forces being equal and opposite, in the nature of an action and reaction. The set of forces on the fluid on one side of S is equivalent to a force and a couple, and this is true for any portion of S. We assume, however, that the resultant force exerted over a vanishingly small area is ultimately proportional to the area: that is, that the ratio of force to area has a definite limit when the area shrinks up to a point; and it follows that the ratio of the couple to the area must ultimately vanish. We can, therefore, specify the intensity of the action at any point of the surface by the limit of the ratio of force to area; this may be called the force per unit area at the point, and is, by definition, the stress at the point. This stress may, in general, be in any direction. For a fluid at rest it is normal to the surface, and is in the nature of a pressure. For fluids in motion, however, tangential stresses occur. The existence of these tangential stresses constitutes the phenomenon known as viscosity or internal friction in fluids.

Similarly, if S is a surface of contact of a fluid with a solid body, forces are exerted between the parts of the solid body and the fluid close to S, and there is a resultant force and couple on the body, and a stress at any point of its surface. Now consider any portion of a vanishingly thin layer of fluid next to the solid body. Its inertia is vanishingly small, and therefore the forces acting on it must be in equilibrium. The resultant of the body forces (such as gravitation) which act on it is also vanishingly small. Hence the forces exerted on it across a portion of S must balance the forces exerted on it across its surface of separation from the remainder of the fluid. But the forces exerted on it across a portion of S are equal and opposite to the forces exerted on the body across the portion of S. It follows, by taking the portion of S in question to be small, that the stress on the surface of the solid body at any point is the same as the stress at a neighbouring internal point of the fluid. Thus if the fluid and the solid body are at rest, the solid body will be subjected to normal pressures only; but if the fluid is in motion, there will also be tangential stresses on the solid body, giving rise to the phenomenon called skin-friction.

Neglect of the internal tangential stresses for a fluid in motion leads to the theory, very highly developed mathematically, of the so-called ideal or perfect fluid. There is, however, another fundamental difference between a real fluid and the ideal fluid of that theory. At a surface of contact of an ideal fluid and a solid body continuity requires that the normal velocity of fluid and solid should be the same, but there is a relative tangential velocity, or velocity of slip. In a real fluid, on the other hand, there can be no relative velocity at all at such a surface, the velocity of the fluid in contact with the solid being exactly the same as that of the solid itself.† This impossibility of slip persists no matter how slightly viscous the fluid may be.

The existence of tangential stresses and the impossibility of slip constitute, then, the differences between a real fluid and a theoretically ideal one. In this book we are concerned with the motion of those fluids whose viscosity is small: the phenomena in such motions sometimes approximately agree, sometimes violently disagree, with the predictions of ideal fluid theory; and the explanation of such agreements and discrepancies is one of the first objects of the book. For such an explanation, both the impossibility of slip and the existence of internal friction (no matter how small) must be taken into account.

2. The measure of viscosity.

If a shaft of circular cross-section is placed centrally within a rotating circular tube, so that a narrow annular space is left between the two cylindrical surfaces, and if this space is filled with any fluid, either gas or liquid, then there is a tendency for the shaft to rotate on account of the rotation of the tube and the friction of the fluid, and a torque is required to hold the shaft stationary. This torque is found to be proportional to the relative velocity of the two surfaces. It is also inversely proportional to the distance between the surfaces, so long as this distance is small compared with the radii. With given values of the relative velocity and the distance, the torque will have a value depending on the nature of the fluid; and its magnitude is a measure of the viscosity of the fluid.

† See the note on pp. 676–680.

The conditions in this experiment approximate to the ideal (but less easily realizable) conditions which are postulated in the definition of viscosity given (following Maxwell[†]) in most text-books of physics: 'The viscosity of a substance is measured by the tangential force on the unit area of either of two horizontal planes at the unit of distance apart, one of which is fixed, while the other moves with the unit of velocity, the space between being filled with the viscous substance.'[‡]

It is implied in this definition that if a stratum of fluid, of thickness a, is contained between two horizontal planes of indefinite extent, one (AB) fixed and the other (CD) moving from C to D with velocity u, then when the fluid in the

different parts of the stratum has taken up its final steady velocity, the tangential force exerted on an area S of either plane, from A to B on the lower plane and from D to C on the upper, is $\mu Su/a$, where μ, the measure of viscosity, is independent of u, S and a, depending only on the nature of the fluid. The tangential stress is then $\mu u/a$, where u is the relative velocity of the two planes or of the layers of fluid in contact with them.

Now the tangential stress at any point of a plane, in a fluid moving everywhere in the same direction parallel to the plane, can depend only on the motion in the neighbourhood of the point. Hence we are led to replace the relative velocity and distance of the two layers by differentials, and to write $\mu du/dz$ for the tangential or shearing stress in such motions, where u is the velocity of a layer at a distance z from a fixed point, measured perpendicular to the layers, and μ is a characteristic constant for each fluid, which, in all simple fluids, is independent of du/dz. (The restriction that the layers should be horizontal, put into the definition originally in order that the motion might be unaffected by gravity, may now be removed, since the tangential stress in a shearing motion cannot depend on gravity.)[||]

[†] *Theory of Heat* (London, 1871), p. 278.

[‡] The experiment above, with a coaxial cylinder system, is not, in fact, the best experiment for the measurement of viscosity; but more accurate methods are less suitable illustrations of the definition. The most widely used method is that in which fluid is forced through a circular tube of small diameter, and the viscosity deduced from the volume discharged in a measured time, the pressure fall along the tube, and its dimensions. See § 6.

[||] The idea of a formula such as this was first given by Newton in the 'Hypothesis'

Since a stress is a force per unit area, it follows that the dimensions of μ are $[ML^{-1}T^{-1}]$. In the centimetre-gramme-second system of units, in which the unit of force is a dyne, the unit for μ is called a poise.†

The viscosity is small both for air and for water. Thus at atmospheric pressure and 20° C., while the viscosity of glycerine is about 8·7, and that of cylinder oil (Mobiloil BB) about 9·5, the value for water is about 0·01 and that for air about $1\cdot9\times10^{-4}$.‡ The viscosity of air is, in fact, so small that the stress corresponding to a change of velocity of 100 miles per hour over 1/100th of an inch is about 1 oz. wt. per square foot.

In liquids μ diminishes fairly rapidly as the temperature rises.‖ A table of values of 100μ for water at intervals of 1° C. from 0° C. to 50° C., and of 2° C. from 50° C. to 100° C., is given on pp. 5 and 6 (Table 1 (a)). The table is abridged from one calculated by Bingham and Jackson,†† using an empirical formula with four constants, from weighted averages of a number of determinations by various observers. μ is in poises, or gm. per cm. per sec. The various determinations differ fairly considerably among themselves (from 1·776 to 1·796 at 0° C., for example), and for further details reference should be made to the original papers. Table 1 (b) contains the values of $1,000\mu$ in lb. per ft. per sec. Since there are 2·2046 lb. in 1 kg. and 3·2808 ft. in 1 m., the value of μ in lb. per ft. per sec. is found by multiplying its value in gm. per cm. per sec. by 0·06720, so that the entries in Table 1 (b) are found by multiplying those in Table 1 (a) by 0·6720.

As we shall see later (pp. 11, 12 and p. 96), although the viscous stresses in different fluids themselves depend upon μ, yet their effects

just before Prop. LI, Lib. II, of the *Principia*: 'Resistentiam quae oritur ex defectu lubricitatis partium fluidi, caeteris paribus, proportionalem esse velocitati, quâ partes fluidi separantur ab invicem.' In Prop. LI and Prop. LII Newton calculates, incorrectly, the steady flow of an infinite viscous liquid due to a rotating cylinder and rotating sphere respectively. (See Stokes, *Trans. Camb. Phil. Soc.* 8 (1845), 303, 304; *Math. and Phys. Papers*, 1, 103.) Navier (*Mémoires de l'Académie des Sciences*, 6 (1823), 416) gives almost exactly Maxwell's definition.

† In honour of Poiseuille, a physician interested in the circulation of the blood, who, in a series of careful and beautiful experiments, established experimentally the laws of discharge of fluid flowing through capillary tubes (*Mémoires des Savants Étrangers*, 9 (1846), 433–544).

‡ These values are taken from a chapter by A. G. M. Michell in *The Mechanical Properties of Fluids, a Collective Work* (London, 1925), p. 112.

‖ Data for a number of liquids are given by Hatschek, *The Viscosity of Liquids* (London, 1928), chap. v, and Erk, *Handbuch der Experimentalphysik*, 4, part 4 (Leipzig, 1932), 538 *et seq.* Figures for a number of lubricating oils are given by Michell, *loc. cit.*

†† *Bulletin of the Bureau of Standards*, 14 (1919), 75.

TABLE 1

The Viscosity and Kinematic Viscosity of Water

Temp.	TABLE 1 (a). 100μ in gm./(cm. sec.)	TABLE 1 (b). 1,000μ in lb./(ft. sec.)	TABLE 1 (c). 100ν in cm.²/sec.	TABLE 1 (d). 10⁵ν in ft.²/sec.
0°	1·792	1·204	1·792	1·929
1	1·731	1·163	1·731	1·863
2	1·673	1·124	1·673	1·801
3	1·619	1·088	1·619	1·743
4	1·567	1·053	1·567	1·687
5	1·519	1·021	1·519	1·635
6	1·473	0·990	1·473	1·586
7	1·428	0·960	1·428	1·537
8	1·386	0·931	1·386	1·492
9	1·346	0·905	1·346	1·449
10	1·308	0·879	1·308	1·408
11	1·271	0·854	1·271	1·368
12	1·236	0·831	1·237	1·331
13	1·203	0·808	1·204	1·296
14	1·171	0·787	1·172	1·261
15	1·140	0·766	1·141	1·228
16	1·111	0·747	1·112	1·197
17	1·083	0·728	1·084	1·167
18	1·056	0·710	1·057	1·138
19	1·030	0·692	1·032	1·110
20	1·005	0·675	1·007	1·084
21	0·981	0·659	0·983	1·058
22	0·958	0·644	0·960	1·034
23	0·936	0·629	0·938	1·010
24	0·914	0·614	0·917	0·987
25	0·894	0·601	0·897	0·965
26	0·874	0·587	0·877	0·944
27	0·855	0·575	0·858	0·924
28	0·836	0·562	0·839	0·903
29	0·818	0·550	0·821	0·884
30	0·801	0·538	0·804	0·866
31	0·784	0·527	0·788	0·848
32	0·768	0·516	0·772	0·831
33	0·752	0·505	0·756	0·814
34	0·737	0·495	0·741	0·798
35	0·723	0·486	0·727	0·783
36	0·709	0·476	0·713	0·768
37	0·695	0·467	0·700	0·753
38	0·681	0·458	0·686	0·738
39	0·668	0·449	0·673	0·724
40	0·656	0·441	0·661	0·712
41	0·644	0·433	0·649	0·699
42	0·632	0·425	0·637	0·686
43	0·621	0·417	0·627	0·674
44	0·610	0·410	0·616	0·663
45	0·599	0·403	0·605	0·651
46	0·588	0·395	0·594	0·639
47	0·578	0·388	0·584	0·629
48	0·568	0·382	0·574	0·618

TABLE 1 (cont.)

Temp.	TABLE I (a). 100μ in gm./(cm. sec.)	TABLE I (b). 1,000μ in lb./(ft. sec.)	TABLE I (c). 100ν in cm.²/sec.	TABLE I (d). 10⁵ν in ft.²/sec.
49°	0·559	0·376	0·565	0·609
50	0·549	0·369	0·556	0·598
52	0·532	0·358	0·539	0·580
54	0·515	0·346	0·522	0·562
56	0·499	0·335	0·506	0·545
58	0·483	0·325	0·491	0·528
60	0·469	0·315	0·477	0·513
62	0·455	0·306	0·463	0·499
64	0·442	0·297	0·451	0·485
66	0·429	0·288	0·438	0·471
68	0·417	0·280	0·426	0·459
70	0·406	0·273	0·415	0·447
72	0·395	0·265	0·404	0·435
74	0·385	0·259	0·395	0·425
76	0·375	0·252	0·385	0·414
78	0·366	0·246	0·376	0·405
80	0·357	0·240	0·367	0·395
82	0·348	0·234	0·358	0·386
84	0·339	0·228	0·350	0·376
86	0·331	0·222	0·342	0·368
88	0·324	0·218	0·335	0·361
90	0·317	0·213	0·328	0·353
92	0·310	0·208	0·322	0·346
94	0·303	0·204	0·315	0·339
96	0·296	0·199	0·308	0·331
98	0·290	0·195	0·302	0·325
100	0·284	0·191	0·296	0·319

on the motions of the fluids are determined by the ratio of μ to the density ρ, which is called the kinematic viscosity and denoted by ν. In Table 1 (c) values of 100ν are given, where ν is in cm.² per sec., while Table 1 (d) gives the values of $10^5\nu$ in ft.² per sec. The value of ν in ft.² per sec. is found by multiplying its value in cm.² per sec. by $1\cdot0764.10^{-3}$, so that the entries in Table 1 (d) are found by multiplying those in Table 1 (c) by $1\cdot0764$.

These values are for pressures of about one atmosphere. The effect of a change of pressure on the viscosity of water depends markedly on the temperature, but is very small for any change likely to occur in ordinary circumstances. Thus the percentage change in the viscosity of water between 1 and 100 atmospheres seems to vary from about $-1\cdot2$ at 0° C. to about $+0\cdot7$ at 75° C.†

† See Bridgman, *The Physics of High Pressure* (London, 1931), p. 346. For most other liquids the viscosity increases with increase of pressure at all temperatures at

TABLE 2

The Viscosity and Kinematic Viscosity of Air

Temp.	TABLE 2 (a) $10^4\mu$ in gm./(cm. sec.)	TABLE 2 (b) $10^5\mu$ in lb./(ft. sec.)	TABLE 2 (c) ν in cm.²/sec.	TABLE 2 (d) $10^3\nu$ in ft.²/sec.
0°	1·709	1·148	0·132	0·142
20	1·808	1·215	0·150	0·161
40	1·904	1·279	0·169	0·181
60	1·997	1·342	0·188	0·202
80	2·088	1·403	0·209	0·225
100	2·175	1·462	0·330	0·248
120	2·260	1·519	0·252	0·271
140	2·344	1·575	0·274	0·295
160	2·425	1·630	0·298	0·321
180	2·505	1·683	0·322	0·347
200	2·582	1·735	0·346	0·372
220	2·658	1·787	0·371	0·399
240	2·733	1·837	0·397	0·427
260	2·806	1·886	0·424	0·456
280	2·877	1·933	0·451	0·485
300	2·946	1·980	0·481	0·518
320	3·014	2·025	0·507	0·546
340	3·080	2·070	0·535	0·576
360	3·146	2·114	0·565	0·608
380	3·212	2·158	0·595	0·640
400	3·277	2·202	0·625	0·673
420	3·340	2·244	0·656	0·706
440	3·402	2·286	0·688	0·741
460	3·463	2·327	0·720	0·775
480	3·523	2·367	0·752	0·809
500	3·583	2·408	0·785	0·845

In gases, on the other hand, μ increases as the temperature rises. It varies only slightly with pressure within fairly wide limits. As regards the viscosity of air, Ruckes[†] found an increase of 20 per cent. in μ for an increase of pressure from 1 to 15 atmospheres; but this result is contested by Wildhagen,[‡] who found an increase of 23 per cent. at 100 atmospheres and 91 per cent. at 200 atmospheres. On the assumption that the increase is parabolic, this would mean an increase of only about 1·5 per cent. at 25 atmospheres, for example; but Boyd[||] criticizes Wildhagen's work, and both on a theoretical

which experiments have been made, and the percentage change is greater than for water (Bridgman, loc. cit.). For lubricating oils reference may be made to Hyde, Proc. Roy. Soc. A, **97** (1920), 240–259; Hersey and Shore, Mechanical Engineering, **50** (1928), 221–232; Kleinschmidt, Trans. Amer. Soc. Mechanical Engineers, Applied Mechanics Section, **49–50**, (1927–1928), 2–5.

† Ann. d. Phys. (4), **25** (1908), 983–1021. See particularly 997.
‡ Zeitschr. f. angew Math. u. Mech. **3** (1923), 181–191.
|| Phys. Rev. (2), **35** (1930), 1297.

basis and by considerations of dynamical similarity for the onset of turbulence in Wildhagen's experiments (cf. §§ 5, 6 and 23 *infra*) he deduces a nearly linear law of increase of μ with pressure, with an increase of about 4 per cent. at 25 atmospheres.

Values of $10^4\mu$ in gm. per cm. per sec. for air at atmospheric pressure, at intervals of 20° C. from 0° C. to 500° C., are given in Table 2 (a) on p. 7. Table 2 (b) gives values of $10^5\mu$ in lb. per ft. per sec., and Tables 2 (c) and 2 (d) give values of ν in cm.² per sec. and of $10^3\nu$ in ft.² per sec., respectively. Table 2 (a) is reproduced from the *International Critical Tables*. A careful survey of the results of the most recent determinations of μ showed that this table gave a very good mean of the best observations. In a few cases individual experimental values depart by about $1\frac{1}{2}$ per cent. from the curve through the plotted values of Table 2 (a), but generally the agreement is much closer.

3. The viscosity and some other properties of gases according to the kinetic theory.

A theoretical explanation of Newton's formula for the shearing stress in a viscous fluid was first given by Maxwell[†] for gases, according to the kinetic theory: a simplified form of the calculations may help to explain several notions which will be useful later. According to the kinetic theory the molecules of a gas are always in motion, with velocities distributed at random, so that there is no motion of the gas as a whole on this account: the kinetic energy of these random motions is the heat energy of the gas. Now suppose that, on the molar scale, the gas has a velocity u everywhere in the same direction AB, with u constant over any one of a series of planes parallel to one another and to AB, and with a constant gradient α at right angles to these planes. Thus, if we suppose that u vanishes over the plane whose trace is AB, its value at a distance z from this plane is αz. Then the molecules of the gas, in addition to their random heat motions, possess the ordered motion and the momentum associated with it.

In consequence of the random heat motion, molecules from below will pass upward, and from above will pass downward, through AB. If we call momentum in the direction AB positive, the molecules from above bring with them positive momentum, and those from

† *Phil. Mag.* (4), **19** (1860), 19–32; *Scientific Papers*, **1**, 377–391.

below negative momentum. Thus the transport of momentum tends to equalize the velocities of the upper and lower layers. If there are N molecules per unit volume of the gas, moving with an average velocity c, then for a simple calculation we suppose that $\frac{1}{3}N$ molecules per unit volume are moving with the velocity c at right angles to the planes of constant u, with $\frac{1}{6}N$ moving in each of two directions parallel to these planes and at right angles to each other. Of the $\frac{1}{3}N$ molecules per unit volume moving at right angles to the

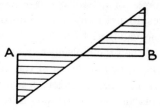

planes of constant u, we suppose that half, i.e. $\frac{1}{6}N$ molecules per unit volume, are moving downwards, and the other half upwards, all with the velocity c; so that, in time dt, $\frac{1}{6}Nc\,dt\,dS$ molecules pass downwards through an area dS of the plane AB, and the same number pass upwards. If the molecules when they pass through AB have on the average the velocity appropriate to a plane at a distance L from AB, and if m is the mass of a molecule, the average momentum of each molecule is $mL\alpha$, and there is a transport of positive momentum downwards through AB, of amount $\frac{1}{6}NcmL\alpha$ per unit area per unit time, and an equal transport of negative momentum upwards. Thus the gas below AB is gaining momentum $\frac{1}{3}NcmL\alpha$ per unit area per unit time, and this gives the tangential stress on AB. Since α is the velocity gradient, Newton's formula gives the tangential stress equal to $\mu\alpha$; and since Nm is the total mass per unit volume, i.e. the density ρ of the gas, it follows that μ is $\frac{1}{3}\rho cL$.

This calculation is extremely rough, and the method of averaging is probably the simplest and roughest possible. More accurate calculations (in which account is taken of the correct distribution of random velocities among the molecules, and of the change in this distribution due to the ordered motion) give the value $0.499\rho cL$ for μ, where c is the average random velocity of a molecule, and L the mean free path, calculated in a certain way.†

According to this formula it may be shown that the usual ideas of the kinetic theory would make μ independent of the pressure and directly proportional to the square root of the absolute temperature.

† The calculations are due to Enskog and Chapman. For an account of the application of the kinetic theory of gases to hydrodynamics reference may be made to Rocard, *L'Hydrodynamique et la Théorie Cinétique des Gaz* (Paris, 1932).

The former result is, as we have noted, experimentally confirmed within fairly wide limits; but the increase of viscosity with temperature is more rapid than the latter result asserts. Formulae more in harmony with experimental results have been found by allowing for forces of attraction or repulsion between the molecules; but the results naturally depend on the model chosen, and the discussion of the validity of the formulae is complicated.†

When the molecules cross the plane AB they carry with them not only the momentum of their ordered motion but also their mass and their energy. In a gas in which the density is not constant the transport of mass corresponds to the phenomenon of diffusion; if the temperature is not constant the transport of energy gives rise to the phenomenon of the conduction of heat. Thus on the simplest theory the mechanisms of the transport of a component of ordered momentum, of heat energy, and of mass are identical; and as a result it is found that, according to the simplest possible calculations, the co-efficient of conduction of heat (k) is equal to the product of the viscosity (μ) and the specific heat at constant volume (C_v), while the coefficient of self-diffusion (D) is equal to the viscosity (μ) divided by the density (ρ). Both experiment and more accurate calculations give values round about 2 for $k/(\mu C_v)$, the value for air at $0°$ C. being 1·91. If C_p is the specific heat at constant pressure, C_p is equal to $1·401C_v$ for air, so that $k/(\mu C_p)$ is about 1·36. Similarly, the values of $D\rho/\mu$ appear to lie between 1·2 and 1·5.‡

Throughout this book, with the exception of the present section, we shall regard a fluid as a continuum. In order that this view may be justified it must be possible to define a volume, very small from the molar point of view, which nevertheless includes so many molecules that it possesses the average, or molar, properties of the fluid. Ordinarily this condition presents no difficulties (thus a cube of air at atmospheric pressure, of side one-hundredth of a millimetre, contains about $2·7.10^{10}$ molecules), but it is violated in the case of gases at very low pressures. Again, in order that an element of volume, so defined, may possess an individuality of its own for a sufficient time to permit us to reason about its motion, its dimensions must not be small compared with the molecular mean free path of

---

† For a discussion of some of the more recent theoretical results reference may be made to Fowler, *Statistical Mechanics* (Cambridge, 1929), pp. 229–234.

‡ See, for example, Jeans, *The Dynamical Theory of Gases* (Cambridge, 1925), chaps. xi, xii, and xiii.

a gas (and, as we have seen, even when this condition is satisfied, transport phenomena across its boundaries must still be taken into account). It follows that the mean free path must be very small compared with the dimensions of the apparatus or other system with which we are concerned.

Finally, we remark that the mechanism of viscosity in liquids is quite different from that in gases, and that its theory has not been developed to anything like the same extent.†

4. The compressibility of air.

In this book we shall usually neglect the compressibility of air, and treat its density as constant. This procedure naturally involves some departure from the facts, but we can see that the error introduced is small so long as the velocities with which we are concerned are not too large. The percentage change in density is small so long as the percentage change in pressure is small: now the maximum pressure change associated with motion is of the order of $\rho_0 v^2$, where ρ_0 is the density and v the maximum velocity, and thus the approximation will be satisfactory so long as this quantity is small compared with the undisturbed pressure, p_0. Near the ground the pressure of the atmosphere is about 2,100 lb. wt. per square foot, and for a speed of 100 miles an hour $\rho_0 v^2$ is about 52 lb. wt. per square foot or about $2\frac{1}{2}$ per cent. of p_0. Quite generally we can say that the condition required is that v should be small compared with $(p_0/\rho_0)^{\frac{1}{2}}$: since a, the velocity of sound, is about $1 \cdot 2(p_0/\rho_0)^{\frac{1}{2}}$, the condition is then that v/a should be small. At a temperature of $0°$ C. the velocity of sound in dry air at atmospheric pressure is about 331·5 metres per second.

An exact evaluation of the error involved for a particular value of v/a, and a description of what happens either when v is a considerable fraction of a (as for motion near the tips of airscrew blades) or when v is greater than a (as for the flight of bullets and shells) is outside the scope of this book.

5. Kinematic viscosity and Reynolds number. Force coefficients. Scale effect. Non-dimensional parameters.

The viscous stresses in different fluids depend on the velocity gradients and on μ; but when an element of the fluid is accelerated in passing from point to point, the effect of the viscous stresses on

† For a discussion and references see 'A Discussion on Viscosity of Liquids', *Proc. Roy. Soc.* A, **163** (1937), 319–337.

its motion is determined by the ratio of their resultant to its inertia. The determining quantity is then the ratio μ/ρ, where ρ is the density, rather than μ itself. This ratio is usually called the kinematic viscosity,† and denoted by the special symbol ν.

Since the dimensions of μ are $[ML^{-1}T^{-1}]$ and those of ρ are $[ML^{-3}]$, the dimensions of ν are $[L^2T^{-1}]$. At atmospheric pressure and 20° C. ν has the values 6·9 for glycerine, 10·4 for cylinder oil, 0·01 for water, and 0·15 for air (in c.g.s. units). Thus viscosity has more effect on the motion of air than on the motion of water. (Moreover, as we have seen in Tables 1 (c) and 2 (c), with increase of temperature ν decreases for water but increases for air.) Nevertheless, the value of ν for air is only about one-seventieth of that of an ordinary cylinder lubricating oil.

We can now go farther and ask what is the determining quantity for the flow of different fluids at different speeds and on different scales for systems which are in all respects geometrically similar. In the first place we may suppose the effects of forces such as gravity acting on the fluid eliminated by the following device:—If the fluid were in equilibrium, a certain system of hydrostatic pressures would be set up whose effects would just balance the effects of these forces,—that is, their effects would be equal and opposite to those of the forces. If, then, we assume that when the fluid is moving, instead of the actual system of stresses we have the differences of these actual stresses from the hydrostatic pressure (i.e. the actual stresses minus the hydrostatic pressure) the effect will be exactly the same as for the actual stresses together with the external forces. We shall suppose this done (except in Chap. III, §§ 30–36, and Chaps. XIV, XV), so that whenever we speak of the pressure in a moving fluid we mean the difference of the actual pressure from the hydrostatic pressure; and, as a consequence, whenever we speak of the force on a solid body immersed in a moving fluid we mean the excess of the actual force experienced by the body over the force of buoyancy.

The arguments are now quite general, but to fix ideas we may consider the flow of fluid past a stationary obstacle, any other boundaries being so far away from the obstacle that their influence may be neglected. The shape of the obstacle, and its orientation with regard to the direction of the undisturbed stream, are supposed

† This name and symbol are due to Maxwell, *Theory of Heat* (London, 1871), p. 279.

fixed. If d is some representative length of the obstacle—for example, its diameter, if the obstacle is a sphere—and U is the undisturbed velocity of the stream, then the whole system is fixed if we know U and d, together with ρ and ν for the fluid. Now if u is a component of fluid velocity in some arbitrarily chosen direction, if p is a pressure and τ a shearing or tangential stress, then u/U, $p/(\rho U^2)$, and $\tau/(\rho U^2)$ are non-dimensional quantities in the sense that their values will be the same whatever the units chosen to measure mass, length, and time. They will depend in the first place on the position at which they are measured; but if we fix our attention on corresponding points in our systems, then their values can depend only on U, d, ρ, and ν, and being themselves non-dimensional they must depend on some non-dimensional combination of these quantities which is entirely independent of the units chosen. Remembering that the dimensions of U are $[LT^{-1}]$, of d are $[L]$, of ρ are $[ML^{-3}]$, and of ν are $[L^2T^{-1}]$, we easily see that the only non-dimensional combination possible does not contain ρ and is $R = Ud/\nu$, or some function of R. Thus at corresponding points u/U, $p/(\rho U^2)$, and $\tau/(\rho U^2)$ must be functions of R only. More generally, if in any system of coordinates three lengths x, y, z fix the position of a point in any one of our systems, then x/d, y/d, and z/d are non-dimensional, and we may say that u/U, $p/(\rho U^2)$, and $\tau/(\rho U^2)$ depend on x/d, y/d, z/d, and R, and on these only.

Again, if F is the component in an arbitrarily chosen direction of the force on the obstacle due to the system of stresses over its surface, $F/(\frac{1}{2}\rho U^2 d^2)$ is a non-dimensional quantity. Instead of writing d^2 we usually write S, where S is some representative area associated with the obstacle: for example, for a sphere of which d is the diameter, S may be the area opposed to the stream, $\frac{1}{4}\pi d^2$. Then the non-dimensional quantity $F/(\frac{1}{2}\rho U^2 S)$ is called a force coefficient. It can depend only on a non-dimensional combination of U, d, ρ, and ν, and must therefore be a function of R only. The component of the force in the direction of the undisturbed stream is called the drag force, and denoted by D; any component at right angles to this is a component of lift,[†] and the resultant lift force is denoted by L; the drag and lift coefficients are denoted by C_D and C_L, so

---

[†] The word lift suggests a force vertically upwards, and the orientation of the undisturbed stream and of the obstacle may usually be considered to be such that the force actually is in that direction; but the word lift will be used in this book quite generally for a component force perpendicular to the main stream, without any necessary relation to the direction of gravity.

that, for an obstacle of given shape at a given orientation to the stream,

$$C_D = \frac{D}{\frac{1}{2}\rho U^2 S} \quad \text{and} \quad C_L = \frac{L}{\frac{1}{2}\rho U^2 S}$$

are functions of R only.

In the special but important case of flow past an infinite cylinder, D and L are used to denote the drag and lift forces per unit length of the cylinder, so that they have one less dimension in length than a force has. The drag and lift coefficients are then defined by

$$C_D = \frac{D}{\frac{1}{2}\rho U^2 d}, \qquad C_L = \frac{L}{\frac{1}{2}\rho U^2 d};$$

they are still functions of R alone. In this case, the motion being two-dimensional, the direction of the lift—at right angles to the undisturbed stream—is quite definite.

The non-dimensional quantity Ud/ν, denoted by R, is usually called a Reynolds number, in honour of Osborne Reynolds, who (in his researches on the flow of water through pipes)† first applied the idea that the state of affairs in geometrically similar systems depends only on R, in the sense outlined above. The dimensional argument was given by Lord Rayleigh.‡

The advantages of using non-dimensional quantities, and of the arguments given above, are considerable. In the first place a force coefficient or a Reynolds number will have the same value whatever units are employed for measurement, though it is to be remarked that different velocities and different lengths may, in different connexions, be used for U and d in systems geometrically similar. Thus for flow along a pipe U may be either the maximum velocity or the mean velocity across a section; d may be the diameter or the radius of a circular pipe, or the hydraulic radius—the ratio of the area of the section to its perimeter, which, for a circular pipe, is half the radius. But the importance of the ideas arises mainly from the fact that, although we can make out theoretically that $C_D = f(R)$, for example, the form of the function involved cannot be theoretically determined, except perhaps for certain restricted ranges of values of R. Generally recourse must be had to experiment; and the values of C_D for a series of values of R can then be found by varying U or d

---

† *Phil. Trans.* **174** (1883), 935–982; *Scientific Papers*, **2**, 51–105.

‡ *Phil. Mag.* (5), **34** (1892), 59, 60; *Phil. Mag.* (6), **8** (1904), 66, 67; *Advisory Committee for Aeronautics, Reports and Memoranda*, No. 15 (1909); *Scientific Papers*, **3**, 575, 576; **5**, 196, 197, and 532, 533.

or ν or any combination of them, as may be most convenient. Thus in Fig. 1 the graph of C_D as a function of R is given for the flow of a stream past a circular cylinder (U is taken as the undisturbed velocity of the stream, and d as the diameter of the cylinder).† A similar graph for a sphere is given in Fig. 2 (d is taken as the diameter of the sphere, and S as the area opposed to the stream, $\frac{1}{4}\pi d^2$).

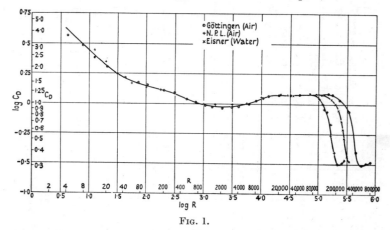

Fig. 1.

Fig. 2, for example, represents in one curve the results of a large number of measurements of the drag of spheres, with spheres of different sizes, streams of different velocities, and fluids of different densities and viscosities.‡ If the function $f(R)$ were a constant, one experiment would suffice to determine the drag of all spheres in all fluids, and similar statements would be true for all other cases. To what extent the non-dimensional coefficients vary with Reynolds number must in general be a matter for experiment; this variation is referred to as scale effect. If we wish to study scale effect in con-nexion with model experiments on aeroplanes, for example, we should

---

† For an explanation of the sudden drop in the drag coefficient in the neighbour-hood of $R = 2.10^5$, see Chap. II, §24. The fact that C_D may take different values for Reynolds numbers in this neighbourhood is due to different degrees of turbu-lence in the main stream. See p. 18, and Chap. IX, §184. The experiments in air were carried out at the Aerodynamische Versuchsanstalt, Göttingen, Germany, and the National Physical Laboratory, Teddington, England; those in water by Dr. Eisner in Berlin.

‡ Fig. 2 is reproduced with little alteration from an article by Muttray in the *Handbuch der Experimentalphysik*, **4**, part 2 (Leipzig, 1932), 304. For Göttingen, see above. The Variable Density Tunnel, U.S.A.. is of the compressed air type (see pp. 17, 237, 238). The other names with dates are those of the experimenters.

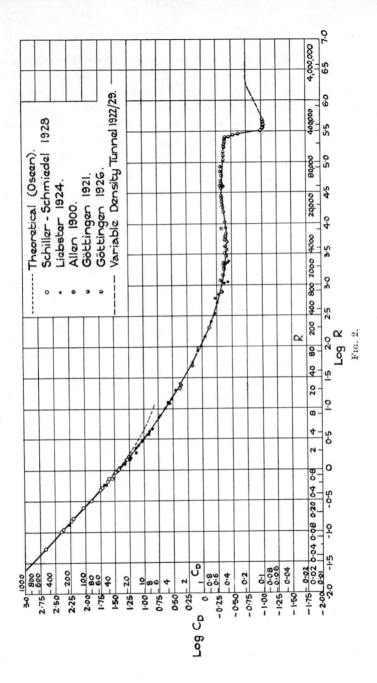

Fig. 2.

have to be able to make Ud/ν as large for the model as for the full-scale aeroplane: since d is much smaller this would mean making U much larger if ν is unaltered. This is difficult, and is in any case undesirable, partly because of the effects of compressibility at large values of U. Considerations such as these have led to the use of a compressed air wind tunnel (Chap. VI, § 102) as a means of diminishing ν or μ/ρ. Since μ is not much altered if the pressure and density are increased, ν can thus be diminished and R increased.

An interesting interpretation of R for a gas, according to the kinetic theory, has been given by Kármán.† Apart from a numerical constant, ν or μ/ρ is cL for a gas, where c is the average molecular velocity and L is the molecular mean free path (p. 9). Thus apart from a numerical constant, R is $U/c \times d/L$. Now in ordinary problems of hydrodynamics d/L must be very large and U/c very small, otherwise the phenomena will depend not only on R but on U/c and d/L separately. Thus if d/L is not very large we can no longer regard the gas as a continuum,—we must take molecular phenomena into account; if U/c is not very small, compressibility and thermal effects in the gas must not be ignored.

The conditions under which we have established that the various non-dimensional coefficients are functions of R only must be carefully noted. In the first place geometrical similarity is postulated throughout: thus if experiments are performed, for example, on solid bodies of the same shape but different sizes in one or in several wind tunnels (Chap. VI, § 99 *et seq.*), the tunnel boundaries must in every case be so far from the solid body that they do not influence the results, if the simple laws enunciated above are to apply. Otherwise some correction must be made for the influence of these boundaries; and, if this is not done, then even for the same or geometrically similar tunnels the ratio of the linear dimensions of the tunnel section to the linear dimensions of the solid body enters as a second non-dimensional parameter, in addition to the parameter R. Again, strictly speaking, the geometrical similarity of two solid bodies must extend also to the roughnesses of their surfaces. (To what extent varying roughness affects the results must be a matter for experiment. Some such experiments, and attempts to interpret them by introducing further parameters to characterize the roughness, are reported in later chapters. See especially Chap. VIII, §§ 167, 168.)

† *Zeitschr. f. angew. Math. u. Mech.* **3** (1923), 395, 396.

Moreover, when a model is placed in a stream of air in a wind tunnel, this stream is not completely smooth, but is, to a greater or less extent, eddying or turbulent (see Chap. II, §§ 23, 24, and Chap. V). Thus, in addition to the main velocity of the stream, the air at any point has an eddying or irregular velocity; and the conditions of geometrical similarity will not be satisfied in different tunnels as regards the flow past the model, unless these eddying velocities have the same periodicity, structure and magnitude (in proportion to the velocity of the main stream) at a section sufficiently far in front of the model. This explains why different results may be obtained in different tunnels for the lift and drag coefficients of the same model at the same Reynolds number. The influence of the various factors is again a matter for experiment. (See Chaps. IX, X and XI.)

We must next note that our previous reasoning will not apply if the system includes a free surface, or surface of separation of one fluid from another, such as water from air. For at such a surface the stresses must be continuous,—and not only the differences of the stresses from the hydrostatic pressure, but the actual stresses; so that for fluid subject to gravity only, for example, our quantities may depend on the acceleration, g, due to the earth's attraction, as well as on U, d, ρ, and ν. Therefore another non-dimensional parameter, U^2/gd, usually called the Froude number,† enters as well as R. Now work must be done to supply the kinetic energy of the system of waves caused by the motion of a ship, or to overcome the wave-making resistance, as it is called; and if, in model ship experiments, both the frictional and wave-making resistances are to be accurately determined at once, both Ud/ν and U^2/gd will have to be the same in the model experiment as for the motion of the full-scale ship: this is impossible. It is easy to make U^2/gd the same for both, since U must be diminished when d is; and the usual procedure is to estimate the frictional resistance for the model, subtract it from the total resistance to give the wave-making resistance, calculate from this the wave-making resistance on the full-scale, and add to this the estimated full-scale frictional resistance. But the difference of the total resistance and frictional resistance is not entirely independent of the Reynolds number; and the possible

† After the discoverer of its significance, William Froude. *39th Report of the British Association, Exeter* (1869), 43–47; also *Trans. Inst. Naval Arch.* **11** (1870), 87–93.

errors so introduced are greater with smaller Reynolds numbers or smaller models, so that fairly large models are usually used.†

Other non-dimensional parameters may enter in other circumstances. Thus, if the compressibility of a gas has to be taken into account, the various non-dimensional coefficients depend on the ratio of the typical velocity U to the velocity of sound in the gas,‡ as well as on R; if surface tension, γ, is important, then the non-dimensional parameter $\gamma/(\rho d U^2)$ enters; and so on. In particular, in phenomena in which the conduction of heat is involved, we can first define a quantity analogous to the kinematic viscosity ν. Thus the rate of flow of heat at any point depends on the conductivity k and the temperature gradient; but the effect of conduction on change of temperature is determined by the ratio of the resultant heat flow into any volume to the amount of heat necessary to raise the temperature of this volume by $1°$ C.; so the determining quantity is the ratio $k/(\rho C)$, where ρ is the density and C the specific heat. This ratio is called the thermometric conductivity, and denoted by κ. Its dimensions are the same as those of ν, namely $[L^2 T^{-1}]$, so that, for heat conduction in a moving viscous fluid, κ/ν enters as well as R. We shall see later that in a gas moving with a velocity small compared with the velocity of sound, the relative specific heat is C_p, the specific heat at constant pressure; and we have already seen (p. 10) that for air κ/ν is about 1.36. For water at $10°$ C. it is about 0.1, and for mercury about 30. If Q is the total rate of heat transfer from any surface S, and if T is a typical temperature difference, then $Qd/(kTS)$ is a non-dimensional coefficient, the coefficient of total heat transfer, analogous to a force coefficient; and such non-dimensional quantities as this depend on R and on κ/ν.

6. Steady flow through a circular tube.

Some of the results of the preceding section may be illustrated by considering the steady motion of fluid through a circular tube under the influence of a pressure gradient. A knowledge of the characteristics of this motion will, moreover, be required later.

† Scale effect on the frictional resistance also demands a fairly high Reynolds number if the results are to be capable of extension to full-scale (cf. Chap. VII, § 151).

‡ For geometrically similar systems in different gases the non-dimensional coefficients will be the same function of this parameter and of R only if the connexion between pressure and density is the same. For adiabatic changes in a perfect gas, for example, the ratio of the specific heats will enter in general.

If the flow is steady and the same across all sections, then at all points in the tube at the same distance r from the axis the velocity u, which is along the tube, has the same value; in other words, u is a function of r only. Now consider a cylinder of fluid of length l and radius r, with its axis along the axis of the tube. Under the conditions previously specified, this fluid is neither gaining nor losing momentum, and hence the forces on it must balance. The tangential stress over its curved surface is $\mu \, du/dr$. The velocity u must fall to zero at the wall, and is biggest in the middle, so that du/dr is negative. The effect of the viscous stress is to retard the motion of the fluid considered, so that there is a retarding pull $-\mu \, du/dr$ per unit area over its curved surface. This is the same at all points of that surface, and since the area of the surface is $2\pi r l$, the total retarding force due to friction is $-2\pi\mu l r \, du/dr$. The area of either flat end is πr^2, and, if the pressures over them are p_1 and p_2, there is a force $\pi r^2 p_1$ pushing the fluid forward, and a force $\pi r^2 p_2$ pushing it back. Since the forces as a whole must balance, we must have

$$\pi r^2 (p_1 - p_2) = -2\pi\mu l r \, du/dr,$$

or

$$\frac{du}{dr} = -\frac{1}{2\mu} \frac{p_1 - p_2}{l} r.$$

Since nothing else in this equation depends on l, $(p_1 - p_2)/l$ must be independent of l. This means that there must be a constant pressure gradient, P, along the tube, and $(p_1 - p_2)/l$ is equal to P. Also u must be zero at the wall, so that, if the tube is of radius a, $u = 0$ when $r = a$, and hence

$$u = \frac{P}{2\mu} \int_r^a r \, dr = \frac{P}{4\mu}(a^2 - r^2).$$

The graph of u across a meridian section of the tube is therefore parabolic. The maximum velocity u_{max} is $Pa^2/4\mu$. The flux between two circles of radii r and $r+dr$ is $u \, . \, 2\pi r \, dr$, and the flux across any section is

$$Q = \int_0^a u \, . \, 2\pi r \, dr = \frac{\pi P}{2\mu} \int_0^a (a^2 - r^2) r \, dr = \frac{\pi P a^4}{8\mu}. \, \dagger$$

The average velocity u_m is $Q/\pi a^2$ or $Pa^2/8\mu$, and is equal to $\frac{1}{2}u_{max}$. The velocity—either average or maximum—is directly propor-

<hr />

† This formula provides the starting-point for the most widely used method of measuring viscosity. For the various precautions and corrections necessary, reference may be made to Hatschek, *op. cit.*

tional to the pressure gradient. The tangential stress, τ_0, at the wall is the value of $-\mu\, du/dr$ when $r = a$, and is $\frac{1}{2}Pa$ or $4\mu u_m/a$. Hence $\tau_0/(\rho u_m^2)$ is $4\nu/(u_m a)$, or $8/R$, if R is the Reynolds number $u_m d/\nu$, where d is the diameter of the tube, equal to $2a$.

The parabolic distribution of velocity is attained only after a sufficient distance from the entry. The distribution of velocity in this 'inlet length' depends on the conditions at the entry (Chap. VII, § 139).

If the Reynolds number is increased beyond a certain limit, the motion ceases to be of the rectilinear type here considered, and becomes turbulent (Chap. II, § 23, and Chap. VIII).

7. Some results of ideal fluid theory, and comparison with observation.†

We have seen that for air and water the viscosity is small, and for ordinary motions of these fluids the Reynolds number is high. Indeed, in most cases of fluid motion of technical importance we are dealing with motions at very high Reynolds numbers; and it might perhaps be anticipated that fairly close agreement with observation would be obtained from a theory which, as a simplifying assumption, neglected the viscosity altogether—that is, regarded the Reynolds number as infinite. Since ideal fluid theory is based on this simplifying assumption, it is natural to look first to this theory, especially as it has been developed into an instrument of great elegance and power, and in some classes of problems the expectation of fairly close agreement with observation has been realized, notably for tides and waves. But in the problems with which we shall be chiefly concerned in this book—namely, the prediction of the motion of a solid body through air or water, or the flow of air or water past a solid body or along a pipe, and of the forces that arise—progress along these lines appears to be obstructed by the second property of real fluids, that, however low their viscosity, they are incapable of slipping (with any velocity that can be measured) over the surface of a solid body, whereas the only solutions of these problems yielded by the theory all involve very considerable slip. In these circumstances it is perhaps surprising, not that the results of theory and observation often disagree violently, but rather that they sometimes agree fairly well, as for the motion of airship bodies. In any case a correct theory

† A closer discussion of many of the points raised in this and the next two sections, together with references to the original papers, will be found in Lamb's *Hydrodynamics* (Cambridge, 1932).

must explain both the agreements and the discrepancies. Before attempting to set forth such a theory we recall some of the results of the ideal fluid theory.

The most striking of these results is that on a solid body moving with uniform velocity through otherwise still fluid the pressure of the fluid produces no resultant force at all, although, in the general case, there may be a resultant torque.† In particular, a solid body should experience no resistance to motion through the air or, if submerged to a sufficient depth, to motion through water. This is definitely in contradiction with observation: in the words of Rayleigh, 'On this principle the screw of a submerged boat would be useless, but, on the other hand, its services would not be needed.'‡ Nevertheless it is to be remarked that for bodies with what are called good stream-line shapes, such as airships, the drag coefficient as defined above is fairly small. In general the designer is interested in reducing resistance as much as possible, and hence in solid bodies for which this contradiction between ideal fluid theory and observation is a minimum.

To examine the theoretical results in more detail let us consider as an example steady two-dimensional flow past a circular cylinder. The stream-lines—a stream-line is such that the tangent to it at any point is in the direction of the velocity at the point—are, at some distance from the cylinder, almost undisturbed, and so are parallel straight lines in the direction of the undisturbed velocity, U, of the stream. A diagram of the stream-lines is given in Fig. 3.

When the motion is steady, as here, the stream-lines are the actual paths of particles of fluid. The same amount of fluid flows, per unit time, across any section between the same two stream-lines, and hence a crowding together of the stream-lines denotes an increase in the velocity. Thus the crowding together of the stream-lines at B and D shows that the velocity there is greater than the velocity, U, upstream. At A and C two stream-lines intersect. At a point of

---

† Since, according to the laws of mechanics, the superposition on the whole system of a uniform velocity, equal and opposite to that of the body (so that the body is brought to rest), can make no difference to mechanical phenomena, these results also hold for an obstacle anchored in a stream, uniform apart from the disturbance caused by the obstacle.

The pressure of the fluid denotes here, and from now on throughout the book unless otherwise stated, the difference between the actual and the hydrostatic pressures, so that the resultant force is meant to exclude the force of buoyancy.

‡ *Proc. Roy. Institution*, **21** (1914), 70; *Scientific Papers*, **6**, 237.

intersection of two stream-lines the fluid cannot possess a finite velocity, since this would mean that it was moving in two directions at once. At such a point the velocity is zero or (on the mathematical theory) infinite. At A and C the velocity is zero. Points of zero velocity are called stagnation points. Thus along the cylinder the velocity rises from zero at A to B or D, then falls again to zero at C. The mathematical result is that at any point P on the surface of the

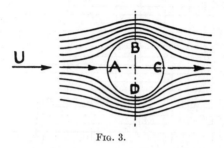

Fig. 3.

cylinder the velocity is $2U \sin \theta$, where θ is the angle subtended by the arc AP at the centre of the section.

The fluid is accelerated in passing from places of higher pressure to places of lower pressure, so that where the pressure is less the velocity is greater, and conversely. The mathematical result for an ideal fluid is that $p + \frac{1}{2}\rho q^2 = H$, where p is the pressure, q the velocity, and H is a constant, called the total pressure head, for reasons connected with its measurement (see Chap. VI, § 111). If p_0 is the pressure upstream, where the velocity is U, H is $p_0 + \frac{1}{2}\rho U^2$, and this is the pressure at stagnation points such as A and C. The increase of pressure, $\frac{1}{2}\rho U^2$, at a stagnation point may be called the kinetic pressure. At the point P of the cylinder the non-dimensional pressure coefficient $(p - p_0)/(\frac{1}{2}\rho U^2)$ is equal to $1 - q^2/U^2$ or $1 - 4\sin^2\theta$. The pressure is then greatest at A, where it is H; it falls to $H - 2\rho U^2$ at B or D, and rises again to H at C. The stream-lines close in again behind. In moving down the pressure gradient from A to B or D the fluid acquires momentum and energy, just sufficient, in the absence of friction, to carry it up the pressure gradient again to C. The whole diagram is symmetrical about BD. The resultant of the pressures on the front portion BAD is exactly balanced by the resultant of the pressures on the rear portion BCD, so that in this case it is clear that there will be no resultant drag. The theoretical result for the pressure coefficient $(p-p_0)/(\frac{1}{2}\rho U^2)$ is plotted against θ in Fig. 4,† which also contains graphs of the measured pressure distribution for two values of the Reynolds number R or Ud/ν, where d is the diameter of the cylinder. It will be seen that there is fair agreement with the theoretical result in the neighbourhood of the forward stagnation point, especially at the larger Reynolds number,

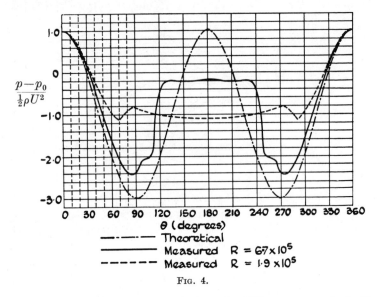

$$\frac{p-p_0}{\frac{1}{2}\rho U^2}$$

θ (degrees)

——·—— Theoretical
———— Measured R = 6·7 × 10⁵
———— Measured R = 1·9 × 10⁵

FIG. 4.

but that the actual and theoretical results differ enormously in the rear of the cylinder.

A similar diagram for the pressure distribution over any meridian section of a sphere is given in Fig. 5, where θ is again the angle measured from the forward stagnation point. It will be seen that the results are very similar to those for a cylinder.‡ In Fig. 6 a meridian section is shown of a body of revolution of good stream-line shape (an airship body), together with the pressure distributions over either the top or the bottom of the section, both from calculation and from measurement at a Reynolds number $Ud/\nu = 1\cdot2\,.\,10^5$, where d is the

† Figs. 4, 5, and 6 are reproduced, with very little alteration, from an article by H. Muttray in the *Handbuch der Experimentalphysik*, **4**, part 2 (Leipzig, 1932), 316, 306, and 309 respectively, the first two from measurements by O. Flachsbart and the last from measurements by G. Fuhrmann. See also Chaps. IX and XI, §§ 187, 217, 228.

‡ The breaking of the full line curve between $\theta = 150°$ and $\theta = 210°$ indicates that the shape of the curve there is uncertain.

maximum diameter of a cross-section. It will be seen that in this case
there is very good agreement over the whole of the body, except
right at the tail, where the theoretical rise of the pressure to $p_0+\frac{1}{2}\rho U^2$
does not take place. The theoretical results in this case differ from

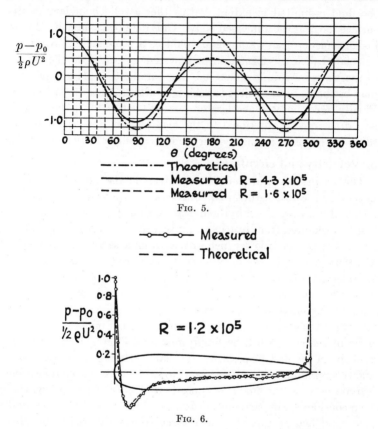

FIG. 5.

FIG. 6.

those for a cylinder or sphere very markedly in that the pressure
rise towards the rear is very gradual over most of the length.

It is to be expected that these results, that the calculated and
observed pressure distributions agree fairly well near the front
stagnation point for a bluff obstacle and over almost all the surface
for a stream-line one, will apply also to cases when the undisturbed
stream is not necessarily straight and uniform. This is verified by
the agreement of calculation and experiment on the orientations that

would be assumed by bodies of certain shapes suspended in curved or converging streams.†

We may here state explicitly that the theorem that the force on a solid body moving uniformly in an ideal fluid is zero will not apply if the fluid is limited in extent, with either a solid boundary or free surface too near the immersed body. Thus for a body submerged to an insufficient depth in water there would be a wave-making resistance associated with the formation of a system of waves on the surface of the water. Again, a sphere moving parallel to a plane rigid wall, may be shown to be subject to a force of attraction towards the wall. Finally, for a body in accelerated motion relative to the fluid, there is a drag force proportional to the acceleration, and this force has the same effect as an increase in the inertia of the body.

8. Vorticity and circulation.

The results of ideal fluid theory given in the preceding section depend on the absence of two quantities known as vorticity and circulation. Proofs are given in the literature that, for any motion which can be generated from rest in an inviscid fluid, these two quantities are zero under conditions which we may assume satisfied.‡ Nevertheless (fortunately for the development of hydrodynamics) important and elegant investigations of the nature of the motion of an inviscid fluid possessed of circulation or vorticity have been published without any close consideration of their production: these investigations find a place in the treatises on the motion of inviscid fluids, and some of the results will be briefly mentioned here. It will be convenient, in the first place, to recapitulate certain general definitions and theorems, and, where necessary, to explain also the modifications introduced when the fluid is viscous. In the following sections we shall then consider again particular examples of the flow of inviscid fluids past solid bodies, this time with circulation or vorticity included. We shall then be in a position to pass on to our proper subject—the main features of the flow of fluids of small viscosity past solid bodies.

† G. I. Taylor, *Proc. Roy. Soc.* A, **120** (1928), 260–283.

‡ The density must be uniform or a function of the pressure only ; and any field of external force acting on the fluid must be such that, if a particle were taken round any closed path in the field, the work done by the forces on the particle would be zero— that is, the field of force must be conservative. The former condition is violated in meteorological phenomena, where temperature differences play a part ; the only common field of force violating the second condition would be a magnetic field of electric currents. (See, however, the discussion on p. 46 for a closer examination of the theorem stated in the text.)

The vorticity is a vector quantity, of the same nature as angular velocity, and its meaning may be explained in the manner of Stokes†
by imagining an infinitesimally small sphere at any point of a fluid in motion to be suddenly solidified, as by freezing, in such a way that its angular momentum about its centre is unchanged; if the resultant solid is found to have rotation, then the fluid was possessed of vorticity, which by definition is equal to twice the initial angular velocity of the solid sphere. A vortex-line is then defined as a line drawn in the fluid so that the tangent to it at any point has the direction of the axis of the vorticity at the point. The vortex-lines through every point of a small closed curve form a tube, called a vortex-tube. For such a vortex-tube, of small cross-section, it may be shown that the product of the magnitude of the vorticity and the area of a normal cross-section at any point has the same value all along the tube: this constant product is called the strength of the tube. As a consequence of the constancy of the strength, vortex-tubes—and therefore also vortex-lines—cannot begin or end in the fluid. The vortex-lines form closed curves, or begin or end on the boundaries of the fluid, or—if we suppose the fluid unbounded—go to infinity.

Motions in which the vorticity is zero everywhere are called irrotational motions, or, occasionally, potential motions, for reasons connected with the mathematical similarity of their theory with those of other subjects, such as gravitation and electricity. The absence of vorticity introduces an enormous simplification into the mathematics, and this is one of the reasons why the theory of irrotational motion has been so highly developed.

Circulation is associated with a closed circuit drawn in the fluid. Mathematically, the circulation round such a circuit is defined by the integral $\oint v_s\,ds$ taken once completely round the circuit, where v_s is the component of the fluid velocity in the direction of the tangent at the element ds of the circuit. This circulation may be shown to be equal to the total strength of all the vortex-tubes that thread through the circuit; and the difference of the circulations in any two circuits is equal to the total strength of all the vortex-tubes that pass between them. Thus, if there is no vorticity in the fluid, the circulation must be the same in any two circuits that can be made to coincide with one another without passing out of the fluid.

† *Trans. Camb. Phil. Soc.* **8** (1845), 309, 310; *Math. and Phys. Papers*, **1**, 112.

We have now to distinguish carefully between two possible cases. If we have any ordinary finite solid body, such as a sphere, in a fluid, then any circuit in the fluid may be so moved and deformed without passing out of the fluid that it shrinks up into a point, the circulation becoming zero. Hence, if there is no vorticity in the fluid, the circulation must have been zero originally; in other words, absence of vorticity implies zero circulation in every circuit. But if we think of an infinite cylinder in the fluid then a circuit that encloses the cylinder cannot be made to shrink up into a point without passing out of the fluid. In such a case we cannot assert that absence of vorticity implies that the circulation round such a circuit must be zero. All we can assert is that the circulation must then be the same for all circuits enclosing the cylinder; this we naturally call the circulation round the cylinder.

In an inviscid fluid vorticity may be imagined concentrated on sheets or along lines. To explain this, we may first consider a motion of any fluid, similar to one already considered in §§ 2 and 3. Thus

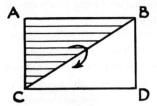 between two planes, whose traces are AB and CD, we imagine the fluid to be moving parallel to AB or CD. If the velocity is u, and if z is distance perpendicular to AB or CD, and if u is a function of z only, then it may be shown that the vorticity in this layer is about an axis at right angles to the plane of the paper, in the direction shown by the arrow, and of magnitude du/dz. If we consider two planes at a distance dz apart, the total strength of all the vortex-tubes between them, per unit length of the planes in the direction AB, is simply du (since dz is the total area of the cross-sections). This is the relative velocity of the two planes: hence the total strength of all the vortex-tubes in the layer, per unit length, is the relative velocity of the two planes AB and CD—that is, the difference in the velocities at A and C. We arrive at the same result by calculating the circulation round the rectangle $ABCD$, if AB and CD are of unit length. This circulation is equal to the total strength of all the vortex-tubes that pass through the rectangle, and is also equal to the difference in the velocities at A and C. We may call it the strength of the layer. Then so long as the velocity-difference is unaltered, the strength of the layer is unaffected by any change in its thickness. If, the

velocity-difference remaining constant, this thickness becomes zero, we get a surface at which the velocity is discontinuous. Such a surface is called a vortex-sheet, and the strength of the sheet is equal to the discontinuity in the velocity. More generally, if we have any surface at which the normal velocity is continuous but the tangential velocity discontinuous, this surface is a vortex-sheet. The vorticity at any point of the sheet is tangential to the sheet and at right angles to the discontinuity in the velocity; and the magnitude of this discontinuity measures the magnitude of the strength of the vortex-sheet.

Vortex-sheets may be regarded as an idealization, for inviscid fluids, of thin layers of vorticity in a fluid whose viscosity is small but not zero; we shall meet such layers later. Again, in the motion of fluids of small viscosity we may often observe cases in which the vorticity is sensibly concentrated into narrow tubes, in which case the tubes are called simply vortices. Such concentrated vortices may be observed if a blade is dipped into running water, or the point of a spoon moved across the surface of a liquid. In these cases observation is facilitated by the depression of the free surface where the vortex meets it.† In the motions with which we shall be concerned there is, in general, no free surface to facilitate the observation of concentrated vortices; but such vortices often exist behind solid bodies in motion relative to the fluid, in much the same way as in the cases mentioned above with a free surface. In the theory of inviscid fluids such concentrated vortices are often idealized by supposing the vorticity concentrated along a line, the total strength remaining finite. In this way we arrive at the conception of a line vortex, with a certain finite strength. Then the circulation in any circuit which is threaded by the line vortex is equal to the strength of the vortex.

The definitions of vorticity, vortex-lines, vortex-tubes, and circulation, together with the theorems given above concerning the strength of a vortex-tube and the connexion of circulation therewith, all apply equally well to a viscous as to an inviscid fluid. They are, in fact,

---

† This depression is easily explained. For the fluid in the vortex is rotating, and there must be a pressure gradient to balance the centrifugal force, so that the kinetic pressure is less in the middle than in the outer parts of the vortex. But at the free surface the total pressure, including the hydrostatic, must be constant. The hydrostatic pressure is therefore greater in the middle, which must be at a lower level than the outer parts.

purely kinematical or geometrical matters, completely independent of the presence or absence of shear stress. In the theory of inviscid fluids, however, it is proved in addition that if a circuit always passes through the same fluid particles, then the circulation round that circuit remains the same for all time. In other words, the

circulation in a circuit moving with the fluid is invariable.† This theorem concerning the circulation is fully equivalent to two theorems concerning the vorticity. The fluid inside any small portion of a narrow vortex-tube at any time remains a portion of a vortex-tube during the whole of its motion; that is, if a small portion of a narrow tube of fluid is in the direction of the vorticity at any time, then it moves in such a way that at any subsequent

Fig. 7.

time it is in the direction of the vorticity at its new position. Further, the strength of the tube remains constant as it moves. These two theorems may be summed up by saying that the vorticity is convected with the fluid. It follows that vorticity can neither be created nor destroyed in the interior of any finite portion of an inviscid fluid. In particular, any vortex-lines or vortex-sheets that may exist in an inviscid fluid move with the fluid and persist indefinitely. The strength of a vortex-sheet at any point changes, however. A vortex-sheet is, in fact, unstable; a plane vortex-sheet, if given a small sinusoidal displacement, rolls up in the manner shown in Fig. 7.‡ The vorticity becomes more and more concentrated in the rolled-up portions, and the appearance of the flow approximates more and more to that due to a set of concentrated vortices.

In a viscous fluid, as we shall see in Chap. III, § 36, the rate of change of the circulation in a circuit moving with the fluid depends only on the kinematic viscosity and on the space rates of change of the vorticity components at the contour, so that it is zero if there is no vorticity near the contour, and is in any case small, for small

† The conditions specified in the footnote on p. 26 are supposed satisfied.
‡ See Rosenhead, *Proc. Roy. Soc.* A, **134** (1931), 170–192.

viscosity, unless the space rates of change of the vorticity components are large.† Again, the theorem concerning the convection of the vorticity is modified. Any component of the vorticity of a fluid element has the variation it would have in the absence of viscosity, but has also an additional variation that follows the law of conduction of heat, the kinematic viscosity v taking the place of the thermometric conductivity. We may express this by saying that the vorticity is convected with the fluid, but at the same time diffuses like heat. It follows that even in a viscous fluid vorticity cannot originate in the interior of the fluid, but must arise from the boundaries.†

We may also note explicitly that vortex-sheets and lines could not exist in a real fluid, since the vorticity would diffuse. But a thin vortex-layer would still be unstable, and would roll up somewhat in the manner of Fig. 7.

9. The motion of inviscid fluids with circulation. Lift.

We have already remarked on the enormous simplification of the mathematical theory introduced by the absence of vorticity. This simplification extends also to motion past infinite cylinders when there is circulation but no vorticity. According to this theory there is a definite lift force on the cylinder per unit length, but still no drag force for steady motion. On the other hand, the motion of a solid body in an inviscid fluid endowed with vorticity is not, in general, easily amenable to mathematical treatment; but considerable progress has been made for those cases in which the vorticity is supposed concentrated on sheets or along lines; and in such cases, for the first time in the theory of inviscid fluids, calculation did at any rate give a definite, non-zero, drag.‡

In order to consider the former case, with circulation but no vorticity, in more detail, let us return to the steady two-dimensional flow past an infinite circular cylinder. The flow without circulation has been considered in § 7. If there is circulation but no general streaming flow, then the stream-lines are circles, as in Fig. 8, and the velocity in any circle is constant, so that, if K is the circulation, the

---

† The conditions in the footnote on p. 26 are again supposed satisfied.

‡ Kirchhoff, *Vorlesungen über mathematische Physik, Mechanik* (Leipzig, 1876), p. 307. See also Kirchhoff, *Journal für die reine und angew. Math.* **70** (1869), 295, 296; Rayleigh, *Phil. Mag.* (5), **2** (1876), 430–441; *Scientific Papers*, **1**, 287–296.

velocity at a distance r is $K/(2\pi r)$. In particular, the velocity at the surface is $K/(2\pi a)$, where a is the radius of the cylinder. If now there is both a circulation K and a general streaming with velocity U, the velocity at any point is simply the resultant of the velocities for the two motions separately. In particular, the velocity at the surface is $2U \sin \theta + K/(2\pi a)$, where θ is measured from A as before. If then

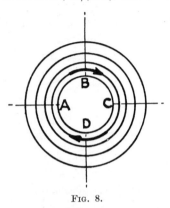

K is less than $4\pi a U$, there are two points on the circle where the velocity is zero. The stream-lines for this case are drawn in Fig. 9 (a), where the stagnation points are at A_1 and C_1. If K becomes equal to $4\pi a U$, these two stagnation points both coincide at D, as in Fig. 9 (b). The velocity at B is then $4U$. If K increases still further, then the velocity at the cylinder is everywhere in the direction corresponding to the circulation, and the stagnation point moves down

Fig. 8.

in the fluid along the prolongation of the line BD, as in Fig. 9 (c). In all cases the effect of the circulation is to increase the velocity, and therefore diminish the pressure, above the cylinder, and to diminish the velocity, and therefore increase the pressure, below the cylinder. The result is that there is a lift force on the cylinder. It may be shown that the magnitude of this force per unit length is $K\rho U$, and that, moreover, this formula applies whatever be the section of the cylinder. On the other hand, there is no drag force. This also is a general result for any section: for the circle it is clear from the diagrams, since they are symmetrical about BD. In Fig. 9 (a) the pressure falls from A_1 to B or D and then rises again to C_1; in Figs. 9 (b) and 9 (c) the pressure falls from D to B round the front or upstream side of the cylinder, and rises again round the back.

The formula $K\rho U$ for the lift per unit length has been shown experimentally to apply remarkably well to the two-dimensional flow of real fluids, when the measured value of K is inserted.† In

† See, for example, Bryant and Williams, *Phil. Trans.* A, **225** (1925), 199–237. The theoretical derivation of the formula for a real fluid, with vorticity present, when the contour around which the circulation is taken is suitably chosen, was given by G. I. Taylor, *Phil. Trans.* A, **225** (1925), 238–245, and Filon, *Proc. Roy. Soc.* A, **113** (1926), 7–27.

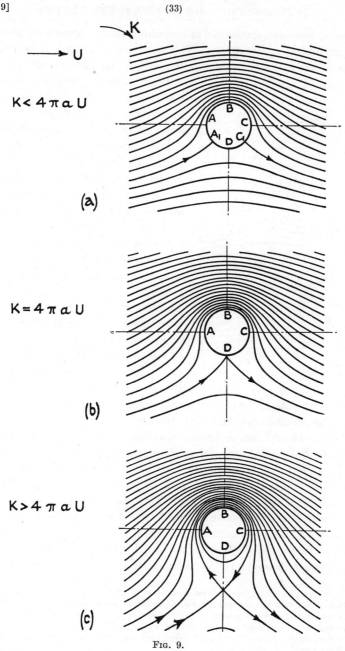

K < 4πaU

(a)

K = 4πaU

(b)

K > 4πaU

(c)

Fig. 9.

general, however, the theory of inviscid fluids can provide no means of calculating a circulation. This is possible only when the contour of the cylinder has a salient point, as for an aerofoil† with a sharp trailing edge. In such a case there is one and only one value of

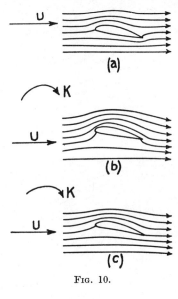

(a)

(b)

(c)

Fig. 10.

the circulation K which does not make the calculated velocity infinite at that point; and this provides a criterion for choosing one particular value for K.

The theoretical stream-lines for two-dimensional flow past such an aerofoil without circulation are shown in Fig. 10 (a). The rear stagnation point lies on the upper side of the aerofoil, and the fluid is forced to flow round the sharp trailing edge, where the velocity would become infinite. If too large a circulation were present, the rear stagnation point would lie on the lower side of the aerofoil, as in Fig. 10 (b), and the fluid would again have to flow round the sharp trailing edge. For one particular value of the circulation, the stream-lines come smoothly off from the trailing edge, as in Fig. 10 (c).‡

When, in addition to having a salient point, the section of the cylinder has a good stream-line shape, as for an aerofoil at a small inclination to the stream, the circulation calculated in this way shows fairly good agreement with the measured values in a real fluid of small viscosity. The calculated value is too large, for reasons that will be given later (Chap. II, § 25). The calculated lift coefficient is therefore also a little too large. This is illustrated in Fig. 11, where the calculated value of C_L and the measured values of C_L and C_D are plotted against the inclination α to the stream for the aerofoil

† An aeroplane wing, when considered apart from the rest of the aeroplane, is called an aerofoil. We are here considering two-dimensional motion past an aerofoil —motion past an infinitely long aerofoil or past an aerofoil between parallel walls. The motion past an aerofoil of finite length is considered in § 12.

‡ Figs. 10 (a), (b), and (c) are reproduced from an article by A. Betz in the *Handbuch der Physik*, **7** (Berlin, 1927), 221.

section shown. (The lift and drag coefficients for two-dimensional flow past an aerofoil are, by definition, $L/(\frac{1}{2}\rho U^2 c)$ and $D/(\frac{1}{2}\rho U^2 c)$ respectively, where L and D are the lift and drag per unit length and c is

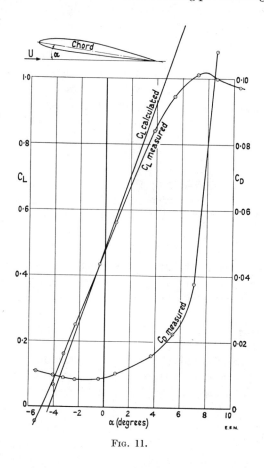

FIG. 11.

the length of the chord of the aerofoil section, as shown in the diagram.) The calculated value of C_L increases linearly with α; the calculated value of C_D is, of course, zero. It will be seen that the measured value of C_L does at first rise linearly (though with a smaller gradient than the calculated one), and that the measured value of C_D is fairly small until α is equal to about 6°. Thereafter the drag rises rapidly and the lift falls. The aerofoil is then said to be stalled. This is a phenomenon to which we shall return later (Chap. II, § 25 and Chap. X, § 209).

If the measured value of the circulation is used to calculate the pressure distribution round the body, then for a good stream-line shape there is fair agreement between the calculated and observed

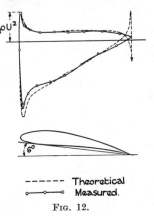

values, except near the rear, with some discrepancies also in the region of greatest suction near the nose. This is illustrated in Fig. 12, where the results for the aerofoil section shown are reproduced: the pressure defect, or suction, relates to the upper side of the aerofoil, and the pressure excess to the lower side.†

------ Theoretical
o——o——o Measured.
FIG. 12.

When the cylinder section has no salient point, the value of the circulation can be foretold only for bodies symmetrical about a line in the direction of the stream, for which the circulation must be zero. Thus, for the circular cylinder previously considered, a circulation arises, in the absence of other boundaries, only if the cylinder is rotating. (See Chap. II, § 27.)

10. The motion of inviscid fluids with concentrated vorticity. Drag.

The first theoretical deduction of a formula for the drag was provided by the so-called theory of free stream-lines, developed, for flow past a flat plate, by Kirchhoff and Rayleigh according to the methods used by Helmholtz for two-dimensional jets, and extended by Levi-Civita and others to the case of curved rigid boundaries.‡ According to this theory there is, in two-dimensional flow past a flat plate, for example, a mass of fluid at rest behind the plate, separated from the stream by two stream-lines springing from the edges of the plate, as in Fig. 13. The velocity is discontinuous across these stream-lines, which are therefore the traces of vortex-sheets. The velocity just outside the 'free' stream-lines is constant, and

† A. Betz, *Handbuch der Physik*, **7** (Berlin, 1927), 288; *Zeitschr. f. Flugtechn. u. Motorluftschiffahrt*, **6** (1915), 173.

‡ See Lamb's *Hydrodynamics* (Cambridge, 1932), pp. 94–105, and Villat, *Mécanique des Fluides* (Paris, 1933), pp. 141–154, where further references will be found.

PLATE 1

Direction of flow →

equal to the velocity U of the undisturbed stream. The pressure in the stagnant fluid is constant and equal to p_0, the pressure at infinity. This theory has considerable theoretical, but very little practical importance, its results being largely in disagreement with the results of observation in real fluids of small viscosity. Thus, for two-dimensional motion past a flat plate at right angles to the stream, the theoretical result for the drag coefficient, $D/(\frac{1}{2}\rho U^2 b)$, is 0.880, where b is the breadth of the plate: the measured value is nearly 2. The discrepancy arises largely from the fact that there is actually a defect of pressure, or suction, at the rear, the pressure being much less than p_0; for the plate at right angles to the stream it is nearly constant and equal to $p_0 - 0.7\rho U^2$ right across the rear,[†]

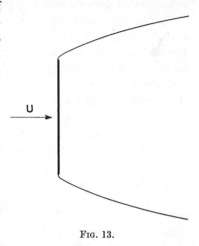

Fig. 13.

and similar features are present in other typical cases. In other important respects the theory is widely at variance with reality, since behind a bluff obstacle in a stream the observed motion either is an irregular, eddying one, or for two-dimensional motion at certain Reynolds numbers has, for some distance behind the obstacle, the appearance of a double trail of vortices with opposite rotations, as in Pl. 1.[‡] Even if a motion like that in Fig. 13, or any similar one with vortex-sheets, be supposed set up in an inviscid fluid, it would not persist, since it would be unstable.|| The notion that the stream leaves the plate at the edges is, however, valuable and in accordance with reality; and a vortex-sheet (more accurately, for real fluids, a thin vortex-layer) does begin to be formed from the edges of the plate. But this vortex-sheet or layer is not fully developed either

[†] Fage and Johansen, *Proc. Roy. Soc.* A, **96** (1927), 173.

[‡] From a paper by G. J. Richards, *A.R.C. Reports and Memoranda*, No. 1590 (1934), plate 3; *Phil. Trans.* A, **233** (1934), 279–301, plate 3, fig. 16.

|| On the other hand, the theory provides a better approximation to actual conditions when water is flowing against the plate, and the region behind the plate is filled with air or water vapour, as in the phenomenon of cavitation. In certain cases of this kind the vortex-sheets are actually much more fully formed than in motions without cavitation.

in a real or an inviscid fluid; it curls round on itself, and something much more in the nature of concentrated vortices is formed. (See Pl. 2 and p. 40 *infra*. This is not quite the phenomenon shown in Fig. 7, since the vortex-sheet begins, as it were, to curl up into a concentrated vortex before it is properly formed.)

The double row of vortices shown in Pl. 1 can be idealized, for an inviscid fluid, so that each vortex is supposed concentrated along a line at right angles to the plane of the motion. The resulting arrangement has been studied by Kármán and others. It appears that such a double row of vortices could keep its configuration unchanged, and would not be unstable for any slight displacements of the vortices parallel to themselves, only if the vortices in one row are opposite the points half-way between the vortices in the other row, as in the annexed figure, and if the distance, h, between the rows is 0·281

times the distance a between two consecutive vortices in a row.†
A double row of this type is called a Kármán vortex-street. The stream-lines for such a vortex-street, relative to the vortices, are shown in Fig. 14. Such a vortex-street would move, relative to the fluid, parallel to itself with a velocity u depending on the strength of each individual vortex. The vortex-street may be regarded as an idealization of the conditions behind a bluff obstacle in a stream; and on this basis a theory of the drag on the obstacle may be constructed, which gives for the drag force per unit length‡

$$D = \rho U^2 h \left\{ 2\cdot 83 \frac{u}{U} - 1\cdot 12 \left(\frac{u}{U}\right)^2 \right\}.$$

The double row of vortices may be observed for some distance behind any bluff obstacle, although there is a transition region just behind the obstacle before the double row may be regarded as

† The mathematical condition is $\sinh \pi h/a = 1$. Lamb, *Hydrodynamics* (Cambridge, 1932), §156, pp. 228, 229.

‡ The stability calculations are given by Lamb, *loc. cit.* For a derivation of the drag formula, see Chap. XIII, §243. The fluid is supposed unlimited in the calculations. The effect of boundaries, both on the stability and on the drag, has been considered by Rosenhead, *Phil. Trans.* A, **208** (1929), 275–329, who has also shown that, with vortices of finite cross-section, instability arises for certain longitudinal deformations (*Proc. Roy. Soc.* A, **127** (1930), 590–612). See Chap. XIII, §§244, 245.

formed, and the motion becomes irregular farther downstream, so that the regularity does not persist. Exact observation is somewhat difficult on account of the diffuse nature of the vortices in the actual flow. The results obtained, and their comparison with theory, are referred to later, in Chap. XIII, § 246.

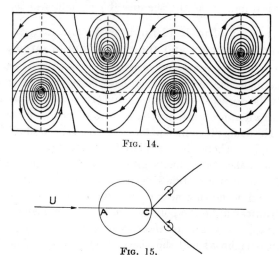

FIG. 14.

FIG. 15.

When a motion past a bluff obstacle is started from rest, then at a stage prior to that at which the double vortex row is formed there are two symmetrical vortices at the back of the obstacle, as in Chap. II, Pls. 7 and 8 (p. 63).† These may be idealized into two concentrated line vortices with opposite circulations, called shortly a vortex-pair. The motion with such a vortex-pair sym-metrically placed behind a circular cylinder in a stream has been investigated mathematically by L. Föppl,‡ who found that the vortices can maintain their position relative to the cylinder pro-vided that they lie one on each of the two symmetrically placed curves shown in Fig. 15, and have an appropriate strength, which increases with the distance of the vortices from the cylinder. Thus, by an extension of the exact theory, if we suppose the strengths of the vortices gradually to increase, they might be supposed to move gradually farther and farther from the cylinder. But the symmetrical position is found to be unstable for antisymmetrical disturbances, so

† Rubach, *Göttingen Dissertation*, 1914.
‡ *Sitzungsberichte d. k. bayer. Akad. d. Wissensch. zu München* (1913), 1–17.

that it could not be indefinitely maintained. We shall consider the observed motion later (Chap. II, § 20), noting only for the present that if the vortex-pair is in motion relative to the cylinder, or if the vortex strength is changing, or both, a drag force is exerted on the cylinder which it is possible to calculate.† But the calculation is deprived of any practical importance by the unstable character of the motion.

11. The motion of inviscid fluids with concentrated vorticity. The cast-off vortex and the production of circulation.

We have already remarked in connexion with flow past a plate that the stream leaves the plate at each edge, where a vortex-sheet begins to be formed, and that each vortex-sheet curls round on itself, with an appearance approximating to that of a concentrated vortex. The same phenomenon takes place wherever fluid flows past a salient edge, where the calculated irrotational motion, without circulation, makes the velocity infinite. We shall see later that the same phenomenon also takes place even when there is no salient edge, if the fluid flowing near a solid surface is being retarded: but then we can calculate the point where the stream leaves the surface only by taking account of the viscosity of the fluid; and this is true no matter how small the viscosity may be. In fact, if motion of a solid body relative to a fluid is started from rest, then the initial motion is the calculated irrotational motion without circulation: this changes rapidly—very rapidly if there is a salient edge—into a motion with separation of flow from the surface, as above. In order to understand the change, regard must be had to viscosity, no matter how small it may be. But the rolling up of the vortex-sheet, and the concentration of the vorticity into the rolled-up portion, is again a process which might perhaps be calculated theoretically for an inviscid fluid, and some steps in this direction have been taken by Prandtl,‡ to whom Pl. 2 a is due. A photograph of the phenomenon in a real fluid is shown in Pl. 2 b, which is also due to Prandtl.‖ When the vortex-sheet is rolled up, and the vorticity concentrated in the rolled-up portion, the further course of events depends on the circumstances, and we shall return to the subject later.

For two-dimensional flow past an aerofoil, however, we can proceed

† Föppl, *loc. cit.* See also Bickley, *Proc. Roy. Soc.* A, **119** (1928), 146–151.

‡ *Vorträge aus dem Gebiete der Hydro- und Aerodynamik, Innsbruck*, 1922 (Berlin, 1924), 18–33.

‖ *Handbuch der Experimentalphysik*, **4**, part 1 (Leipzig, 1931), 20.

PLATE 2

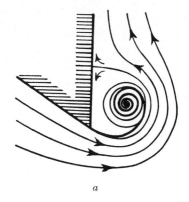

a

b

a little further immediately. The process may be described roughly
as follows:—When the motion is started from rest, then in the initial
stages of the motion a vortex-sheet begins to be formed from the
trailing edge and rolls up with the formation of a concentrated
vortex (Fig. 16), called the cast-off vortex; when the vortex has

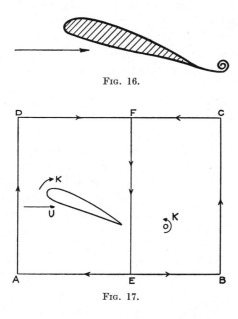

Fig. 16.

Fig. 17.

reached a certain strength, it moves away downstream (Fig. 17).
The circulation round the large circuit $ABCD$, fixed relative to the
aerofoil, was initially zero; it remains zero since no vorticity has come
near to it. But the circulation round $ABCD$ is the sum of the circulations round $AEFD$ and $EBCF$, which are, therefore, equal and
opposite to each other; the circulation round $EBCF$ is in the
direction shown by the arrows and is equal to the strength K of the
vortex; there is, therefore, a circulation K in the opposite sense
round $EADF$, or round any circuit in the fluid including the aerofoil
but not the vortex. This process may be supposed repeated, if
necessary, until there is such a circulation round the aerofoil that
the velocity at the trailing edge is finite and the flow comes smoothly
off there without any discontinuity. In this way the establishment
of such a circulation may be held to be at least partly explained.

12. The motion of inviscid fluids with concentrated vorticity. Three-dimensional aerofoil theory.

The preceding explanation refers to two-dimensional motion; that is, to motion past an aerofoil of infinite span—the span is the distance between the wing-tips—or past an aerofoil between parallel walls. The cast-off vortex is either infinitely long or ends on the walls. For motion past an aerofoil of finite span without walls there will still be a cast-off vortex, but it will be of finite length, and it will end in the fluid. It is a general theorem, however, that vortex-lines cannot begin or end in the fluid: there must, therefore, be vorticity elsewhere in the fluid. We may also argue thus:—In order that there should be a lift on the aerofoil the pressure above it must be diminished and the pressure below it increased, and hence the velocity above must be increased and the velocity below diminished from what it would be in an irrotational motion without circulation. This is accomplished if we suppose that there is a circulation round any section of the aerofoil in the correct sense. But the aerofoil being of finite span, it is now possible, without passing out of the fluid, so to move and deform any circuit that it shrinks up into a point. Hence, as explained on pp. 27, 28, if there were no vorticity in the fluid, the circulation round any circuit would be zero. It follows that there must be vorticity in the fluid, and the vortex-lines must be cut if any circuit surrounding the aerofoil is moved and deformed without passing out of the fluid so that it shrinks up into a point. The vortex-lines must, therefore, stretch from the aerofoil to the cast-off vortex.

Again, it is theoretically possible to replace the aerofoil by fluid at rest at a certain pressure with a vortex-sheet or surface of slip coincident with its surface, the whole being acted upon by certain forces so that it maintains the position that would have been occupied by the aerofoil. The vorticity so introduced is, therefore, referred to as bound vorticity, since its position and motion are prescribed. The usual theory of the aerofoil of finite span now proceeds to approximate to these conditions by supposing the bound vorticity concentrated into a single line with length equal to the span of the aerofoil. (In order that this approximation should be valid it is theoretically necessary that the thickness of the aerofoil should be small compared with the chord, a condition usually realized in practice; and also, theoretically, that the chord should be small compared with the span,—although, rather surprisingly perhaps, laboratory experiments have shown that the theory applies fairly well even when the chord and span are nearly equal. In practice the chord of an aeroplane wing may vary along the span: the mean chord is defined as the ratio of the area of the plan form of the aerofoil to its span; and the ratio of the span to the mean chord, called the aspect ratio, varies in practice from about 4 to 10.) The strength of the bound vortex-line at any point is equal to the circulation round the corresponding section of the aerofoil, and is a maximum in the middle, falling to zero at both ends.

When, for theoretical purposes, we have replaced the aerofoil by the bound vortex-line, our previous reasoning shows that there must be vortex-lines in the fluid connecting the bound vortex with the cast-off vortex: these are referred to as trailing vortices. Theory shows that they must coincide with the stream-lines. Altogether the trailing vortex-lines form a vortex-sheet or surface of discontinuity in the velocity. This discontinuity will be in the transverse component of the velocity, the longitudinal component being continuous and the transverse components equal and opposite on the two sides of the sheet,—a result which may be demonstrated theoretically from the condition that the pressure must be continuous on both sides of the sheet. As time goes on the vortex-sheet increases in length and the kinetic energy of the fluid associated with the trailing vortex system increases, so that work is being done by external agencies. This manifests itself as a drag force on the aerofoil, called the induced drag.

In the mathematical theory a second approximation is now made. It is assumed that the velocities due to the whole vortex system—bound vortex, cast-off vortex, and trailing vortices—are small compared with the velocity of the fluid relative to the aerofoil; so that the trailing vortex-lines, which must in any case coincide with the stream-lines, are assumed to be in the direction of this undisturbed relative velocity, with the cast-off vortex at their end (Fig. 18). For this approximation to be valid the circulation K round the section of the aerofoil where it is greatest must be small compared with the product of U, the undisturbed relative velocity of aerofoil and fluid, and the mean chord c. Since the lift on the aerofoil is of order $K\rho Us$, where s is the span, and the lift coefficient C_L is the lift divided by $\frac{1}{2}\rho U^2 sc$, so that it is of order $2K/Uc$, the lift coefficient must be small compared with 2. Again, the theory is experimentally verified for rather surprisingly high values of C_L.

On this basis a highly successful mathematical theory has been built up, which has served, for example, to bring into agreement results of lift and drag measurements on aerofoils of different aspect ratios, and has also provided formulae for the effects of the boundaries

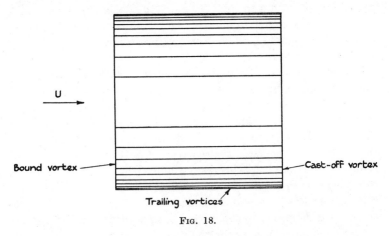

Fig. 18.

of a wind tunnel on such measurements. Two further observations may be made. First, the existence of a discontinuity in the transverse component of velocity behind an aerofoil of finite span may be physically explained from the fact that below the wing there must be an excess of pressure and above it a defect of pressure or suction, the pressures above and below becoming equal at the tips. Hence there is a pressure gradient tending to make the fluid flow outwards towards the tips below, and inwards from the tips above, as it passes over the aerofoil. This is illustrated in Fig. 19, where the first diagram represents a section of the wing perpendicular to the direction of flight, the second a view of the suction side of the wing, and the third a section of the surface of discontinuity behind the wing. Second, the trailing vortex-sheet illustrated in Fig. 18 is not a possible stable form. It would roll up at its edges, the vorticity being concentrated more and more in the rolled-up portions, until it presented the appearance of two concentrated vortices at a distance apart somewhat less than the span of the aerofoil. The process, which would take place somewhat after the manner illustrated in

PLATE 3

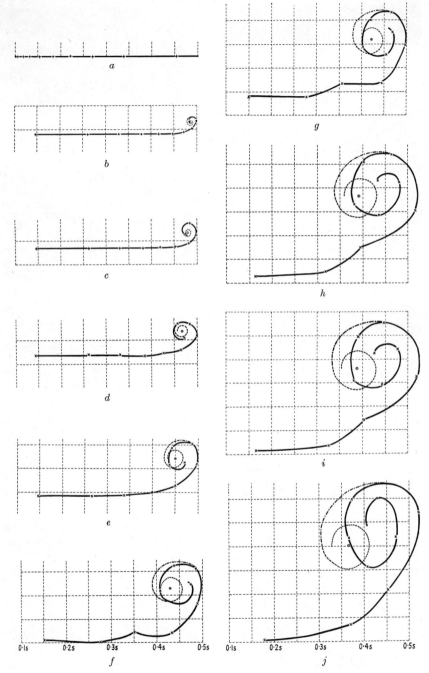

s = span

PLATE 4

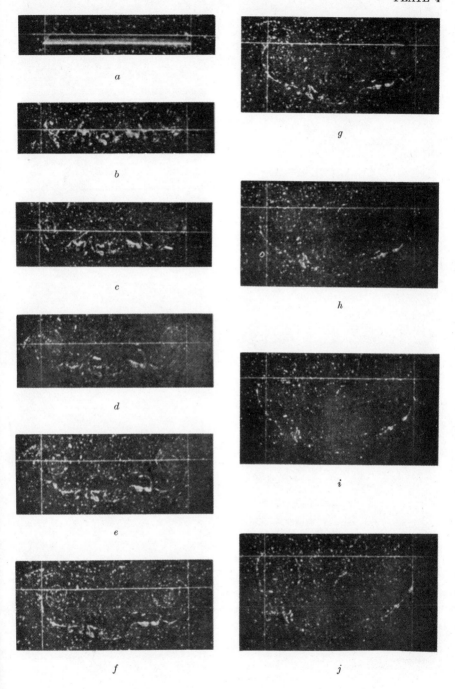

Fig. 20,† has not yet been followed through mathematically. Approximate calculations for the rolling-up of a vortex-sheet of finite breadth, but extending to infinity along its length in both directions, have been carried out by Westwater,‡ some of whose results are shown in Pl. 3. (The full-line curves are drawn through the calculated positions of individual vortices by which, as an approximation, the sheet was replaced. The dotted curves are spirals calculated by a slight

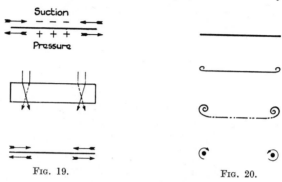

Fig. 19.   Fig. 20.

extension of a method due to Kaden, and the broken lines simply represent a plausible join between the other two sets of curves.) Photographs of the process taking place in a real fluid are reproduced in Pl. 4.‖ It will be seen that the calculated drawings and the photographs here reproduced roughly correspond to each other, in order. In an inviscid fluid this transformation of a vortex-sheet does not affect the energy and momentum associated with it, and so the mathematical calculations mentioned above, based on its continued existence without deformation, are still valid, In any case, the deformation is due to the velocity induced by the vortex system itself, which has already been assumed small; and so, logically, the process could in any case be neglected for a first approximation.

The theory is known as the Lanchester-Prandtl theory.†† It should

† For Figs. 19 and 20 compare Betz, *Handbuch der Physik*, **7** (Berlin, 1927), 239, 241.

‡ *A.R.C. Reports and Memoranda*, No. 1692 (1936). See also Prandtl, *Göttinger Nachrichten* (1919), reprinted in *Vier Abhandlungen zur Hydrodynamik und Aerodynamik*, L. Prandtl and A. Betz (Göttingen, 1927; see particularly pp. 60–67); Kaden, *Ingenieur-Archiv*, **2** (1931), 140–168; Betz, *Zeitschr.f. angew. Math. u. Mech.* **12** (1932), 164–174.   ‖ Kaden, *op. cit.*, p. 166.

†† Lanchester, *Aerodynamics* (London, 1907), chap. iv; *The Flying Machine* (London, 1915), being a reprint from the *Proc. Institution of Automobile Engineers*, **9** (1915), 171-259; Prandtl, *Göttinger Nachrichten* (1918), 451–477; (1919), 107–137.

be noticed that a trailing vortex system and an induced drag, connected with an increase of energy of that system, are associated with flow past any finite body on which a lift is exerted; and that a circulation arises round each section of any body and a lift force results unless the body is symmetrical about a plane parallel to the velocity of the fluid. But it is only for a stream-line body with a salient edge, like an aerofoil with a sharp trailing edge, that anything approaching a valid mathematical theory can be constructed by using the conception of an inviscid fluid.

This closes our account of the attempts of inviscid fluid theory to imitate, with the help of circulation and concentrated vorticity, the actual flow of a fluid of small viscosity past solid bodies. We must now point out that, as a consequence of the theorems on p. 30 concerning the vorticity in an inviscid fluid, any finite portion of a fluid in motion, if once moving irrotationally, continues to move irrotationally ever afterwards. In general, it follows that a motion which has originated from rest is irrotational, since the vorticity is originally everywhere zero; exceptionally, the theorems do not forbid the appearance of vortex-sheets springing from the boundaries of immersed solid bodies, something after the manner of Figs. 13, 16 and Pl. 2, since the continued absence of vorticity is asserted, not for regions of space, but for portions of matter. The same result may be otherwise expressed:—All valid proofs of the impossibility of the appearance of vorticity in an inviscid fluid, when the motion is started from rest, depend on the hypothesis that the velocity is continuous; so they do not exclude concentrated vorticity. That Kelvin's theorem on the constancy of the circulation is not violated by vortex-sheets springing from the boundaries of immersed bodies, has been clearly explained by Prandtl.† But it may be felt that the existence of such vortex-sheets, which are surfaces of discontinuity in the fluid, still stands in considerable need of elucidation: so too, therefore, does the appearance of circulation; and all the more so because of the theorem that if a motion is started impulsively from rest, the initial motion is irrotational without circulation.

13. The motion of a solid body in a uniformly rotating fluid.

Even if we are willing to assume the existence of diffused vorticity, and thereafter to neglect viscosity, the motion of a solid body in a

† *Journ. Roy. Aero. Soc.* **31** (1927), 722, 723.

fluid possessing vorticity is not in general amenable to calculation. There is one exception, which, though rather apart from our main line of investigation, is of considerable interest, since theoretical predictions can be made which either do not depend on the conditions at the boundary of the solid body, or which give no relative velocity of solid and fluid at such a boundary. We refer to motion in a uniformly rotating fluid.† Thus certain predictions concerning the differences to be expected between the motion of a solid body in a fluid when the whole system is rotating from when it is not rotating do not depend on the boundary conditions. For example, it may be shown that if in the rotating system a cylinder between parallel walls at right angles to its axis and to the axis of rotation has the same density as the fluid and is acted on by an external force through the axis of rotation, then it moves in the direction of the force; but that if a symmetrical three-dimensional body, such as a sphere, of the same density as the fluid, is so acted upon, it follows a curved path; and, if the fluid is rotating in the clockwise direction when seen from above, it leaves the axis of rotation on its right. This has been experimentally confirmed. Again, it may be shown that any small steady motion of a rotating fluid relative to the rotating system must be two-dimensional. This also is confirmed by experiment. If a three-dimensional body is moved slowly and uniformly through water rotating at a considerable speed, the motion produced is, in fact, steady and two-dimensional. When, for example, a cylinder with generators parallel to the axis of rotation is moved slowly in a closed rotating tank whose height is greater than that of the cylinder, the motion of the fluid relative to the rotating system is the same as if the cylinder had extended from the top to the bottom of the tank. Thus, if the generators of the cylinder be supposed produced to meet the top and bottom of the tank, the fluid inside the surface so formed moves like a solid body. There is a stagnation point at the front of every section of this partly fluid cylinder, and the motion of the fluid outside this cylinder is in all other respects the same as if the whole cylinder were truly solid, provided that the rotation is fast enough. Similar results are obtained with a sphere. In a rather different category is the calculation of the steady motion of a non-rotating sphere along the axis of rotation in a rotating fluid. Here

† G. I. Taylor, *Proc. Roy. Soc.* A, **93** (1907), 99–113; **100** (1921), 114–121; **102** (1922), 180–189; **104** (1923), 213–218; *Proc. Camb. Phil. Soc.* **20** (1921), 326–329.

it is possible to obtain a solution of the equations of motion of an inviscid fluid which does not involve slip at the surface of the sphere. (It should be again emphasized that such a solution is impossible in a non-rotating fluid.) Since the relative velocity of the fluid at the surface of the sphere is zero, the fluid streaming past the sphere as it moves along the axis does not tend to rotate it. This also has been experimentally verified. A ping-pong ball, initially rotating with the water contained in a tall rotating jar, stops rotating as soon as it is moved along the axis of the jar and starts rotating again as soon as its motion along the axis ceases, provided that its motion along the axis is not too slow. A physical explanation of this phenomenon is obtained by considering that the fluid flowing past the surface of the sphere was all in the neighbourhood of the axis. As it flows over the sphere its distance from the axis is increased. Its angular momentum remains unchanged, and so its velocity of rotation about the axis is reduced practically to zero. On the other hand, if the motion of the sphere along the axis is too slow, the motion tends to become two-dimensional, with the formation of a cylindrical dead-water region extending above the sphere and moving with it.

14. Inviscid fluid theory and observation in real fluids.

The interest and importance of the calculations and experiments described in the preceding section lie in the demonstration they afford of the manner in which the motion of a real fluid of small viscosity may be foretold by calculation for a fluid of zero viscosity, when the boundary conditions are either satisfied or not involved. Apart from them we may say, in general terms, that inviscid fluid theory can reproduce conditions near the forward stagnation point of a bluff obstacle, or over most of the surface of a stream-line body, if the circulation is suitably chosen. Skin-friction is naturally beyond its scope, and the drag of a stream-line body is mainly, though not entirely, due to skin-friction. The drag of a bluff obstacle, on the other hand, is mainly the resultant of normal pressure, called form drag; and (apart from the theory of the induced drag associated with trailing vortices for a body such as an aerofoil of finite span) the theory of the vortex-street is the only theory we possess for form drag. When we consider fluids of small viscosity, we shall have to explain first why inviscid fluid theory ever gives approximately correct results, since it involves slip over the surface; how circulation and vorticity make their appearance; how to calculate skin-friction; how to calculate the circulation and the lift for a stream-line body without a salient edge; and how to calculate the pressure distribution, the drag, and the lift for a bluff body. We may state at once that we can make very little progress indeed with this last calculation beyond what has already been mentioned in connexion with the theory of the vortex-street.†

† For certain mathematically elegant attempts of Oseen and others to find the limit of the steady motion of a viscous fluid when the viscosity tends to zero, reference may be made to Oseen, *Hydrodynamik* (Leipzig, 1927), where further references will be found. It seems probable that the limit is given by the motion of the free stream-line theory which, as we have already pointed out, is unstable. Compare Friedrichs and Prandtl, *Vorträge aus dem Gebiete der Aerodynamik und verwandter Gebiete, Aachen*, 1929 (Berlin, 1930), pp. 51–53. See also Squire, *Phil. Mag.* (7), **17** (1934), 1150–1160.

INTRODUCTION. BOUNDARY LAYER THEORY

15. Boundary layer theory.† Flow along a solid surface.

WHEN a fluid flows past a fixed solid boundary the fluid immediately in contact with the wall is at rest. It is, however, a matter of common observation that, for a fluid of small viscosity like water or air, if

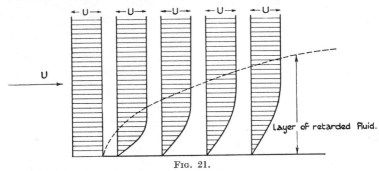

FIG. 21.

the distance the fluid has travelled along the wall is not too long, then the velocity rises rapidly from zero at the wall to its value in the main stream, the rise taking place within a thin layer of fluid next to the wall. In this layer the velocity gradient is very large, so that, even if the viscosity is small, the tangential stresses may exert a considerable influence upon the motion. If, for example, fluid is flowing along a flat plate and the velocity in the stream has a constant value U, then the velocity rises from zero at the plate to the value U within a very small distance from the plate. When the stream arrives at the forward edge of the plate the fluid practically has the velocity U at all distances from the plate: the fluid next to the plate is then forced to remain at rest while the main stream flows on with velocity U. In this way tangential stresses are brought into play, which retard the fluid next to that in contact with the plate. This retarding effect of the internal tangential stresses gradually spreads farther and farther, so that as the fluid flows along the plate the width of the layer of retarded fluid at the plate continually increases. This is illustrated in Fig. 21, where graphs of the velocity

† The theory is due to Prandtl, *Verhandlungen des dritten internationalen Mathematiker-Kongresses, Heidelberg*, 1904 (Leipzig, 1905), 484–491; reprinted in *Vier Abhandlungen zur Hydrodynamik und Aerodynamik*, L. Prandtl and A. Betz (Göttingen, 1927).

against distance from the plate are shown for various sections, the distance from the wall being shown on a greatly enlarged scale.

Since the velocity parallel to the wall, which we now denote by u, is changing, continuity requires that there should be a velocity perpendicular to the wall,† and this velocity we denote by v. The velocity v is small. Thus, if AB and CD represent sections inside the retarded layer, with AC along the wall, the flow across the section AB is greater than that across CD, so that there must be a flow out through BD; but since the lengths of AB and CD are small, of the same order of magnitude as the width δ of the retarded layer, v is also small, of the same order of magnitude. The argument may be given in greater detail in a dimensionally correct form. The differ-

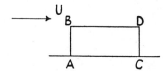

ence in the forward velocities at corresponding points of AB and CD is of the same order as U, and hence the difference in the volumes of fluid flowing per unit time across two sections, each of breadth b, represented by AB and CD respectively, is of the order of $Ub\delta$. If AC or BD is of length l, the volume flowing per unit time outwards across a surface of breadth b, represented by BD, is of order vbl; and since no fluid flows across the surface of the wall, represented by AC, continuity requires that the flux across BD should balance the excess of the flux across AB over that across CD. Hence v must be of the same order as $U\delta/l$. In this expression l may for the present be supposed to be any moderate fraction of the length of the plate measured from its leading edge.

Again, the mass of the fluid flowing per unit time across a section of breadth b, represented by AB, is of the order of $\rho Ub\delta$, and its forward momentum of the order of $\rho U^2 b\delta$, where ρ is the density. The momentum flowing per unit time across a section of the same breadth represented by CD is of the same order. The mass flowing across the surface represented by BD is of order ρvbl, and its forward momentum is of order $\rho Uvbl$. By the result above concerning the order of

† We are considering a two-dimensional motion, so that, if, for example, the flow is along a flat plate of finite breadth, we restrict our considerations to the portion of the plate far from the side edges.

magnitude of v, this is of the same order as $\rho U^2 b\delta$. Thus, if we consider the fluid inside a volume of breadth b and section $ABDC$, the rate at which forward momentum is being carried across its surface per unit time is of order $\rho U^2 b\delta$, and this also represents the change in the forward momentum of the fluid in unit time. We have so far considered the lengths of AB and CD as equal, as in the previous figure; but the argument remains unaltered if they are somewhat different, so long as each is of the same order of magnitude as δ. In particular, the result still applies if AB and CD have the thickness of the retarded layer at their respective sections, so that $ABDC$ represents the whole of the retarded layer between the two sections, as in the figure below. In that

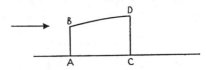

case it is the frictional force on the portion of the wall represented by AC which produces the change in the momentum of the fluid, and this frictional force must therefore be of order $\rho U^2 b\delta$. The area on which it acts is bl, and so the shearing stress at the wall must be of order $\rho U^2 \delta/l$. But the velocity rises from zero at the wall to U in the main stream over a length δ, so that the velocity gradient at the wall is of order U/δ, and the shearing stress of order $\mu U/\delta$ or $\rho \nu U/\delta$, where μ is the viscosity and ν the kinematic viscosity. This must be of the same order, then, as $\rho U^2 \delta/l$. Hence δ^2 must be of the same order as $\nu l/U$, and δ of the same order as $(\nu l/U)^{\frac{1}{2}}$. Now Ul/ν is a Reynolds number; if we denote it by R, then δ/l is of order $R^{-\frac{1}{2}}$. We may also notice that the skin-friction drag on an area bl is of order $\rho U^2 b\delta$, or $\rho \nu^{\frac{1}{2}} U^{\frac{3}{2}} bl^{\frac{1}{2}}$. In particular, then, the skin-friction drag varies as $U^{\frac{3}{2}}$. To find the coefficient of skin-friction drag we must divide by $\frac{1}{2}\rho U^2 bl$, so that this coefficient varies as $(\nu/Ul)^{\frac{1}{2}}$, or $R^{-\frac{1}{2}}$.[†]

The effect of the velocity v is to give any element of the fluid a small velocity towards or away from the wall; and since u varies very rapidly with distance from the wall, this may have an appreciable effect in changing the forward velocity of the fluid element,— that is, it may have an appreciable effect on its forward acceleration. Apart from this the velocity at right angles to the wall may be neglected and the flow thought of as a simple shearing motion, having

[†] The result does not apply if the motion is turbulent. See § 24 and Chap. VIII, § 163.

only the velocity u in a fixed direction parallel to the wall, with u depending only on the distance y from the wall. The internal friction then gives rise simply to shearing stresses $\mu \, \partial u / \partial y$ parallel to the flow, and the vorticity is $\partial u / \partial y$ in the sense shown by the arrow in the figure on p. 28. The influence of the shearing stresses at right angles to the wall is, then, small. The acceleration at right angles to the wall is also small. The only other cause giving rise to acceleration in addition to shearing stresses is a pressure gradient. Hence the pressure gradient at right angles to the wall must be small. It is of order δ, as we shall see more exactly in Chap. IV. Hence the pressure is very nearly constant throughout any section, and is equal to its value just outside the boundary layer.

We have so far considered the velocity, and therefore also the pressure, just outside the boundary layer to be constant and the walls to be straight. Similar results hold if there is a pressure gradient parallel to the wall, or if the wall is curved. In the latter case, however, there must be a pressure gradient perpendicular to the wall in the retarded layer in order to balance the centrifugal force. The approximation that the pressure is constant across any section is then not as accurate as for a straight wall; but although the pressure gradient perpendicular to the wall is now moderate and not small, the total change of pressure in that direction takes place over a length of order δ and is, therefore, still small. The pressure may still, then, be considered approximately constant over any section. Our other results also apply as before. Thus, if in a two-dimensional motion y is distance perpendicular to the wall and u the velocity parallel to it, the viscous stresses may still be taken as $\mu \, \partial u / \partial y$ tangential to surfaces parallel to the wall, and the vorticity of magnitude $\partial u / \partial y$. Also, if d is a representative length of the system, δ is of order $(\nu d / U)^{\frac{1}{2}}$, or δ / d of order $R^{-\frac{1}{2}}$, where R is the Reynolds number $U d / \nu$. The skin-friction drag on any surface varies (for non-turbulent motion) as $U^{\frac{3}{2}}$,[†] which is expressed non-dimensionally by saying that the coefficient of skin-friction drag varies as $R^{-\frac{1}{2}}$.

In flow along a flat plate parallel to the stream the velocity at any section does not depend sensibly on what happens behind it, and cannot, therefore, depend on the total length of the plate. The correct representative length is not the length of the plate, therefore, but simply the distance x of the section we are considering from the

† This result was given by Lanchester, *Aerodynamics* (London, 1907), p. 51.

forward edge of the plate. In this case δ varies accurately as $(\nu x/U)^{\frac{1}{2}}$, so that the thickness of the boundary layer grows parabolically. The shearing stress at the wall is inversely proportional to δ, so that it varies as $x^{-\frac{1}{2}}$.†

Although we began by suggesting that our approximations are valid only if δ is small, the more accurate criterion expressed non-dimensionally must be, quite generally for any system, that δ/d is small or Ud/ν large. Thus, in particular, although the boundary layer along a flat plate continually increases in thickness with the distance from the forward edge, yet δ/x continually decreases, so that our approximation should get better and better. But, as we shall see later (§ 24), the steady flow breaks down when Ux/ν is too large, and the motion then becomes turbulent.

16. Boundary layers in the inlet lengths of pipes.

Boundary layers are formed whenever a fluid of small viscosity flows past a solid obstacle. They are also formed in the 'inlet lengths' of pipes (p. 21 and Chap. VII, § 139). With certain types of entry, for example, the flow when it enters the pipe is uniform over a cross-section. Later, the fluid near the walls is retarded, with consequent acceleration of the central portions in order to ensure that the flux is the same across all sections. The retarded layer grows in thickness until it fills the whole tube, and ultimately the final distribution of velocity (parabolic for non-turbulent flow) is attained. While the central portions are being accelerated in the inlet length, the pressure gradient along the pipe is greater than when the final stage is established. Further, according to the foregoing results, for steady flow the width of the retarded layer increases at first in proportion to the square root of the distance from the entry; farther downstream the increase is slower (Chap. VII, § 139). The increase is much more rapid when the motion is turbulent (Chap. VIII, § 162).

† That the stress would decrease as x increased, and the reason therefor, were clearly recognized by W. Froude in his *Report on Experiments for the Determination of the Frictional Resistance of Water* (London, 1874), p. 4: 'The portion of surface that goes first in the line of motion, in experiencing resistance from the water, must in turn communicate motion to the water in the direction in which it is itself travelling; and consequently the portion of surface which succeeds the first will be rubbing, not against stationary water, but against water partially moving in its own direction, and cannot therefore experience as much resistance from it.' This explanation is so worded as to apply to a flat plate towed through stationary water, but the frictional stress will depend, of course, only on the relative motion, and the explanation is fundamentally the same for a plate fixed in a stream.

17. Theoretical arguments for the existence of boundary layers. Diffusion of vorticity.

We have so far simply assumed the existence, adjacent to solid boundaries, of thin layers of retarded fluid in which the influence of the viscous stresses was appreciable without being predominant. The existence of such layers cannot, it is true, be demonstrated mathematically with full rigour; but theory does tell us that there must be regions somewhere in the fluid where the viscous stresses have an appreciable though not predominant influence, and it is natural to look for such regions, in the first place, near the boundaries of solid bodies, where theoretical solutions in the absence of viscous stresses would imply a slip that cannot really take place. This does not, of course, preclude their existence elsewhere. Further, the few mathematical solutions of the equations of motion of a viscous fluid that we possess do give, for high Reynolds numbers, results entirely in agreement with the boundary layer theory in all cases where such agreement is to be expected. But perhaps the most satisfactory theoretical explanation of the existence of boundary layers comes from the theorems concerning the convection and diffusion of vorticity. We have seen that vorticity is convected with the stream and at the same time diffuses like heat, with the kinematic viscosity ν taking the place of the thermometric conductivity κ; and we know that, if a concentrated source of heat is applied anywhere to a body, then, after t seconds, its effect is appreciable at distances of the order of $(\kappa t)^{\frac{1}{2}}$ centimetres. Now, when the stream arrives at the forward edge of the flat plate we have previously considered, the fluid in contact with the plate is at rest and the fluid immediately above has the velocity U. This implies very intense vorticity, which diffuses as the fluid flows over the plate. The time required for the fluid to traverse a distance x along the plate is of order x/U. In this time the vorticity has become appreciable in a layer of order $(\nu x/U)^{\frac{1}{2}}$. This is the order of thickness of the boundary layer.†

The argument from diffusion of vorticity is even more satisfactory in explaining the growth of the boundary layer when motion of a solid body is started from rest. The initial motion is found, both theoretically and experimentally, to be irrotational without circulation. This implies slip at the surface. But the fluid immediately in

† Jeffreys, *Phil. Mag.* (6), **50** (1925), 815–819; *Proc. Roy. Soc.* A, **128** (1930), 380, 381.

contact with the surface must be at rest. The fluid next to it is, therefore, slipping over it with a finite velocity. We may express this by
saying that the thickness of the boundary layer is initially zero;
there is a vortex-sheet, or sheet of concentrated vorticity, surrounding the body. This vorticity immediately begins to diffuse, and after
t seconds the thickness of the boundary layer is of the order of $(\nu t)^{\frac{1}{2}}$
centimetres.

The diffusion of vorticity that takes place when fluid flows past a
solid obstacle may be contrasted with that which takes place when
fluid is contained within a vessel—for example, a cylinder—which is
made to rotate. In both cases, vorticity cannot originate in the
interior of the fluid, but must be diffused inwards from the boundaries. In the latter case, initially the fluid is at rest and the surface
is rotating; finally the system is rotating as a whole. Viscosity works
in this case by accumulation of effect. Vorticity, created at the
boundary, is continually being diffused into the fluid; it cannot
escape, and the process goes on until the whole system is rotating
as if solid, when no further vorticity is created at the boundary.
In the former case, however—that of flow past an obstacle—the
vorticity created at the boundary is being convected downstream
with the fluid; the result, as we shall see, is that vorticity is practically
confined to the boundary layer and to a wake behind the body with a
width increasing downstream. Quite generally, if the viscosity is small,
its effects can be important only if there is a region of intense rate
of shear in the fluid, or if the effects can accumulate in a limited
space. It is with the former case that we are more particularly concerned.

18. Separation of the forward flow. Flow through a diffuser. Flow along a curved surface.

We may now consider in more detail the course of events when the
fluid is moving against a pressure gradient parallel to the wall. Since
the pressure is nearly constant across any section of the boundary
layer, this pressure gradient is operative right through the layer.
Now the motion of a thin stratum of fluid adjacent to the wall, and
wholly inside the boundary layer, is determined by three causes. It
is retarded by friction at the bounding wall; it is pulled forward by
the stream above it through the action of viscosity; and it is retarded
by the adverse pressure gradient. If the pressure gradient had been

favourable, it would have continued its forward motion; but, as we
have seen, its forward velocity is small because of the effect of the
wall, and its energy and momentum are therefore small, and may be
insufficient for it to force its way for very long against an adverse
pressure gradient. It is then brought to rest, and, farther on, next
to the wall, a slow back-flow in the direction of the pressure gradient
may set in. The forward stream then leaves the surface. The course

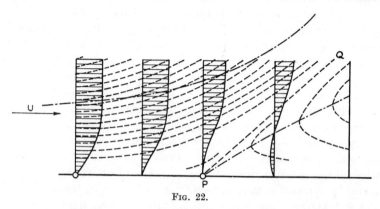

Fig. 22.

of events is illustrated in Fig. 22, where, the wall being drawn straight
for convenience, graphs of the velocity against distance from the
wall are shown for various sections. The upper chain-dotted line
represents the limit of the boundary layer, the lower chain-dotted
line the limit of the small back-flow. The stream-lines are shown as
broken lines across the figure. A thin layer of vorticity thus leaves
the wall and makes its appearance in the interior of the fluid, where
it corresponds, for a real fluid, to the vortex-sheets previously considered in an inviscid one. This explains the statement previously
made (Chap. I, § 11, p. 40) that such sheets (or for real fluids, thin
layers) of vorticity can make their appearance whenever the fluid, in
streaming past a solid surface, is being retarded. The separation of
the flow from the surface may be said to begin at P, where $\partial u/\partial y$
at the wall vanishes.† The position of this point can be calculated if
the pressure distribution outside the boundary layer is given. This
last condition should be emphasized: the mathematical calculations

---

† This explanation was given by Prandtl in his original paper (*loc. cit.*, p. 50),
from which Fig. 22 is taken with some changes. Lanchester gave a similar explanation
in less detail (*Aerodynamics*, p. 134).

based on the theory require the pressure distribution as a datum; they can do nothing to help us find it. If the pressure gradient is in the direction of the flow, or in any case where no separation occurs, the vorticity is confined to the boundary layer; also it is only in that layer that the viscous stresses have an appreciable effect: thus the pressure distribution can be found, at any rate approximately, from the theory of an inviscid fluid without vorticity. If, however, separation takes place, then there is vorticity elsewhere in the fluid: the whole picture is different from any that that theory could give us, and in general the pressure distribution can be found only by experiment. An important conclusion from theory is, however, that if the pressure distribution is unchanged, the position of P will be independent of the Reynolds number. Thus in the limit, if the Reynolds number became infinite and the thickness of the boundary layer zero, we should still have separation of flow from the surface. On the other hand, the angle the stream-line PQ makes with the boundary would decrease as the Reynolds number increased, the whole diagram being reduced in scale perpendicular to the wall in inverse proportion to the square root of the Reynolds number.

A well-known example in which the flow separates from the walls in this way is that of flow through a diffuser, or pipe of increasing cross-section. In this case, since in a steady motion the same amount of fluid must pass through any cross-section if the flow followed the walls, the velocity would decrease and the pressure would increase as the cross-section increased. The fluid in the boundary layers at the walls is, therefore, moving against a pressure gradient; and after a certain distance, which may be expected to be shorter the greater the pressure gradient (i.e. the more rapid the expansion) the stream leaves the walls and forms a jet. This is illustrated by the photograph in Pl. 5 a.† A picture of two single stream-lines is shown in Pl. 5 b.‡ When the fluid leaves the walls the expected pressure increase no longer takes place.‖ That the effect is due to the pressure gradient rather than to

† Prandtl, *Journ. Roy. Aero. Soc.* **31** (1927), 735.

‡ Due to W. S. Farren.

‖ It is interesting to notice that this explanation of the phenomenon, which was itself known long before Prandtl first put forward the boundary layer theory, was to a considerable extent anticipated by W. Froude (*Report of the British Association for 1875*, p. 229). He was exhibiting an experiment in which fluid was flowing from a discharging cistern into a receiving cistern, with a free jet in between, the discharge and reception being through two projecting tubes with cross-sections diminishing from the cisterns. He says: 'You observe as I diminish the supply of water and

PLATE 5

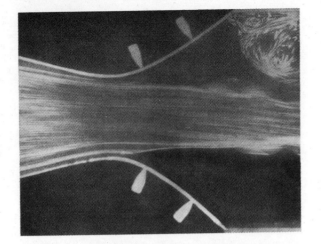

a

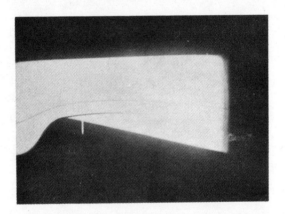

b

c

any other property associated with the expansion is demonstrated by an experiment due to Farren, who constructed a pipe with rectangular cross-section such that the length of one side increased and the length of the other side diminished, the area remaining constant, along the pipe. When fluid flows through such a pipe there is no separation of flow from the walls. A photograph of an expanding longitudinal section of such a pipe is shown in Pl. 5 c.

The same phenomenon of separation of flow, with the appearance of appreciable vorticity in the fluid, takes place in flow past a curved surface. Thus in flow past a circular cylinder, if the motion were irrotational as shown in Fig. 3, p. 23, the fluid flowing over the surface down the pressure gradient from A to B or D would acquire just sufficient momentum and energy to carry it, in the absence of friction, up the pressure gradient again to C. In a real fluid this does not happen. The forward flowing fluid in the boundary layer leaves the surface; the expected rise of pressure towards the rear does not take place, and the pressure distribution over the surface becomes, in consequence, quite different from that corresponding to Fig. 3, except near the forward stagnation point. We proceed to consider in more detail the course of events when the motion past a bluff symmetrical obstacle is started from rest.

19. Motion past a bluff symmetrical obstacle.

When the motion past any body is started from rest, the initial motion is practically irrotational. The thickness of the boundary layer is initially practically zero, with what amounts to a vortex-sheet

allow the excess of head in the discharger to become reduced, a steadily increasing waste becomes established between the orifices; and it is interesting to trace exactly the manner in which the friction operates to produce this result.

'If the conoids of discharge and reception are tolerably short as they are here, it is the outer annuli or envelopes of the stream which are in the first instance affected, that is to say, retarded, by friction; and the escape or waste between the orifices implies that this surface-retardation has reduced the velocity of those envelopes below that due to the head in the recipient; thus an annular counter-current is able to establish itself, and in fact constitutes a counter discharge from the recipient.

'As the head in the discharger is more and more reduced, the diminishing velocity of the central inflow into the recipient offers less and less frictional resistance to the annular counter-current which envelops it, and the waste continually increases.'

In 1918 Lord Rayleigh (*Phil. Mag.* (6), **36** (1918), 315, 316; *Scientific Papers*, **6** 552, 553) remarks that 'if the expansion be made too violently, the fluid refuses to follow the walls, eddies result, and mechanical energy is lost by fluid friction. According to W. Froude's generally accepted view, the explanation is to be sought in the loss of velocity near the walls in consequence of fluid friction, which is such that the fluid in question is unable to penetrate into what should be the region of higher pressure beyond.'

round the body. The vorticity diffuses and the boundary layer grows
in thickness. After a certain short time separation of flow from the
surface of the body begins. For the circular cylinder this time is
roughly proportional to the radius and inversely proportional to the

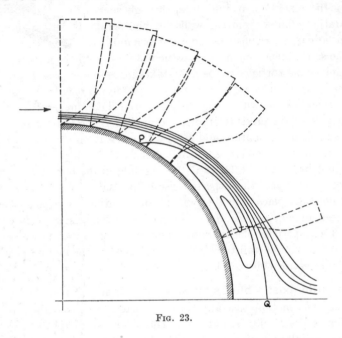

Fig. 23.

speed, and separation begins at the rear stagnation point. In general,
separation begins somewhere near the point where the velocity just
outside the boundary layer is decreasing most rapidly as we go round
the surface in the direction of the flow; and the time required is
shorter the smaller the radius of curvature. The point of separation
then moves forward until it reaches an almost stationary position.
The calculated stream-lines in the boundary layer over the rear portion of a circular cylinder moving with constant acceleration, when
the point of separation has advanced rather more than 60° from the
rear stagnation point, are shown in Fig. 23.† If the radius of the
cylinder is taken as 10 cm., the kinematic viscosity as 0·01 cm.²/sec.,
and the acceleration as 0·1 cm./sec.², this diagram corresponds to

† Blasius, *Zeitschr. f. Math. u. Physik*, **56** (1908), 37. The velocity graphs have been
added.

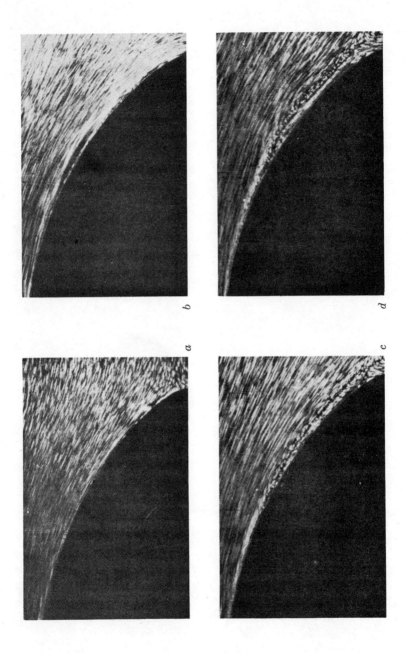

a

b

c

d

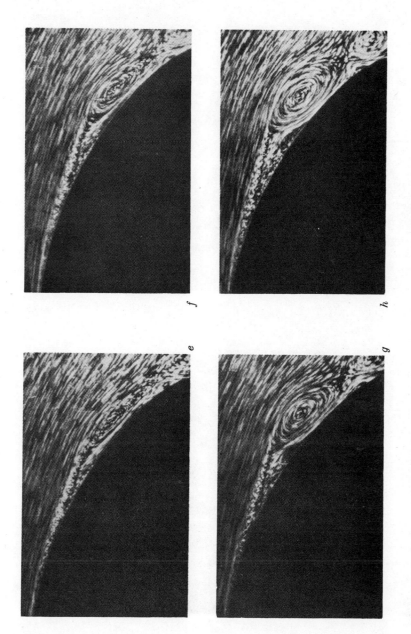

e

f

g

h

PLATE 6   From L. Prandtl and O. Tietjens, *Hydro- und Aeromechanik,* 2 *(Dover reprint)*

(over)

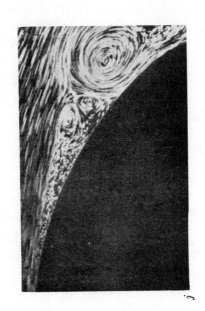

i

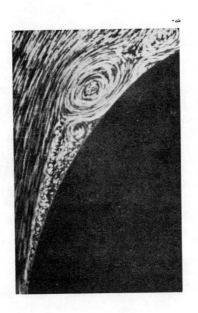

j

PLATE 6 (concluded)

15·8 seconds after the beginning of the motion. If the acceleration were 10 cm./sec.², the diagram would correspond to 1·58 seconds after the beginning of the motion, and the thickness of the boundary layer would be reduced in the ratio of 1 : √10. The dotted lines represent the graphs of the velocity against distance from the boundary. The closed stream-lines represent a vortex, but the velocity and vorticity therein are very small. The vorticity is greatest outside the stream-line PQ. (No claim to great accuracy can be made for the diagram, since the boundary layer thickens considerably beyond the point of separation, and this also has an effect on the pressure distribution.) A general photographic view of the development of the separation over the rear of a solid body is given in Pl. 6.†

The vorticity leaving the surface is meanwhile convected down-stream, diffusing at the same time. The vorticity in the fluid is practically confined to the boundary layer and to a region behind the body known in all cases as the wake. Ultimately the wake must continually increase in breadth owing to the diffusion of vorticity. The ultimate spread of the vorticity in the wake, however, actually takes place by turbulent mixing rather than by the molecular processes giving rise to viscosity.

For the circular cylinder Hiemenz,‡ who was the first to determine simultaneously the final stationary position of the point of separation by experiment and by calculation from an observed pressure distribution, found that it was about 82° from the forward stagnation point (the pressure minimum occurring at about 70° and the Reynolds number being about $1·85 \times 10^4$). Subsequent experimenters have all found values round about 80° at Reynolds numbers sufficiently low to ensure that the flow in the boundary layer up to the point of separation is steady and not turbulent.‖

We have seen that, when a motion is started from rest, the time before separation of flow begins from the surface is shorter the smaller the radius of curvature at the point where it begins. At a sharp projecting edge, where the radius of curvature is zero, the calculations on which the assertion is based cease to be valid; but we might nevertheless expect that separation will begin from the sharp edges

† Prandtl and Tietjens, *Hydro- und Aeromechanik*, **2** (Berlin, 1931), plates 12–14, figs. 24–33.

‡ Hiemenz, *Göttingen Dissertation*, 1911; *Dingler's Polytech. Journ.* **326** (1911), 321–324.

‖ See, for example, Fage, *Phil. Mag.* (7), **7** (1929), 253–273, especially p. 265.

almost instantaneously. This, in fact, does happen. Previously this separation was explained by cavitation: in the initial motion, which is practically irrotational, there would be extremely low pressures at the edges, so that, for water, separation of the dissolved air and evaporation would ensue, and, for air, rapid expansion would take place. But, as a rule, the motion has been modified by viscosity, so that the large suction is avoided, before any rupture or expansion takes place.

The process of the separation of flow takes place in a somewhat similar manner when the flow is three-dimensional. Calculations, for example, for a sphere starting impulsively from rest have been carried out by Boltze,† who showed that separation begins at the rear stagnation point when the sphere has moved a distance equal to about two-fifths of its radius. The line of separation then moves forward, and when it has moved through a fairly big angle, the streamlines in a meridian plane have an appearance somewhat similar to that of Fig. 23.

20. The wake behind a bluff symmetrical obstacle.

We can now follow the processes in the wake behind a bluff symmetrical cylinder more closely for that range of Reynolds numbers in which the theory of the vortex-street has validity. We restrict ourselves to the case of two-dimensional motion.‡ When the motion is started from rest, then in the initial stages two thin vortex-layers, symmetrically situated, leave the surface of the cylindrical body and curl round on themselves, the vorticity becoming more and more concentrated into the rolled-up portions (Fig. 24). The vortices thus formed gain in strength as more and more vorticity, shed from the surface, passes into them from the thin layers; and as their strength increases they move slowly away from the cylinder, a process of which the theory referred to on p. 39 provides a rough explanation. The resulting arrangement is unstable for anti-symmetrical disturbances, and assumes an asymmetrical configuration, as theory teaches us that it should; but before this happens other changes take place to which theory provides no guide. The shape of the vortices changes: they become longer and longer in

---

† *Göttingen Dissertation*, 1908.

‡ Discussion of the processes in the wake for three-dimensional flow past an obstacle is reserved until Chap. XIII, §250.

PLATE 7

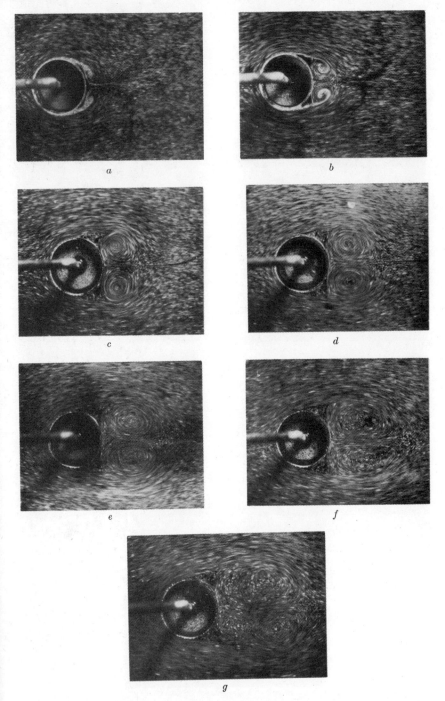

a

b

c

d

e

f

g

PLATE 8

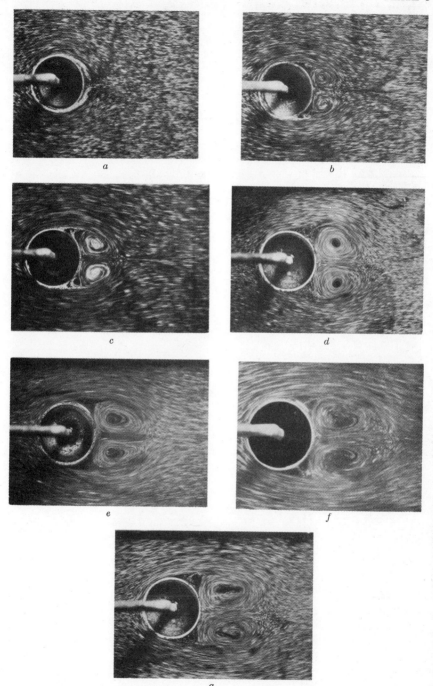

a

b

c

d

e

f

g

the direction of the flow (Fig. 25). Meanwhile each vortex has produced a strong back-flow over the rear portion of the cylinder. This back-flow itself separates from the surface, with the formation of a small secondary vortex having an opposite rotation to the main vortex, with which it proceeds to coalesce. This coalescence naturally contributes to a deformation in the shape of the main vortex. The main vortices continue to move and to spread downstream. Asymmetry now sets in. Vortices are shed alternately from the two sides

FIG. 24.   FIG. 25.

of the cylinder and pass downstream, where they arrange themselves in a configuration corresponding to that of a Kármán vortex-street for some distance, after which the regularity disappears and the motion in the wake becomes irregular. The initial stages of the motion are shown by the photographs in Pls. 7 and 8.† In Pl. 7 the cylinder, starting from rest, has been given a constant velocity as rapidly as possible (impulsive start): in Pl. 8 the cylinder is moving with uniform acceleration. The velocities are equal when the cylinders have moved through about 15 cm., corresponding to the third photograph in each series. The asymmetry begins to make its appearance in about the sixth photograph of each series, when the cylinder has moved through 30 cm.

Before leaving the flow past a symmetrical obstacle we might perhaps mention that, for two-dimensional flow at Reynolds numbers below those at which a Kármán street is formed, the motion is steady and two weak standing eddies exist behind the obstacle. The calculated stream-lines past a circular cylinder at a Reynolds number Ud/ν equal to 20, where d is the diameter of the cylinder, are shown in Fig. 26,‡ and correspond roughly to Fig. 27,‖ prepared from measurements of two actual photographs of the flow,

---

† Rubach, *Göttingen Dissertation* (1914), plates A and B, figs. 1a–VIIa and 1b–VIIb.

‡ Thom, *Proc. Roy. Soc. A,* **141** (1933), 658.

‖ Fage, *Proc. Institution of Mechanical Engineers,* **130** (1935), 30.

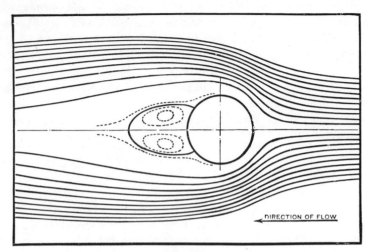

FIG. 26.

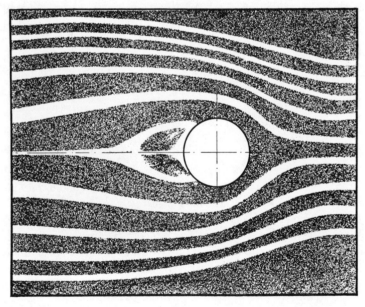

FIG. 27.

at Reynolds numbers of 23 and 29 respectively.† Similar phenomena are observed for other bluff obstacles, although the Reynolds numbers for transition to a Kármán street will alter with the shape and with the degree of turbulence in the stream, etc. For very small Reynolds numbers, in the neighbourhood of unity, the two standing eddies are not formed, and the Stokes-Oseen approximations‡ apply.‖

21. Form drag and skin-friction.

When the final stage of a motion at the higher Reynolds numbers is reached, the separation of the flow prevents the expected rise of pressure towards the rear of the obstacle. This explains the origin of form drag,†† the magnitude of which is closely correlated with the position of separation: the farther the separation towards the rear, the smaller the form drag. For stream-line bodies separation, if it takes place at all, does so very near the rear of the body, and the form drag (apart from any induced drag in the sense of Chap. I, § 12) is exceedingly small. This may, in fact, be taken as a rough definition of a stream-line body. For bluff obstacles, on the other hand, the skin-friction drag is small compared with the form drag. If the position of separation does not change very much, we might expect that the form drag will not change very much; and so, as regards the drag coefficient, scale effect will be small for bluff obstacles except when the position of separation is changing rapidly. For bodies with sharp edges, such as a flat plate or a circular disk, since the separation must take place from the sharp edge, we might expect practically no scale effect. This is borne out by experiment: the drag coefficient of a circular plate normal to the stream, referred to the surface of one side of the disk, is constant at about 1·12. For stream-line bodies, on the other hand, the drag is mostly due to skin-friction. The skin-friction drag, as we have seen (p. 53), varies as $U^{\frac{3}{2}}$, and the coefficient of skin-friction drag as $(\nu/Ud)^{\frac{1}{2}}$, or $R^{-\frac{1}{2}}$, for non-turbulent motion. But this does not apply when the flow in the boundary layer becomes turbulent (pp. 71, 72 and Chap. VIII, § 163).

† Thom, *op. cit.* figs. 9 and 12 (*d*).
‡ Lamb, *Hydrodynamics* (Cambridge, 1932), §§ 335–343.
‖ For a rather fuller description of the sequence of changes in the final flow at different Reynolds numbers (as distinct from the development from rest of the flow at one Reynolds number) see Chap. IX, § 183.
†† Apart from the induced drag (see Chap. I, § 12) in three-dimensional flow past an obstacle on which there is a lift force.

22. The production of circulation.

When a cylindrical obstacle is symmetrical, the same amount of vorticity is shed in any time from the top and from the bottom: the vorticity shed from the top is of opposite sign to that shed from the bottom, and so the total amount of vorticity crossing any contour surrounding the body is zero. The circulation round such a contour, originally zero when the motion is started from rest, therefore remains zero. This is true on the average even if the motion itself is not steady. (The argument is similar to that given on p. 41 and illustrated in Fig. 17. For a real fluid of small viscosity the circulation round $ABCD$ still remains practically zero, since no vorticity has come near to it. The total strength of the vortex-tubes enclosed by $EBCF$ is, on the average, zero, so that the circulation round it is zero, and the circulation round $AEFD$ remains zero on the average. $AEFD$ may be taken as any circuit surrounding the cylinder and cutting the wake at right angles.)

If the obstacle is not symmetrical, however, different amounts of vorticity are shed from the top and from the bottom, and as a result a circulation is produced round any contour surrounding the body. Now in the boundary layer the vorticity is $\partial u/\partial y$. The rate at which vorticity flows across any section of the boundary layer, per unit breadth along the cylinder, is the integral of $u(\partial u/\partial y)\,dy$ taken right across the boundary layer. This is $\frac{1}{2}u_1^2$, where u_1 is the velocity in the main stream just outside the boundary layer. The rate at which vorticity is leaving the surface is, therefore, the value of $\frac{1}{2}u_1^2$ at the section where separation of the flow takes place. Hence more vorticity is shed from the top than from the bottom if u_1 at the point of separation is greater on the top than on the bottom, and conversely. Outside the boundary layer, however, the total head may be taken as constant, and the bigger the velocity the smaller the pressure. Hence the smaller the pressure the greater the rate at which vorticity is shed. The exact conditions for the separation of the flow from the surface are complicated; but we may say in a general way that when the thickness of the boundary layer and the momentum of the flow in it are roughly about the same, the retarded fluid is able to follow the surface longer if it is moving up a gentle pressure gradient than up a sharp one, and makes its way, before leaving the surface, into regions of higher pressure in the former case than in the latter. Hence more vorticity is shed on the side on which the pressure gradient is sharper.

The growth of the circulation may now be illustrated by consideration of flow past an elliptic cylinder. The initial motion, when the system is started from rest, is irrotational without circulation. The

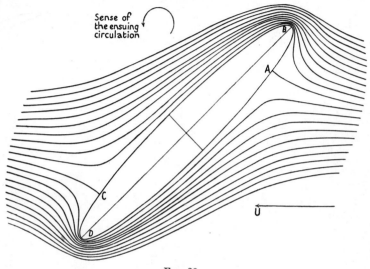

Sense of the ensuing circulation

FIG. 28.

calculated stream-lines, when the axes are in the ratio 1:6 and the major axis is inclined at 45° to the stream, are shown in Fig. 28, and the corresponding pressure distribution in Fig. 29. A and C are stagnation points. The fluid flows down a pressure gradient from A to B or D, and up a pressure gradient again from B or D to C. The pressure gradient from B to C is more gradual than that from D to C, and when separation takes place it may therefore be expected to do so at a lower pressure between D and C than between B and C, so that more vorticity will be shed between D and C than between B and C. Between D and C the sense of the vorticity is clockwise when the figure is viewed from above; between B and C it is anti-clockwise. The net transport is, therefore, of vorticity with clockwise rotation, and a circulation in an anti-clockwise sense, as indicated by the arrow, is produced round the body. This circulation has the effect of increasing the velocity and decreasing the pressure along ABC, and of decreasing the velocity and increasing the pressure along ADC. The pressure gradient up to C along ABC is made steeper and that along ADC more gradual. The difference in the amounts of vorticity shed becomes less, and the rate of growth

(The letters A, B, C, D, refer to the points similarly denoted in Fig. 28.)

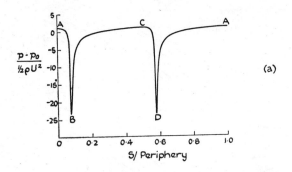

(a)

S is the distance round the cylinder measured from the forward stagnation point A.

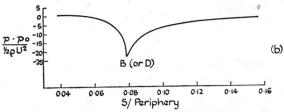

(b)

Portion of (a) near B (or D) to enlarged S scale and reduced pressure scale.

Fig. 29.

of the circulation is diminished, until eventually a steady value of the circulation, or at any rate one steady on the average, is reached. Theoretically this steady state will be reached asymptotically: in practice the whole process is completed fairly rapidly. In the final stage the pressures are equal at the two points of separation, and as a rough generalization we may say that the pressure remains constant round the rear of the body. It may also be noticed that the average curvature is greater between D and C than between B and C; and in general terms we may say that the net amount of vorticity shed

PLATE 9

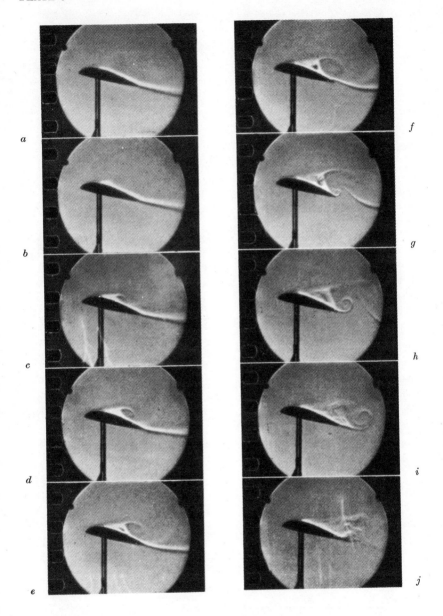

from a body is of the same sense as that in the boundary layer towards the rear on the side where the curvature is greater.[†]

When the final stage is reached, the conditions in the wake for a bluff obstacle are somewhat similar to those in the symmetrical case, with the formation of a vortex-street for the right range of Reynolds numbers. The early stages of the motion past a stalled aerofoil are shown in Pl. 9. The photographs[‡] were taken by fixing a hot wire along the suction side of the aerofoil, so that the wake and eddies were made visible by the change of the refractive index of the heated air from the wire, and using the 'Schlieren' method (Chap. VI, § 134, p. 290). Pl. 9a was taken about 2 seconds from the start, when the relative displacement of the aerofoil was about 1 chord length. The interval between the photographs here reproduced was about $\frac{1}{10}$ second.

23. Turbulence in a pipe.

When fluid is flowing along a circular pipe, then in the calculated steady motion every element of the fluid moves in a straight line parallel to the axis of the pipe. At a sufficient distance from the inlet the pressure gradient is proportional to the first power of the velocity, and the distribution of velocity across a section is parabolic (Chap. I, § 6). When the Reynolds number is not too high, these conditions are found to be fulfilled. A filament of coloured liquid introduced into water flowing along a tube, with a smooth entry, extends down the tube in a straight line, increasing in width only very slowly through diffusion. After a sufficient distance from the entry for the permanent régime to have become established, the above laws concerning the pressure gradient and the velocity distribution are satisfied. If the speed of the flow is increased, a stage is reached at which the straight line motion breaks down. The coloured filament mixes with the surrounding water and the tube appears to be filled with colour, while a close examination reveals that the stream is constantly varying, with irregular motions across the tube. The experiments with coloured filaments were first carried out by Osborne Reynolds,[‖] whose own description of the phenomenon may be quoted:

'When the velocities were sufficiently low, the streak of colour extended in a beautiful straight line across the tube, Fig. 30 a. If the water in the tank had

---

† Betz, *Handbuch der Physik*, **7** (Berlin, 1927), 223, 224.
‡ Due to H. C. H. Townend.
‖ *Phil. Trans.* **174** (1883), 935–982; *Scientific Papers*, **2**, 51–105.

not quite settled to rest, at sufficiently low velocities, the streak would shift
about the tube, but there was no appearance of sinuosity. As the velocity was
increased by small stages, at some point in the tube, always at a considerable
distance from the trumpet or intake, the colour band would all at once mix
up with the surrounding water, and fill the rest of the tube with a mass of
coloured water, as in Fig. 30 b. Any increase in the velocity caused the point

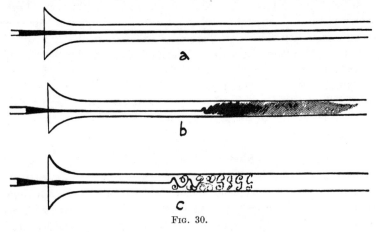

FIG. 30.

of break-down to approach the trumpet, but with no velocities that were tried
did it reach this. On viewing the tube by the light of an electric spark, the
mass of colour resolved itself into a mass of more or less distinct curls showing
eddies, as in Fig. 30 c.'

The value of $U_m d/\nu$ for which break-down occurred in Reynolds's
experiments, where U_m is the mean velocity across a section and d
the diameter of the tube, was about $1\cdot3 \times 10^4$. After break-down has
occurred the motion is said to be turbulent. The motion at any
point is then no longer steady, but we can consider the main characteristics of the flow by taking into consideration only the average
velocity over a time sufficient for the fluctuations to be smoothed
out. (This time is usually very short. The averaging process and the
nature of the fluctuations will be considered in more detail in Chap. V).
In the turbulent flow through the tube the distribution of this
mean velocity across a section of the tube is no longer parabolic.
There is a very sharp rise of velocity near the walls, and over the
rest of the tube the distribution is considerably flatter than in
non-turbulent flow. The pressure gradient is no longer proportional
to the velocity, but varies as the nth power of the velocity, where n
lies between 1 and 2 and depends on the Reynolds number.

The value 1.3×10^4, found by Reynolds for $U_m d/\nu$ at break-down, referred to smooth conditions of entry. When disturbances are introduced at the entry, values round about 2,000 are found by measurements of the pressure gradient, for example. (The use of colour filaments is precluded by the disturbances introduced at the entry.) The critical Reynolds number thus depends considerably on the disturbances present, and, when care is taken to avoid disturbances, subsequent experimenters have found values considerably higher than 1.3×10^4;[†] and it would appear that if disturbances could be avoided altogether, the critical Reynolds number might be pushed up indefinitely. On the other hand, for no initial disturbances does the critical Reynolds number fall below about 2,000.[‡]

24. Turbulence in boundary layers. Sharp fall in the drag coefficient. Interference effects. Scale effect.

Motion in a boundary layer also becomes turbulent if the Reynolds number is too high. For flow along a flat plate this appears to have been known to Lanchester.[||] It was noticed by Blasius,[††] and has been studied by Burgers and van der Hegge Zijnen,[‡‡] by Hansen,[||||] and by Dryden.[†††] In a moderately steady air stream, when the front of the plate is sharpened to a knife edge, the transition to turbulence takes place when $U\delta/\nu$ is about 3,000, where δ is the thickness of the boundary layer. This corresponds to a value of about $3 . 10^5$ for Ux/ν, where x is the distance from the leading edge. The critical Reynolds number depends here also on the disturbances present and on the conditions at the front of the plate. Values varying from 1,650 to 5,750 for $U\delta/\nu$, corresponding roughly to $9 . 10^4$ to $1 . 1 . 10^6$ for Ux/ν, have been observed. In the transition from the steady to the turbulent motion the thickness of the boundary layer increases

---

† Barnes and Coker, *Proc. Roy. Soc.* A, **74** (1904), 341–356; Ekman, *Ark. f. mat., astr. och fys.* **6** (1910), No. 12; Schiller, *Forschungsarbeiten des Ver. deutsch. Ing.* **248** (1922), 15, 16. See Chap. VII, § 148.

‡ This was the value found by Reynolds himself for the disturbed entry in the paper previously referred to. For further details and references see Chap. VII, § 146.

|| *Aerodynamics* (London, 1907), § 37.

†† *Forschungsarbeiten des Ver. deutsch. Ing.*, No. 131 (1913), 27.

‡‡ *Proc. Roy. Acad. Sci.*, Amsterdam, **13** (1924), 3–33; *Mededeeling No. 5 uit het Laboratorium voor Aero- en Hydrodynamica der Technische Hoogeschool te Delft*; van der Hegge Zijnen, *Mededeeling No. 6*; Burgers, *Proc. 1st Internat. Congress for Applied Mechanics, Delft*, 1924 (Delft, 1925), p. 113.

|||| *Zeitschr. f. angew. Math. u. Mech.* **8** (1928), 185–199.

††† *Proc. Fourth Internat. Congress for Applied Mechanics, Cambridge*, 1934 (Cambridge, 1935), p. 175; *N.A.C.A. Report* No. 562 (1936).

rapidly. Whilst in the non-turbulent flow the tangential stress on the plate varies as $U^{\frac{3}{2}}$, in turbulent flow it varies as U^n, where n is a variable index between $\frac{3}{2}$ and 2. The distribution of velocity across the boundary layer is also quite different in turbulent and non-turbulent flow.

In a similar way, the boundary layer along any solid surface becomes turbulent if the velocity or the thickness of the boundary layer becomes large enough. For flow round the surfaces of solid obstacles for which separation is to be expected, this transition to turbulence may take place before the position of separation is reached. Now we have already seen that the motion of a stratum of fluid next to a solid surface is determined by the retarding action of the boundary, the pressure gradient, and the forward pull of the fluid farther from the wall. When the motion is steady, this forward pull arises from the viscosity, which is due to molecular causes. When the motion is turbulent, fluid is moving irregularly backwards and forwards through the boundary layer, continually crossing from the slower to the faster moving strata and *vice versa*. Thus fluid elements with a slower forward velocity are mixed with the fluid in the faster moving strata, and conversely. This produces an interchange of momentum between the different strata. Since the process takes place on a molar scale, the interchange of momentum thus produced is much more vigorous than that produced by the molecular processes giving rise to the ordinary viscosity. Thus, in the first place, the retarding action of the surface spreads farther and the boundary layer thickens. In the second place, the forward pull exerted on a stratum adjacent to the wall by the fluid farther away is considerably greater when the motion is turbulent than when it is steady, in consequence of the more vigorous interchange of momentum. In turbulent motion, therefore, we should expect the retarded fluid to be pulled farther along the surface and to make its way into regions of higher pressure. The position of separation should be farther towards the rear: the loss of pressure in the rear should be restricted to a smaller area, and the form drag diminished. In consequence, we should expect a fairly abrupt drop in the drag coefficient of an obstacle when the speed of the main stream becomes sufficiently high to ensure that the boundary layer becomes turbulent before separation. This extremely important phenomenon is actually found experimentally, and is now well known. Thus, in Figs. 1 and 2, pp. 15 and

PLATE 10

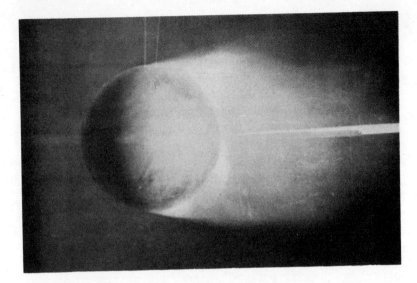

a

b

16, C_D drops from 1·2 to 0·3 approximately as R increases from 2×10^5 to $5·5 \times 10^5$ for a circular cylinder (Göttingen curve), and from 0·4 to 0·09 for a sphere in about the same range of Reynolds numbers (2×10^5 to 4×10^5). The first demonstration of the phenomenon for a sphere was given by Eiffel,[†] who experimented with spheres of three different diameters and, as was pointed out afterwards by Rayleigh,[‡] found critical speeds roughly in inverse proportion to the diameters. The above explanation of the phenomenon was given by Prandtl,[||] who demonstrated its correctness by inducing artificial turbulence in the boundary layer. To do this a wire hoop was fixed on the sphere: small drag coefficients were then obtained even with fairly low Reynolds numbers. Smoke photographs of the flow, reproduced in Pl. 10, show how separation is delayed and the breadth of the wake lessened with the hoop in place. Fage[††] has made a detailed study of the boundary layer for a circular cylinder over the critical range of Reynolds numbers for which the drag coefficient falls sharply, and has verified that the decrease in drag coefficient is associated with a backward movement of the position of separation. Above the critical range of Reynolds numbers no trace of regularity is to be found in the flow in the wake, which becomes everywhere irregularly eddying or turbulent.

The critical ranges of Reynolds numbers and values of the drag coefficients are found to depend, as would be expected, on the degree of turbulence in the main stream.[‡‡] They are also affected by protuberances, hooks, or other attachments on the surface, which, small though they may be in themselves, may have a marked effect on the flow in the boundary layer, especially when this is in any way sensitive to small changes in the external circumstances. These interference effects are particularly marked in the case of a sphere. Further details are given in Chap. XI, § 216.

For bluff obstacles without sharp edges we have noted previously (§ 21) that scale effect may be expected to be appreciable at large Reynolds numbers when the position of separation is changing rapidly. This happens in the critical range, when the boundary layer becomes

---

† *Comptes Rendus,* **155** (1912), 1597–1599.
‡ *Ibid.* **156** (1913), 109; *Scientific Papers,* **6**, 136.
|| *Göttinger Nachrichten* (1914), 177–190; *Journ. Roy. Aero. Soc.* **31** (1927), 730. See also Wieselsberger, *Zeitschr. f. Flugtechn. u. Motorluftschiffahrt,* **5** (1914), 142–144.   †† *Loc. cit.* p. 61.
‡‡ This explains the differences in the curves in Fig. 1, p. 15.

turbulent before separation and the drag coefficient falls rapidly. Although we have illustrated this by reference to the circular cylinder and the sphere, it is a quite general phenomenon; and it shows that experiments on models at Reynolds numbers below the critical would not apply to full-scale bodies if the Reynolds numbers in the latter case were above the critical. The experiments would give too large values for the drag coefficient.

For spheres or circular cylinders, and Reynolds numbers above the critical range, the drag coefficient appears to be increasing gradually with increase of Reynolds number. This increase can be accounted for by a gradual shift farther forward, with increase of Reynolds number, of the transition to turbulence. The consequent thickening of the boundary layer produces a shift forward of the position of separation, with consequent increase of drag.†

25. Stream-line bodies. Aerofoils. The stall.

Stream-line bodies have already been described (§ 21) as those for which separation of flow from the surface, if it takes place at all, does so very near the rear, so that the fluid closes in again behind the body, the wake is very narrow, and the drag (apart from any induced drag) is mainly due to skin-friction.‡ Experiment shows that such bodies must be well rounded and rather slender. The surface must come gradually almost to a point or an edge at the rear, with a very gentle curvature. Towards the front the body may be blunter, with rather sharper curvature at the shoulders. The effect of the gentle curvature towards the rear is to delay any steep pressure rise, and the farther back the steep pressure rise the better the claim of the body to be called stream-lined. This is illustrated in Pls. 11a ‖ and 11b,†† which show photographs of motion past an elliptic cylinder and a symmetrical aerofoil respectively. It will be seen that the wake for the aerofoil is narrower than that for the elliptic cylinder. The pressure distributions for the irrotational motion of an inviscid fluid round the two bodies are shown in Fig. 31.

The drag coefficients of good stream-line bodies are exceedingly

---

† Prandtl, *Aerodynamic Theory* (edited by Durand), **3** (Berlin, 1935), 160; Gruschwitz, *Zeitschr. f. Flugtechn. u. Motorluftschiffahrt*, **23** (1932), 311, 312.

‡ Compare Lanchester (*Aerodynamics*, p. 27): 'A stream-line body is one that in its motion through a fluid does not give rise to a surface of discontinuity.'

‖ Prandtl, *Handbuch der Experimentalphysik*, **4**, part 1 (Leipzig, 1931), 6.

†† Due to H. C. H. Townend.

PLATE 11

a

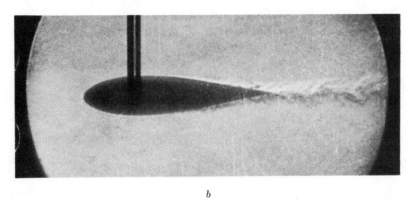

b

S is the distance round the section measured
from the forward stagnation point.

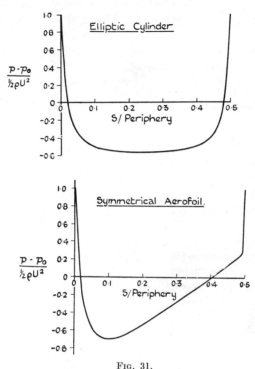

Fɪɢ. 31.

small. Thus, for the solid of revolution (or airship model) whose
section is shown in the figure below, the drag coefficient, referred

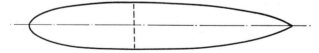

to the area of the maximum cross-section, is 0·054 at a Reynolds
number of $2·2 \times 10^6$. (The length used in forming this Reynolds
number is the diameter of the maximum section.) For a circular
disk facing the stream the drag coefficient is 1·12, or nearly 21
times as large; while if the body shown in the figure were separated
into two at its maximum cross-section, the drag coefficient of the

forward part alone would be roughly about 0·3, or about 5 or 6 times that for the whole body. This result, at first sight probably rather surprising, arises, of course, from the fact that in motion past the front portion alone the flow breaks away at the edge with the formation of an eddying region behind and suction in the rear.

As an example of a stream-line body round which circulation arises, we may consider an aerofoil at a small inclination to the stream. When the motion is started from rest, thin vortex-layers of unequal strength leave the top and the bottom, and the circulation grows as described in § 22. In the case of the aerofoil the two vortex-layers unite and curl up, with the formation of a single vortex—the cast-off vortex—which grows stronger and stronger until the two vortex-layers, which are supplying it with vorticity of opposite senses, have become of equal strength. The cast-off vortex then moves away from the aerofoil with the stream, leaving a circulation round the aerofoil equal and opposite to the circulation round itself.

If the system is now suddenly brought to rest, a second cast-off vortex, with equal and opposite circulation to the first, is formed. The two vortices constitute a vortex-pair, and move, relative to the fluid, perpendicular to the line joining them. A photograph of the vortex-pair formed in this way is shown in Pl. 12a.†

The pressure distribution round an aerofoil, when the fluid is flowing past it uniformly and the final stage is reached, is shown in Fig. 12 (p. 36). If we start from the front stagnation point and go round the bottom or pressure side of the aerofoil, there is a gradual fall of pressure towards the rear; whilst if we go round the top or suction side there is first a very rapid fall of pressure, followed by a rise towards the rear, at first rather steep and then more gradual. These features are common to all thin aerofoils at small inclinations to the stream. There is, therefore, no tendency to separation on the pressure side. On the suction side, if the retarded fluid gets past the rather steep pressure increase on the shoulders, it will be able to flow along the surface almost, if not quite, to the trailing edge.

At small angles of incidence we may say that the stream remains in contact with the surface practically up to the trailing edge. There will be a very narrow wake, shown diagrammatically in Fig. 32. Apart from the flow in the wake and in the boundary layer,

† Prandtl and Tietjens, *Hydro- und Aeromechanik*, **2** (Berlin, 1931), plate 22, fig. 55.

PLATE 12

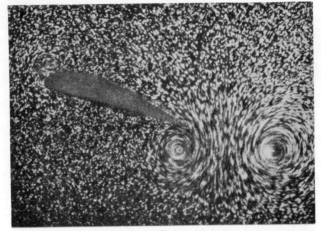

a

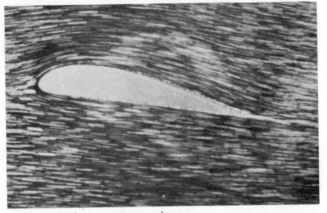

b

c

the motion round the aerofoil is practically irrotational. The stream-lines are displaced upwards somewhat from their position in the calculated motion without a wake, in which they come smoothly off from the trailing edge, as in Fig. 10 (c) (p. 34),—rather as if there were a stream-line along the middle of the wake, with a stagnation point on the top of the aerofoil just before the trailing edge, as indicated in Fig. 32. This corresponds to a potential flow

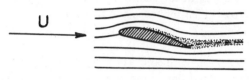

FIG. 32.

with less circulation than that required to bring the flow smoothly off at the trailing edge.† The effect of the wake is, then, to make the lift less than its theoretical value (p. 34).

If, however, the inclination of the aerofoil to the stream is in-creased, a stage is reached at which the retarded layer is unable to negotiate the steep part of the pressure rise near the shoulders on the top of the aerofoil. The flow then separates from the surface very near the nose, with the formation of a large eddying wake and a consequent sharp drop in the lift and rise in the drag. Alternatively, the position of the separation of the flow on the upper surface may have moved forward continuously to such an extent that a large eddying wake is formed. The lift begins to fall, and the drag to increase. When the lift begins to fall, the aerofoil is said to be stalled. Photographs of the flow in the unstalled and stalled condi-tions are shown in Pls. 12b and 12c.‡ The drop in the lift and the rise in the drag can be seen in Fig. 11 (p. 35), where they take place at inclinations between 6° and 8°.

We have already remarked on the effect of turbulence in the boundary layer in delaying separation. A body which is a good stream-line body at large Reynolds numbers, when the boundary layer flow is turbulent, may have a much higher drag coefficient at smaller Reynolds numbers, when the boundary layer flow is non-turbulent or laminar. It is, in fact, because of turbulence in boundary

† Betz, *Handbuch der Physik*, **7** (Berlin, 1927), 222.
‡ Prandtl, *The Physics of Solids and Fluids* (London, 1930), 321, 322.

layers, with the consequent delay in separation, that the engineering problem of designing bodies of small resistance can be solved.

The effect of turbulence in the boundary layer on the stalling of aerofoils is also extremely marked. At lower Reynolds numbers, when the boundary layer is laminar, the stalling inclination of the aerofoil in Fig. 11, p. 35 would be less than that shown in the figure, and the maximum lift would also be less. The maximum lift and the stalling incidence are also affected to some extent by all those factors which influence the transition to turbulence in the boundary layer,—e.g. turbulence in the main stream, roughness of the surface, etc. (see Chap. X). In practice, for thin aerofoils, it has usually been supposed that the boundary layer becomes turbulent near the front stagnation point. It appears that the maximum lift coefficient increases with increase of Reynolds number, and is determined by the relative positions of separation of a laminar boundary layer and of transition to turbulence (see Chap. X, § 213). For thick aerofoils with well-rounded leading edges, on the other hand, it appears that the maximum lift coefficient may fall with increase of Reynolds number until quite a high Reynolds number is reached, after which it increases (see Chap. X, § 197). This may perhaps be explained by a moving forward of the transition to turbulence as the Reynolds number increases, with consequent thickening of the boundary layer and forward shift of separation (as for spheres and circular cylinders: see § 24, p. 74). In cases where this takes place the maximum lift coefficient may fall as the Reynolds number increases until the transition to turbulence is well forward.[†] Then the influence of the thinning of the boundary layer, or of separation of the laminar portion, may become prominent. But the exact details of the change of behaviour with change of shape are difficult of explanation.

26. Artificial prevention or delay of separation.[‡]

The methods that may be used for preventing or delaying separation may be roughly classified as (1) motion of the solid boundary in the direction of the stream; (2) increase of the momentum of the retarded fluid by the use of jets; (3) prevention of accumulation of retarded fluid by suction.

When the surface of an obstacle is made to move sufficiently

[†] Prandtl, *Aerodynamic Theory* (edited by Durand), **3** (Berlin, 1935), 160. Gruschwitz, *Zeitschr. f. Flugtechn. u. Motorluftschiffahrt*, **23** (1932), 311, 312.
[‡] See also Chap. XII.

PLATE 13

a

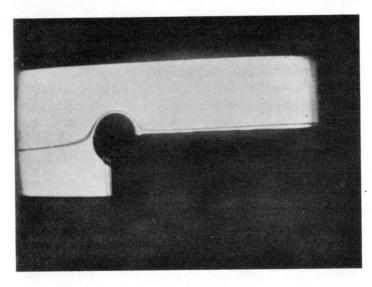

b

rapidly in the direction of the current, it has no retarding action on the fluid; consequently there is no separation. Thus an aerofoil would not stall if the top surface were part of a rotating band (Fig. 33). This method of preventing separation is well illustrated in Pl. 13,† which shows a photograph of a stream-line in flow past half a circular cylinder and then along a wall. In the first photograph the cylinder is at rest and separation takes place. In the second the

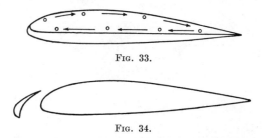

Fig. 33.

Fig. 34.

cylinder is rotating in a clockwise direction and the flow moves right round its surface and then along the wall.

The separation will also be delayed if momentum is supplied to the retarded fluid by jets. This may be done by forcing fluid into the retarded layer from the inside of the obstacle; but a more common method is to use the accelerating effect of the main stream by allowing the more rapidly moving fluid to pass through a slot and push the retarded fluid at the wall, as in the Handley Page slotted wing. In this device there is a small secondary aerofoil at the nose of the main wing, which may either lie against the main wing (slot closed) or maintain a position at a short distance from it, as in Fig. 34 (slot open). By the use of the slot the stall can be delayed. Sketches of the flow with the slot closed and the slot open are shown in Fig. 35.‡ The maximum lift is considerably increased by using the slot. When the slot is open there will, however, be an increase in drag. (The effect of the jet through the slot is only part of the total effect in a Handley Page slot. There is also the action of the down-wash from the small secondary aerofoil. For further information and exact data see Chap. XII, § 237.)

Near a position of separation there is a slow flow towards it on both sides, with a consequent tendency towards accumulation of

† Due to W. S. Farren.
‡ Fage, *Proc. Institution of Mechanical Engineers*, **130** (1935), 23.

Slot closed.

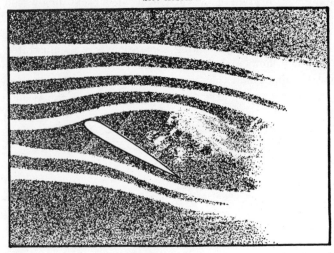

Direction of flow →

Slot open.

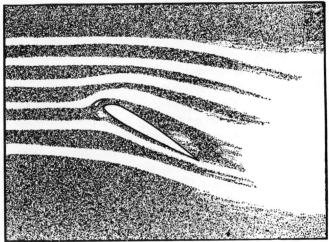

FIG. 35.

retarded fluid. If suction is applied through slits or holes in the surface at points where the back-flow would be set up, the accumulation of retarded fluid is prevented and the separation delayed. This is illustrated in Pl. 14a, which is a photograph of flow through an

expanding canal when suction is applied through the slots shown:†
this photograph should be compared with Pl. 5 a (p. 58). When the
slots on one side only are in use, the flow follows that side (Pl. 14b).†
Pl. 14c‡ shows a single stream-line with suction at the slot, and
should be compared with Pl. 5b (p. 58.)

Although these general explanations give the main features of the
manner in which the second and third methods operate, the exact
manner of operation is by no means so simple as the explanations
might lead one to believe. In the Handley Page slot, for example,
account must be taken of the retarded layer formed at the small
secondary wing. Again, in the case of suction, the pressure is
diminished upstream of the place where suction is applied. This
also tends to prevent separation, but at the same time increases the
drag from the value it would have if the flow followed the surface
without suction.

27. Flow past a rotating cylinder.

An excellent example of the way in which motion of the surface
can be used to prevent separation is afforded by the flow past a
rotating cylinder in a stream. Whether the cylinder is rotating or
not, the initial motion of the fluid, when the stream is started from
rest, is irrotational without circulation, as in Fig. 3 (p. 23). On one
side the surface of the rotating cylinder is moving with the current,
and there is no separation and no detachment of vortices. On the
other side, however, where the surface is moving against the current,
separation takes place; and since there is now a greater production of
vorticity on that side than if the surface were at rest, there is a
correspondingly greater transport of vorticity into the fluid. This
vorticity is practically concentrated into a single vortex, which
moves away downstream, leaving a circulation round the cylinder
in the same sense as the rotation. We see from Fig. 9, (b) and (c),
(p. 33), that if the circulation is large enough, and the motion
outside the boundary layer near the cylinder irrotational, the
velocity of the fluid outside the boundary layer is everywhere in
the same direction as that of the surface. If a is the radius of
the cylinder and U the velocity of the main stream, this stage is
reached when the circulation, K, round the cylinder is $4\pi a U$
(Fig. 9(b)). Again, if the cylinder is moving fast enough, it will nowhere

† Prandtl, *Journ. Roy. Aero. Soc.* **31** (1927), 735, 736.   ‡ Due to W. S. Farren.

exert a retarding action on the fluid. With the above value of K the maximum velocity of the fluid at the surface is $4U$, and if the velocity V of the surface of the cylinder is equal to $4U$, there will be no further tendency for vorticity to be shed into the fluid or for the circulation to change. If, with $V = 4U$, the circulation were less than $4\pi aU$, the cylinder and the fluid would be moving in opposite directions over part of the surface, and there would be a tendency for further vorticity to be shed and for K to increase. When $K = 4\pi aU$, however, there is no further tendency for it to increase, even if V is greater than $4U$. K might still be expected to reach this value even if V is a little less than $4U$, since a retarding action over a small distance near the place where the fluid velocity is biggest will not cause separation, especially when the fluid over the rest of the surface is being urged forward. But if V is much less than $4U$, the maximum circulation will not be reached, and there will be separation of flow from both sides of the cylinder, though naturally asymmetrically, with some circulation in the direction of the rotation. These considerations would lead us to expect a maximum circulation $4\pi aU$, and therefore a maximum lift L per unit length equal to $K\rho U$, or $4\pi\rho aU^2$, and a maximum lift coefficient $L/(\frac{1}{2}\rho U^2 d)$, where d is the diameter, equal to 4π or $12 \cdot 6$, reached with V nearly equal to $4U$.

These considerations can give only a rough indication of what the course of events is likely to be. For one thing fluid elements possessing vorticity may move outwards from the surface on account of centrifugal force when their velocity round the cylinder is greater than that of the fluid outside the boundary layer, if the pressure gradient is insufficient to hold them in position. This causes an increase in the circulation. The circulation on this account increases somewhat with every increase in V, although this effect is secondary to those previously considered. There are other secondary effects which exert considerable influence; and the theory can lay no claim to being more than a rough guide to the circumstances. That it is a rough guide, photographs in Pls. 15, 16† and 17, 18‡ will show. Pls. 15, 16 show the development of the flow from rest when V is equal to $4U$, and Pls. 17, 18 show the final stages for various values

---

† Prandtl, *Journ. Roy. Aero. Soc.* **31** (1927), 736, 737.

‡ Prandtl and Tietjens, *Hydro- und Aeromechanik*, **2** (Berlin, 1931), plates 7–9, figs. 10–16.

PLATE 14

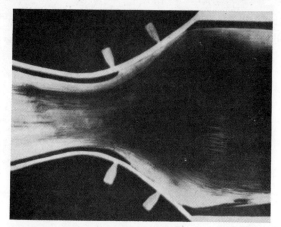

a

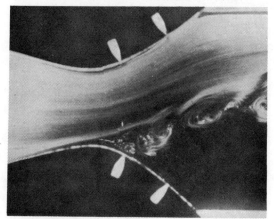

b

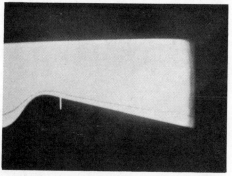

c

PLATE 15

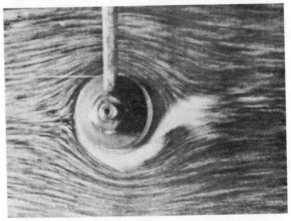

a

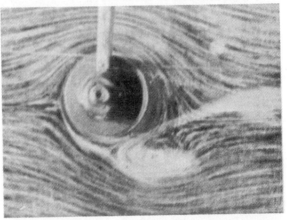

b

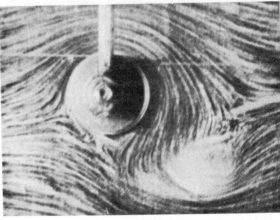

c

PLATE 16

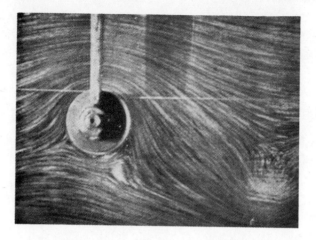

a

b

PLATE 17

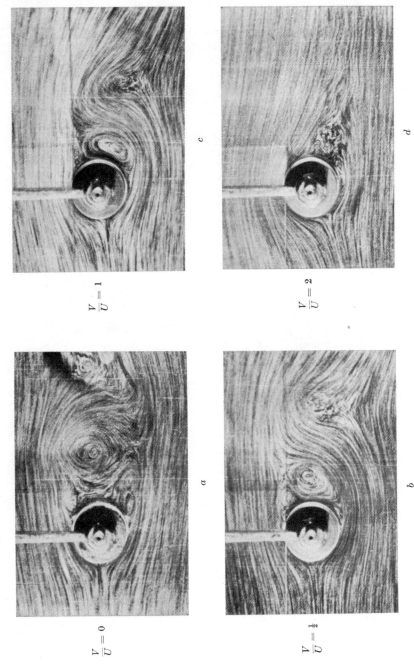

$\frac{V}{U} = 0$

a

$\frac{V}{U} = 1$

c

$\frac{V}{U} = \frac{1}{2}$

b

$\frac{V}{U} = 2$

d

From L. Prandtl and O. Tietjens, *Hydro- und Aeromechanik*, **2** (Springer, Berlin)

PLATE 18

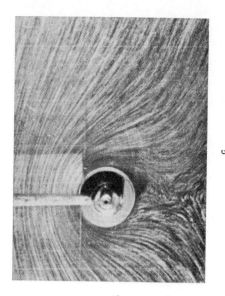

$\dfrac{V}{U} = 6$

c

$\dfrac{V}{U} = 3$

a

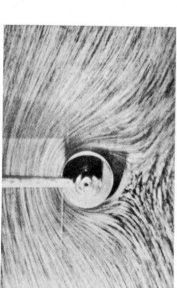

$\dfrac{V}{U} = 4$

b

From L. Prandtl and O. Tietjens, *Hydro- und Aeromechanik*, 2 (Springer, Berlin)

of V/U. These photographs should be compared with Fig. 9 (p. 33). It will be seen that the circulation when V is $6U$ is somewhat greater than when V is $4U$. (Exact information on the lift and drag of rotating cylinders will be given in Chap. XII, § 239.)

The above explanation is due in detail to Prandtl,[†] and we may perhaps mention here that he reports that with V equal to $4U$, and with the cylinder between parallel walls, a lift coefficient of about 4 (instead of 12·6) was found at first in his laboratory. The cause was traced to a separation of the flow from the side walls, where the fluid in the boundary layer would have the same pressure gradient to contend against as along the cylinder. The result was that only the middle portion of the cylinder was functioning properly. To avoid this effect a pair of end-plates was fixed to the cylinder so that they rotated with it. The lift coefficient then rose to 10 for V equal to $4U$.

The considerations above refer to two-dimensional flow. There is also a circulation round any section of a finite rotating cylinder or a rotating sphere, and in consequence there is a lift. Associated therewith, however, is trailing vorticity and induced drag. Moreover, the disturbances caused in a horizontal stream by the presence of the rotating solid have a downward component because of the reaction of the solid on the fluid. In consequence, the trailing vortex-system has a downward inclination to the main stream, and produces not only induced drag but also diminution of lift. In the mathematical theory of the aerofoil of finite span this is a small third-order effect; but for the relatively large lift coefficients of rotating cylinders and spheres it can become so large that the lift actually decreases when the circulation increases. As a result the lift on rotating bodies is fully developed only for two-dimensional flow. But there is nevertheless a lift on rotating spheres,[‡] explained in general terms in the same way as above, which accounts for the irregular flight of tennis balls and golf balls when 'cut' or 'sliced', etc.[||]

[†] *Die Naturwissenschaften*, **13** (1925), 93–108. The notion that separation on one side of the cylinder will be delayed and on the other side hastened is to be found in Lanchester's *Aerodynamics*, pp. 42, 43.

[‡] For a report of lift and drag measurements on a rotating sphere, see Chap. XI, § 221.

[||] The irregular flight of a tennis ball was explained by the lift due to circulation by Lord Rayleigh, *Messenger of Mathematics*, **7** (1887), 14–16; *Scientific Papers*, **1**, 343–346; but he gave no explanation of the origin of the circulation. The first laboratory experiments were made by Magnus, *Poggendorf's Annalen der Physik u. Chemie*, **88** (1853), 1–14. That a rotating sphere experiences a sideways force was known to Newton: see *Phil. Trans.* **6** (1672), 3078.

Circulation round a cylinder can also be caused artificially by suction through a suitably placed slit on one side or the other, causing a delay of separation on that side. This phenomenon is illustrated in the photograph in Pl. 19a.† A small quantity of water is being sucked away through the tube. The flow follows the cylinder at the top until it reaches the slit. Between the top of the cylinder and the wall, after passing the narrowest section, the fluid is flowing against a pressure rise; and it will be seen from the picture that the flow separates from the wall.

28. Curved streams. Secondary flow.

If fluid is flowing along a curved pipe of square cross-section, for example, there must be a pressure gradient across the pipe to

Fig. 36.

balance the centrifugal force. The pressure must be greatest at the outer wall, or wall farther from the centre of curvature, and least at the inner wall, or wall nearer the centre of curvature. The fluid near the top and bottom walls is moving more slowly, however, than the fluid in the central portions, and requires a smaller pressure gradient to balance its centrifugal force. In consequence, a secondary flow is set up in which the fluid near the top and the bottom moves inwards and the fluid in the middle moves outwards (Fig. 36). The pressure at the outer wall is greater at the middle of the pipe than at the top or the bottom, whilst at the inner wall it is less. The secondary flow is superposed on the main stream, so that the resultant flow is helical in the top and the bottom of the pipe. This type of secondary flow is set up whatever be the section of the pipe—if it is circular, for example. It is also set up in open channels, and in rivers at bends. As a result, the region of maximum velocity is displaced from the centre of the pipe or of the free surface of the channel or river towards the outer wall.

A similar phenomenon occurs if fluid is made to rotate in a fixed circular vessel closed at the bottom and open at the top. The layer next to the bottom rotates more slowly than the rest of the fluid, and its

† Prandtl, *Journ. Roy. Aero. Soc.* **31** (1927), 735.

PLATE 19

a

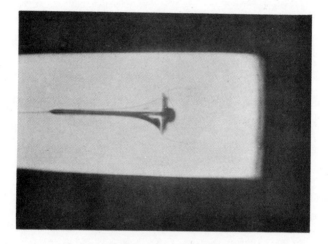

b

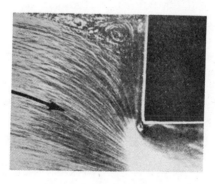

c

centrifugal force is therefore less than for the layers higher up, which determine the pressure gradient. The fluid therefore moves inwards near the bottom, up near the middle, outwards at the top, and down again near the wall. Small bodies at the bottom of the vessel are carried to the centre and deposited there (e.g. undissolved sugar or tea leaves in a tea-cup).†

In rivers sand or gravel is continually being picked up from the bottom, carried along by the current near the bottom for some distance, and then redeposited. The effect of the secondary flow at bends is to remove material from the outer side and pile it up on the inner. This explains the generally observed fact that beds of rivers are scoured near the outer bank and silted near the inner bank, whilst the bend becomes more and more pronounced. This explanation, together with an experimental confirmation, was given by James Thomson.‡

The secondary flow also explains why there is a much thicker layer of slowly moving fluid at the inside wall of a curved pipe than at the outside. The faster-moving fluid at the middle is moving outwards, pushing the fluid in the boundary layer at the outer wall to the top and bottom, and along the top and bottom walls towards the inner wall. Thus fresh fluid is being continually brought into the neighbourhood of the outer wall and then forced round towards the inner wall, being continually retarded. There is thus an accumulation of retarded fluid at the inner wall (Fig. 37).

In a deep and narrow curved channel, on the other hand, exactly

† James Thomson, *British Association Report, Dublin*, 1857, Transactions of the Sections, p. 39; *Papers in Physics and Engineering*, p. 147.

‡ *Proc. Roy. Soc.* A, **25** (1876–7), 5–8 and 356, 357; *Proc. Institution of Mechanical Engineers* (1879), 456–460; *Papers in Physics and Engineering*, pp. 96–106. In the experimental confirmation the inner bank sloped inwards, and in flowing up it the stream separated from the wall, and an eddy was formed near the free surface at the top of the inner bank, whose existence was shown by the use of coloured filaments suggested by Archibald Barr.

A different explanation of the meandering of streams is given by Exner (*Ergebnisse der kosmischen Physik*, **1** (Leipzig, 1931; Supplement to *Gerlands Beiträge zur Geophysik*), 373–445). According to Exner, when a stream silts up at one side lee eddies with vertical axes are formed behind the sandbank (similar to the eddies behind a cylinder described in § 10, p. 38). The stream is thereby deflected towards the opposite bank with extra velocity, and rapid erosion results. The bank farther down is left projecting; lee eddies are formed behind the new projection, with further silting; and so on. The lee eddies probably play some part, but the theory put forward by James Thomson seems to be substantially correct.

For an example of the complicated state of affairs in an actual river, reference may be made to Eakin, *Nat. Res. Counc.* part 2 (1935), 467–472, where a description is given of observations in the Mississippi.

the opposite result is found. There is an accumulation of retarded fluid at the outer wall. To explain this we may first consider two-dimensional flow along a curved channel. In such a curved flow the centrifugal force on a fluid element must be balanced by a pressure gradient inwards. If a particle is going too slowly its centrifugal force is too small, and it moves inwards. Conversely, an element going too fast moves outwards. Near the walls the fluid is retarded. The tendency is, therefore, for particles near the wall to move

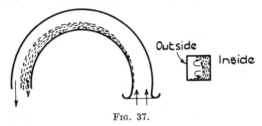

FIG. 37.

inwards, and for particles outside the boundary layer to move outwards. At the outer wall this increases the interchange between the faster and the more slowly moving fluid and thickens the retarded layer. On the other hand, at the inside wall the interchange between the faster and the more slowly moving fluid is hindered. The result is to make the retarded layer thicker at the outer than at the inner wall.

Again, let us suppose that the flow is taking place between two coaxial cylinders, and let us consider its stability. If the angular momentum of the fluid about the axis in the undisturbed flow increases inwards, then if a fluid element moves inwards, keeping its original angular momentum, it has a velocity less than that proper to its new surroundings. According to the argument given above it therefore tends to move farther inwards. Hence such a flow is unstable. On the other hand, a flow in which the angular momentum increases outwards is stable. The argument may be applied to any curved flow so long as the Reynolds number is large and the influence of the viscosity not too large. The flow in the boundary layer is, therefore, unstable at the outer wall and stable at the inner wall. This enlarges the argument previously given, and we see again that the layer of retarded fluid will be wider at the outer wall.

In straight flow there is no pressure gradient across a channel. Hence in a transition from straight to curved flow there is an increase of pressure at the outer wall and a decrease at the inner wall. The increase of pressure at the outer wall assists the thickening of the boundary layer there. But even when the curvature is slight and this effect relatively unimportant, the total thickening is large. The influence of the pressure rise cannot be great.

If now we have a curved channel with a finite rectangular cross-section, but with one side very long compared with the other, the secondary flow is confined to the ends. The path along the outer

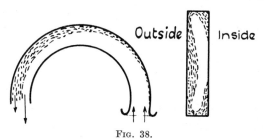

FIG. 38.

wall and the top or the bottom that fluid from the middle of the channel would have to follow in the secondary flow in order to reach the inside wall would be very long—too long to be traversed: that is why the secondary flow is, in fact, confined to the ends. Near the middle there is no noteworthy pressure gradient towards or away from the top or bottom as there is in a square pipe, for example. Hence over the middle of such a channel, with its sides in the ratio of, say, 8:1, the retarded fluid would actually accumulate at the outer wall, and not at the inner wall as for a square section (Fig. 38).†

To prevent misunderstanding it may be remarked here, however, that secondary flow of a different type is found in turbulent flow through straight pipes of other than circular section, and also in the ordinary straight flow of a stream. In the latter case, for example, there is a slow transverse flow outwards from the middle near the bottom, upwards near the sides, inwards near the top, and downwards near the middle, so that, for example, the region of maximum velocity occurs some distance below the middle of the free surface. These are different phenomena from those which we have been considering.‡

† Betz, *Vorträge aus dem Gebiete der Aerodynamik und verwandter Gebiete, Aachen*, 1929 (Berlin, 1930), pp. 10–18, from which Figs. 37 and 38 are taken with some slight changes.

‡ This explanation of the position of the region of maximum velocity is also due to James Thomson (*Proc. Roy. Soc.* A, **25** (1878), 114–127; *Papers in Physics and Engineering*, pp. 106–122, where references to reports of the observational material are given). He explained (1) that the phenomenon of secondary flow is due to turbulence in the stream; (2) that the retarding action of the walls is exercised

29. Some further miscellaneous examples of flow.

(1) If there is a narrow, sharp-edged trough in a surface along which fluid is flowing, as in the adjoining sketch, then initially, if the motion is started from rest, the flow must be nearly irrotational: it turns round the corners and fills the trough. But surfaces of discontinuity and eddies are formed at the corners, and in the final motion the flow goes straight across past the trough, leaving the fluid inside it almost at rest. The pressure in the trough is constant and equal to the pressure in the moving fluid,—a result which is used to measure the pressure at a surface.†

(2) If fluid is flowing along a flat plate, parallel to the stream, to the rear end of which is affixed another plate perpendicular to the stream, then in an irrotational flow the velocity would gradually decrease and the pressure increase along the first plate. In the final motion of a real fluid, therefore, the forward flow separates from the first plate before it reaches its rear end. It passes round the edges of the second plate with the formation of surfaces of discontinuity, and standing eddies are formed in the corners (Pl. 19b).‡ This phenomenon occurs also at a sudden constriction in a channel (Pl. 19c).‖

(3) Pl. 20, a–e, shows photographs of the development from rest of flow past a model of a house with a high roof-slope. It will be seen that the flow breaks away from the ground in front of the house with the formation of a weak eddy in the corner. The flow then breaks away from the roof with the formation of a violent eddying wake behind

almost entirely through the mixture with the main stream of retarded fluid that has been near the walls, except in a thin layer next to them where processes of fluid distortion are taking place with great intensity; elsewhere than in these layers the mere viscosity of the water has an insignificantly small effect; and (3) that the transverse currents are caused by the action of the irregularly moving fluid in the main stream on this retarded layer. He says 'The thin lamina of deadened water will tend by the scour of the quicker going water always moving subject to variations both of velocity and of direction of motion to be driven into irregularly distributed masses; and these, acted on by the quicker moving fluid scouring past them, will force that water sidewise, and will be entangled with it and will pass away with some transverse motion to commingle with other parts of the current'. But this can hardly be described as a complete explanation.

† Cf. Prandtl, *The Physics of Solids and Fluids* (London, 1930), p. 228.

‡ Due to W. S. Farren.

‖ Betz, *Engineering*, **127** (1929), 434.

PLATE 20

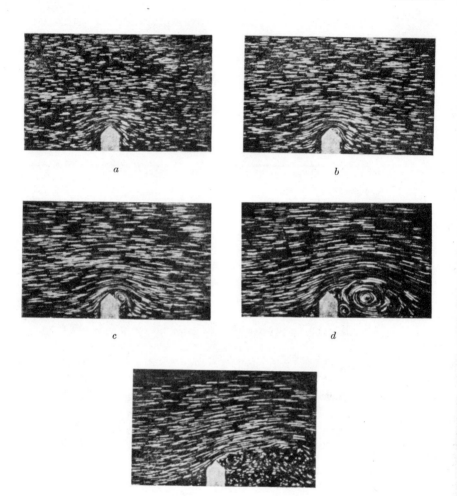

a

b

c

d

e

PLATE 21

a

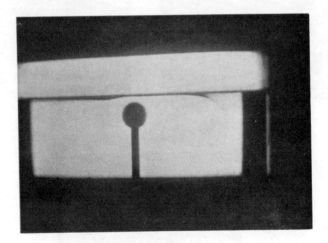

b

the building, and by the time of the fourth picture (*d*) the eddy caused by the roof ridge is so big that it reaches the ground. The counter eddy that it produces in the corner behind the building can also be clearly seen. In the final stage (fifth photograph, *e*), the large vortex at the rear of the building has disappeared, leaving an irregularly eddying region in its place.

Pl. 21*a* shows the flow at the moment when the main stream is stopped. It will be seen that a large eddy, with rotation opposite to that of the eddy in Pl. 20*d*, is shed at the rear of the building. Consequently, in a strong, gusty wind, strong eddies will be formed in the rear of the building, having opposite rotations when the velocity is rapidly increasing and when it is rapidly decreasing. The region immediately in front of the building will be comparatively calm, the most disturbed part being in the rear. This anticipation is confirmed in nature: cases are reported where trees on the windward side of a building were undamaged by storm, whilst others on the leeward side had their tops broken off.†

(4) We have already remarked on several examples in which the flow separated from the wall in flowing past an obstacle. Another example is shown in Pl. 21*b*,† where a circular cylinder is brought near to a wall. Here another phenomenon is also made evident. If the cylinder were touching the wall, the point of contact would be a stagnation point, and the pressure along the wall would be a maximum there. If the cylinder is withdrawn a short distance from the wall, the pressure along the wall is still a maximum at the point of nearest approach to the cylinder. As we go along the wall from a considerable distance upstream, the pressure at first diminishes, and then increases again till we are opposite the cylinder, then as we go along the wall farther downstream behind the cylinder, the pressure at first decreases and then increases again. The result of this last increase is separation from the wall some distance behind the cylinder; and because of the pressure rise just in front of the cylinder, there is a considerable thickening of the boundary layer there, which is clearly shown in the picture.‡

---

† Nøkkentved, *Ingenioren* **41** (1932), 330–339, from which the photographs in Pl. 20*a–e* and Pl. 21*a* are taken.   ‡ Due to W. S. Farren.

THE EQUATIONS OF VISCOUS FLUID FLOW

30. Introduction.

THE present chapter begins with a brief résumé of the mathematical equations governing the motion of a viscous incompressible fluid, and with proofs of general theorems, some of which have been mentioned by anticipation in previous chapters. Certain particular solutions of the equations are then discussed, and the forms assumed by these solutions for large Reynolds numbers are studied. In the next chapter we shall pass on to an exposition of the simplifications introduced in the approximate 'boundary layer theory', and the results that follow therefrom; and to some of the solutions of the approximate equations.

In the derivation of the general theorems and equations it is convenient to use rectangular Cartesian coordinates x, y, z, and to denote the vector velocity of the fluid at the point (x, y, z) by $\mathbf{v}$, its components parallel to the coordinate axes being denoted by (u, v, w). Then u, v, w are, in general, functions of x, y, z and of the time t: if the motion is steady, they are functions of x, y, z alone.

31. The equation of continuity.

The fluid being assumed incompressible, the equation of continuity is[†]

$$\frac{\partial u}{\partial x} + \frac{\partial v}{\partial y} + \frac{\partial w}{\partial z} = 0, \tag{1}$$

or, in vector notation,[‡]
$$\operatorname{div} \mathbf{v} = 0. \tag{2}$$

32. The rate-of-strain components and the vorticity.

The component velocities at a point $P\ (x, y, z)$ being (u, v, w), the components of the relative velocity at an infinitesimally near point $(x + \delta x, y + \delta y, z + \delta z)$ are $(\delta u, \delta v, \delta w)$, where

$$\left. \begin{aligned}
\delta u &= \tfrac{1}{2}(e_{xx}\,\delta x + e_{xy}\,\delta y + e_{xz}\,\delta z) + \tfrac{1}{2}(\eta\,\delta z - \zeta\,\delta y), \\
\delta v &= \tfrac{1}{2}(e_{yx}\,\delta x + e_{yy}\,\delta y + e_{yz}\,\delta z) + \tfrac{1}{2}(\zeta\,\delta x - \xi\,\delta z), \\
\delta w &= \tfrac{1}{2}(e_{zx}\,\delta x + e_{zy}\,\delta y + e_{zz}\,\delta z) + \tfrac{1}{2}(\xi\,\delta y - \eta\,\delta x),
\end{aligned} \right\} \tag{3}$$

† Lamb, *Hydrodynamics* (Cambridge, 1932), p. 6.

‡ For the definitions of scalar product, vector product, gradient, divergence, and curl used in this chapter, a reader unacquainted with vector notation may refer, for example, to Weatherburn, *Elementary Vector Analysis* (London, 1928), chap. iii, and *Advanced Vector Analysis*, chap. i.

and we have written

$$
\left.
\begin{aligned}
& e_{xx} = 2\frac{\partial u}{\partial x}, \qquad e_{yy} = 2\frac{\partial v}{\partial y}, \qquad e_{zz} = 2\frac{\partial w}{\partial z}, \\
& e_{yz} = e_{zy} = \frac{\partial w}{\partial y} + \frac{\partial v}{\partial z}, \qquad e_{zx} = e_{xz} = \frac{\partial u}{\partial z} + \frac{\partial w}{\partial x}, \\
& e_{xy} = e_{yx} = \frac{\partial v}{\partial x} + \frac{\partial u}{\partial y},
\end{aligned}
\right\}
\tag{4}
$$

together with

$$
\xi = \frac{\partial w}{\partial y} - \frac{\partial v}{\partial z}, \qquad \eta = \frac{\partial u}{\partial z} - \frac{\partial w}{\partial x}, \qquad \zeta = \frac{\partial v}{\partial x} - \frac{\partial u}{\partial y}. \tag{5}
$$

Then ξ, η, ζ are the components of curl $\mathbf{v}$, which is a vector that we shall denote by $\boldsymbol{\omega}$. This vector is, as we shall see presently, the vorticity as defined in Chap. I (p. 27).

As regards the quantities e_{xx}, etc., which are called the rate-of-strain components, it is not difficult to see that $\frac{1}{2}e_{xx}$ represents the rate of extension of a line element in the direction of the axis of x, and e_{yz} the rate of change of the angle between the two lines of particles which, at the instant under consideration, lie along the axes of y and z. The other quantities have corresponding interpretations. If we transform from axes (x, y, z) to axes (x', y', z'), where the direction cosines of the axes of x', y', and z', referred to the axes (x, y, z), are (l_1, m_1, n_1), (l_2, m_2, n_2), and (l_3, m_3, n_3), respectively, as in the scheme below,

	x	y	z
x'	l_1	m_1	n_1
y'	l_2	m_2	n_2
z'	l_3	m_3	n_3

then

$$
u' = l_1 u + m_1 v + n_1 w \tag{6}
$$

with two similar equations, where (u', v', w') are the velocity components along the new axes; and

$$
x = l_1 x' + l_2 y' + l_3 z' \tag{7}
$$

with two similar equations. Hence

$$
e_{x'x'} = 2\frac{\partial u'}{\partial x'} = l_1^2 e_{xx} + m_1^2 e_{yy} + n_1^2 e_{zz} + 2m_1 n_1 e_{yz} + 2n_1 l_1 e_{zx} + 2l_1 m_1 e_{xy},
\tag{8}
$$

and

$$e_{y'z'} = l_2 l_3 e_{xx} + m_2 m_3 e_{yy} + n_2 n_3 e_{zz} + (m_2 n_3 + m_3 n_2)e_{yz}$$
$$+ (n_2 l_3 + n_3 l_2)e_{zx} + (l_2 m_3 + l_3 m_2)e_{xy}. \quad (9)$$

The other quantities are transformed similarly.

Now, if we write

$$\Phi = e_{xx}(\delta x)^2 + e_{yy}(\delta y)^2 + e_{zz}(\delta z)^2 + 2e_{yz}\,\delta y\delta z + 2e_{zx}\,\delta z\delta x + 2e_{xy}\,\delta x\delta y, \quad (10)$$

and regard δx, δy, δz as current coordinates, then

$$\Phi = \text{constant} \quad (11)$$

is the equation of a quadric, with its centre at P, called the rate-of-strain quadric. If the quadric be referred to a set of axes through P parallel to the axes of (x', y', z'), then the coefficients in the transformed equation of the quadric will be $e_{x'x'},..., e_{y'z'},...$. When the axes of x', y', z' are taken along the principal axes of the quadric, $e_{y'z'}, e_{z'x'},$ and $e_{x'y'}$ therefore vanish. It follows that the rates of change of the angles between lines of particles along these axes are zero. Hence at any point of a fluid in motion there is a set of three straight lines at right angles to each other such that, if these lines move with the fluid, then after a short time δt the angles between them remain right angles to the first order in δt. These lines are called the principal axes of rate-of-strain. We may also notice that according to equation (8) the rate of extension of a line element drawn in any direction through P is inversely proportional to the square of the radius vector of the rate-of-strain quadric drawn in that direction, and so is stationary, for changes in direction, along the principal axes.

It may be shown from equations (3) (preferably with the axes of coordinates parallel to the principal axes at P, for ease of calculation) that if we imagine an infinitesimally small sphere with its centre at P to be suddenly solidified in such a way that its angular momentum about P is unchanged, then the solid sphere will be rotating with an angular velocity $(\frac{1}{2}\xi, \frac{1}{2}\eta, \frac{1}{2}\zeta)$, or $\frac{1}{2}\boldsymbol{\omega}$, so that $\boldsymbol{\omega}$ is the vorticity as previously defined (p. 27). Equations (3) also show that we could define $\boldsymbol{\omega}$ as twice the angular velocity of the triad of lines forming the principal axes, as this triad moves with the fluid. Quite generally, the first brackets on the right in (3) are $\frac{1}{4}$ of the derivatives of Φ with respect to δx, δy, and δz, respectively; and we may say that the motion of *any* small portion of the fluid in the neighbourhood of P may be analysed into a motion of translation with velocity $\mathbf{v}$, a motion of rotation with angular velocity $\frac{1}{2}\boldsymbol{\omega}$, and a potential, or irrotational, motion of distortion. But it is to be remarked that if any small portion of the fluid with its mass centre at P be imagined suddenly solidified without change of angular momentum about P, it would, in general, be rotating with angular velocity $\frac{1}{2}\boldsymbol{\omega}$ only if the principal axes of rate-of-strain are principal axes of inertia for the resulting solid.

33. The stress components.

The stress at any point P exerted across any surface through P was defined on p. 1. When the normal to the surface at P is in a given direction, the stress itself may be in any direction, and is, in fact, a vector. In the complete specification of stress two directions enter,—that of the normal to the surface, and that of the stress itself. When the normal is in the direction of the axis of x, the components of the stress parallel to the three coordinate axes are denoted by p_{xx}, p_{xy}, and p_{xz}, respectively; when the normal is in the direction of the axis of y, by p_{yx}, p_{yy}, and p_{yz}; when it is in the direction of the axis of z, by p_{zx}, p_{zy}, and p_{zz}; and a tension is reckoned as positive, a pressure as negative.

If we include the kinetic reactions, or reversed mass-accelerations of the particles, we may write down equations of equilibrium for an infinitesimal element of the fluid in the neighbourhood of P. (Actually, in the two cases considered below, the kinetic reactions and body forces may be omitted, since their resultant moments and forces are infinitesimals of higher order than the moments and forces, respectively, due to the surface tractions.) If the element is taken as a cube with its centre at P and edges parallel to the co-ordinate axes, the equations of moments about axes through P give

$$p_{yz} = p_{zy}, \qquad p_{zx} = p_{xz}, \qquad p_{xy} = p_{yx}. \tag{12}$$

If the element is taken as a tetrahedron with three faces meeting in P and parallel to the coordinate planes, the normal to the fourth face having direction cosines (l_1, m_1, n_1), then by resolving the resultant forces along the coordinate axes we find

$$p_{nx} = l_1 p_{xx} + m_1 p_{yx} + n_1 p_{zx}, \tag{13}$$

and two similar equations with y and z, respectively, as the second suffix throughout, p_{nx}, p_{ny}, p_{nz} being the components of the stress exerted across a plane through P whose normal has direction cosines (l_1, m_1, n_1).

If now we transform to axes (x', y', z') as on p. 91, then in the first place $(p_{x'x'}, p_{x'y'}, p_{x'z'})$ and $(p_{x'x}, p_{x'y}, p_{x'z})$ are components, parallel to the new and old axes respectively, of the same vector, and hence

$$p_{x'x'} = l_1 p_{x'x} + m_1 p_{x'y} + n_1 p_{x'z}. \qquad (14)$$

But $p_{x'x}$, $p_{x'y}$, and $p_{x'z}$ are given by three equations of the type (13), so that

$$p_{x'x'} = l_1^2 p_{xx} + m_1^2 p_{yy} + n_1^2 p_{zz} + 2m_1 n_1 p_{yz} + 2n_1 l_1 p_{zx} + 2l_1 m_1 p_{xy}. \quad (15)$$

In the same way we find that

$$p_{y'z'} = l_2 l_3 p_{xx} + m_2 m_3 p_{yy} + n_2 n_3 p_{zz} + (m_2 n_3 + m_3 n_2) p_{yz}$$
$$+ (n_2 l_3 + n_3 l_2) p_{zx} + (l_2 m_3 + l_3 m_2) p_{xy}, \quad (16)$$

and the other stress components are transformed similarly, so that the transformation formulae are exactly the same as for the rate-of-strain components.[†] We may therefore define a stress quadric, and principal axes of stress, in exactly the same way as we defined the rate-of-strain quadric and the principal axes of rate-of-strain; and these axes will have analogous properties. The planes perpendicular to the principal axes of stress are called principal planes of stress; the stress across each of them is purely normal, and these three normal stresses are called the principal stresses.

34. Relations between the stress and rate-of-strain components.

In a fluid at rest, or in a fluid in motion if it be supposed devoid of internal friction, the pressure is wholly normal and is the same in all directions, so that

$$p_{xx} = p_{yy} = p_{zz} = -p, \qquad p_{yz} = p_{zx} = p_{xy} = 0.$$

Again, if a viscous fluid is in motion in such a way that $v = w = 0$, we have seen (p. 3) that

$$p_{zx} = \mu \frac{\partial u}{\partial z},$$

where μ is a constant for any particular fluid. We now seek to generalize these results by assuming that, in general, the stress components are linear functions of the rate-of-strain components, so that the most general expression for each stress component may be equal to the sum of multiples of the six rate-of-strain components plus a quantity independent of them. But in an isotropic

---

† Both the stress and the rate-of-strain are, in fact, symmetrical tensors of the second order. See Jeffreys, *Cartesian Tensors* (Cambridge, 1931).

fluid there are no privileged directions, so the relations between the stress components and the rate-of-strain components must be independent of the choice of axes. If we express mathematically the conditions that this should be so, we find that for an incompressible fluid, in which div **v** = 0, we must have†

$$
\left.
\begin{aligned}
p_{xx} &= -p + \mu e_{xx} = -p + 2\mu \frac{\partial u}{\partial x}, \\[6pt]
p_{yy} &= -p + \mu e_{yy} = -p + 2\mu \frac{\partial v}{\partial y}, \\[6pt]
p_{zz} &= -p + \mu e_{zz} = -p + 2\mu \frac{\partial w}{\partial z}, \\[6pt]
p_{yz} &= \mu e_{yz} = \mu \left(\frac{\partial w}{\partial y} + \frac{\partial v}{\partial z} \right), \\[6pt]
p_{zx} &= \mu e_{zx} = \mu \left(\frac{\partial u}{\partial z} + \frac{\partial w}{\partial x} \right), \\[6pt]
p_{xy} &= \mu e_{xy} = \mu \left(\frac{\partial v}{\partial x} + \frac{\partial u}{\partial y} \right),
\end{aligned}
\right\}
\tag{17}
$$

where p and μ are scalars. Since

$$
e_{xx} + e_{yy} + e_{zz} = 2 \operatorname{div} \mathbf{v} = 0, \tag{18}
$$

p is the mean of the normal pressures over three planes mutually at right angles; it will be called simply the pressure. μ is the viscosity, which, at a given temperature, will be taken to be a constant for any particular fluid. It will be seen that equations (17) include the simple results above for the special cases when the fluid is at rest or in motion in one direction.

35. The equations of motion.

If we include the kinetic reactions and the extraneous forces, and consider the equilibrium of an infinitesimal rectangular parallele-

† See, for example, Jeffreys, *Cartesian Tensors* (Cambridge, 1931), chaps. vii and ix. (The rate-of-strain components as defined in the present chapter are double those used by Jeffreys.) For the related investigation in the mathematical theory of elasticity, in which the calculation differs from that necessary here only in the absence of the terms independent of e_{xx}, etc., reference may be made to Love, *Treatise on the Mathematical Theory of Elasticity* (Cambridge, 1927), p. 102. (In Love's notation e_{xx}, e_{yy}, e_{zz} have half the values corresponding to those by which they are defined in the present chapter; e_{yz}, e_{zx}, e_{xy} have corresponding values.)

It will be seen that, according to equations (17), the principal axes of stress and of rate-of-strain coincide: this may, indeed, be assumed from considerations of symmetry in an isotropic fluid, and the investigation may then be somewhat shortened. See Lamb, *Hydrodynamics* (Cambridge, 1932), p. 574. (Lamb uses a, b, c, f, g, and h for quantities denoted here by $\tfrac{1}{2}e_{xx}, \tfrac{1}{2}e_{yy}, \tfrac{1}{2}e_{zz}, e_{yz}, e_{zx}$, and e_{xy} respectively.)

piped with its centroid at P and its edges parallel to the coordinate axes, then by resolving the resultant forces along the axes, we obtain

$$\rho f_x = \rho X + \frac{\partial p_{xx}}{\partial x} + \frac{\partial p_{yx}}{\partial y} + \frac{\partial p_{zx}}{\partial z}, \qquad (19)$$

and two similar equations, where X, Y, Z are the components of the extraneous force $\mathbf{F}$ acting on the fluid per unit mass, and f_x, f_y, f_z are the components of the acceleration of a particle of the fluid, so that

$$f_x = \frac{Du}{Dt} = \frac{\partial u}{\partial t} + u\frac{\partial u}{\partial x} + v\frac{\partial u}{\partial y} + w\frac{\partial u}{\partial z} = \frac{\partial u}{\partial t} + \frac{\partial}{\partial x}(\tfrac{1}{2}\mathbf{v}^2) - (v\zeta - w\eta),$$
$$(20)$$

with similar equations for f_y and f_z.

It may be verified that when equations (12) and three equations such as (19) are satisfied, then the equations of equilibrium (with reversed mass-accelerations included) are satisfied for any finite portion of the fluid.

If we substitute in equation (19) and the two similar equations from (17), then making use of the equation of continuity (1) we find, with $\nu = \mu/\rho$, where ρ is the density,[†]

$$\left.\begin{array}{l} \dfrac{\partial u}{\partial t} + u\dfrac{\partial u}{\partial x} + v\dfrac{\partial u}{\partial y} + w\dfrac{\partial u}{\partial z} = -\dfrac{1}{\rho}\dfrac{\partial p}{\partial x} + X + \nu\nabla^2 u, \\[2mm] \dfrac{\partial v}{\partial t} + u\dfrac{\partial v}{\partial x} + v\dfrac{\partial v}{\partial y} + w\dfrac{\partial v}{\partial z} = -\dfrac{1}{\rho}\dfrac{\partial p}{\partial y} + Y + \nu\nabla^2 v, \\[2mm] \dfrac{\partial w}{\partial t} + u\dfrac{\partial w}{\partial x} + v\dfrac{\partial w}{\partial y} + w\dfrac{\partial w}{\partial z} = -\dfrac{1}{\rho}\dfrac{\partial p}{\partial z} + Z + \nu\nabla^2 w, \end{array}\right\} \qquad (21)$$

where
$$\nabla^2 \equiv \frac{\partial^2}{\partial x^2} + \frac{\partial^2}{\partial y^2} + \frac{\partial^2}{\partial z^2}. \qquad (22)$$

Now, in vector notation, $\nabla^2 u$, $\nabla^2 v$, $\nabla^2 w$ are the components of grad div $\mathbf{v}$ − curl curl $\mathbf{v}$,[‡] and div $\mathbf{v}$ vanishes, whilst curl $\mathbf{v}$ is the vorticity $\boldsymbol{\omega}$. Hence, if we use the last of the expressions for f_x in equation (20), with the corresponding expressions for f_y and f_z, and if we

---

[†] The equations were obtained by Navier, *Mémoires de l'Académie Royale des Sciences*, **6** (1823), 389–416; Poisson, *Journ. de l'École Polytechnique*, **13** (1831), 139–166; Saint-Venant, *Comptes Rendus*, **17** (1843), 1240–1242; Stokes, *Trans. Camb. Phil. Soc.* **8** (1845), 287–305, or *Math. and Phys. Papers*, **1**, 75–105. For a short account of the various methods and hypotheses adopted by these authors reference may be made to Stokes's Report to the British Association in 1846, reprinted in *Math. and Phys. Papers*, **1**, 182 *et seq.*

[‡] Weatherburn, *Advanced Vector Analysis*, p. 11.

further suppose that ρ is constant and that $\mathbf{F}$ is minus the gradient of a potential Ω, we can write the equations (21) in vector form as

$$\frac{\partial \mathbf{v}}{\partial t} - \mathbf{v} \times \boldsymbol{\omega} = -\operatorname{grad}\left(\frac{p}{\rho} + \Omega + \tfrac{1}{2}\mathbf{v}^2\right) - \nu \operatorname{curl}\boldsymbol{\omega}, \qquad (23)$$

where $\mathbf{v} \times \boldsymbol{\omega}$ denotes the vector product of $\mathbf{v}$ and $\boldsymbol{\omega}$.

36. Equations for the rates of change of circulation and vorticity.

By definition the circulation round any closed circuit drawn in the fluid is given as

$$K = \oint \mathbf{v} \cdot d\mathbf{r}, \qquad (24)$$

where the integral is taken once completely round the circuit, and $\mathbf{v} \cdot d\mathbf{r}$ is the scalar product of $\mathbf{v}$ and $d\mathbf{r}$, where $d\mathbf{r}$ has components dx, dy, and dz, and magnitude ds. Hence, if the circuit moves with the fluid, the rate of change of the circulation is

$$\frac{DK}{Dt} = \oint \frac{D\mathbf{v}}{Dt} \cdot d\mathbf{r} + \oint \mathbf{v} \cdot \frac{D}{Dt}(d\mathbf{r}).$$

But $\dfrac{D}{Dt}(d\mathbf{r})$ is the difference of the velocities at the ends of $d\mathbf{r}$, and is $\dfrac{\partial \mathbf{v}}{\partial s}ds$, so that

$$\mathbf{v} \cdot \frac{D}{Dt}(d\mathbf{r}) = \frac{\partial}{\partial s}(\tfrac{1}{2}\mathbf{v}^2)\,ds.$$

Also $\dfrac{D\mathbf{v}}{Dt}$ is the acceleration $\mathbf{f}$, and is equal to

$$-\operatorname{grad}\left(\frac{p}{\rho} + \Omega\right) - \nu \operatorname{curl}\boldsymbol{\omega},$$

so that $$\frac{D\mathbf{v}}{Dt} \cdot d\mathbf{r} = -\frac{\partial}{\partial s}\left(\frac{p}{\rho} + \Omega\right)ds - \nu(\operatorname{curl}\boldsymbol{\omega}) \cdot d\mathbf{r}.$$

Hence $$\frac{DK}{Dt} = -\oint \frac{\partial}{\partial s}\left(\frac{p}{\rho} + \Omega - \tfrac{1}{2}\mathbf{v}^2\right)ds - \nu \oint (\operatorname{curl}\boldsymbol{\omega}) \cdot d\mathbf{r},$$

and on the assumption that Ω is single-valued this reduces to[†]

$$\frac{DK}{Dt} = -\nu \oint (\operatorname{curl}\boldsymbol{\omega}) \cdot d\mathbf{r}. \qquad (25)$$

This is the first result required, and proves an assertion made previously (pp. 30, 31),—namely, that in a viscous fluid the rate of

† For the general circulation theorem in any fluid, see Jeffreys, *Proc. Camb. Phil. Soc.* **24** (1928), 477–479.

change of circulation in a circuit moving with the fluid depends only on the kinematic viscosity and on the space rates of change of the vorticity components at the contour, so that it is small when the viscosity is small, unless the space rates of change of the vorticity components are large.

To obtain equations for the rates of change, $D\xi/Dt$, $D\eta/Dt$ and $D\zeta/Dt$, of the vorticity components at any fluid element, it is simplest to take the curl of both sides of equation (23). Since $\boldsymbol{\omega}$ is curl $\mathbf{v}$, it follows that div $\boldsymbol{\omega}$ is zero; and since also div $\mathbf{v}$ is zero, the components of curl $(\mathbf{v} \times \boldsymbol{\omega})$ are[†] $\boldsymbol{\omega} \cdot \operatorname{grad} u - \mathbf{v} \cdot \operatorname{grad} \xi$

and two similar expressions, with v and η, w and ζ, respectively, in place of u and ξ. Also the components of curl curl $\boldsymbol{\omega}$ are[‡] $-\nabla^2\xi$, $-\nabla^2\eta$, and $-\nabla^2\zeta$, so that we arrive at the equations

$$\left.\begin{aligned}
\frac{D\xi}{Dt} &= \boldsymbol{\omega} \cdot \operatorname{grad} u + \nu\nabla^2\xi, \\
\frac{D\eta}{Dt} &= \boldsymbol{\omega} \cdot \operatorname{grad} v + \nu\nabla^2\eta, \\
\frac{D\zeta}{Dt} &= \boldsymbol{\omega} \cdot \operatorname{grad} w + \nu\nabla^2\zeta.
\end{aligned}\right\} \qquad (26)$$

The first terms on the right express the rates at which ξ, η, ζ vary for a fluid element when ν is zero, in which case the vortex-lines move with the fluid and the strength of a narrow vortex-tube remains constant; that is, the vorticity is convected with the fluid. The additional variation of ξ, η, and ζ, due to viscosity, is expressed by the last terms, and follows the same law as the variation of temperature in the conduction of heat.|| This proves the second theorem stated in anticipation on p. 31.

It may be remarked that equation (25) and equations (26) are equivalent to each other, and that either may be derived directly from the other.

37. The rate of dissipation of energy.

The rate at which work is being done by surface tractions, per unit time, on the fluid inside any surface is

$$\int (p_{nx}u + p_{ny}v + p_{nz}w)\, dS$$

---

† Weatherburn, *Advanced Vector Analysis*, p. 9.   ‡ Weatherburn, *op. cit.*, p. 11.
|| Lamb, *Hydrodynamics* (Cambridge, 1932), p. 578.

over the surface, where p_{nx}, p_{ny}, p_{nz} are the components of the stress exerted across the element dS of the surface. If (l_1, m_1, n_1) are the direction cosines of the outward normal to the surface, we may substitute for p_{nx} from equation (13), with similar substitutions for p_{ny} and p_{nz}. The surface integral may then be transformed into a volume integral by Green's theorem; and the integrand may be transformed by the use of equations (19) and (4) so as to give, for the rate at which work is being done by the surface tractions, the expression

$$- \int \rho(Xu+Yv+Zw)\, d\tau + \int \rho\left(u\frac{Du}{Dt}+v\frac{Dv}{Dt}+w\frac{Dw}{Dt}\right) d\tau + \int \Phi\, d\tau,$$

(27)

where $d\tau$ is an element of volume and

$$\Phi = \tfrac{1}{2}[p_{xx}e_{xx}+p_{yy}e_{yy}+p_{zz}e_{zz}+2p_{yz}e_{yz}+2p_{zx}e_{zx}+2p_{xy}e_{xy}].$$

If we add to (27) the rate at which work is being done by the extraneous forces, the first term is cancelled. The second term of (27) expresses the rate at which the kinetic energy of the fluid is increasing, and consequently the last term represents the rate at which mechanical energy is disappearing and heat energy is being developed. From (17) and (18) we see that

$$\Phi = \tfrac{1}{2}\mu[e_{xx}^2+e_{yy}^2+e_{zz}^2+2e_{yz}^2+2e_{zx}^2+2e_{xy}^2]$$

$$= \mu\left[2\left(\frac{\partial u}{\partial x}\right)^2+2\left(\frac{\partial v}{\partial y}\right)^2+2\left(\frac{\partial w}{\partial z}\right)^2+\left(\frac{\partial w}{\partial y}+\frac{\partial v}{\partial z}\right)^2+\right.$$

$$\left.+\left(\frac{\partial u}{\partial z}+\frac{\partial w}{\partial x}\right)^2+\left(\frac{\partial v}{\partial x}+\frac{\partial u}{\partial y}\right)^2\right]; \quad (28)$$

and this is the rate of dissipation of energy per unit time per unit volume.†

38. Dynamical similarity.

If p_0 is the pressure when the fluid is permanently at rest, then from (23)

$$p_0/\rho+\Omega = \text{constant};$$

and if in place of p we write p_0+p, so that p is the difference of the actual pressure from the hydrostatic pressure, the equations

† Stokes, *Trans. Camb. Phil. Soc.* **9** (1851), 57–59; *Math. and Phys. Papers*, **3**, 67–70.

(21) become

$$\begin{aligned}
\frac{\partial u}{\partial t}+u\frac{\partial u}{\partial x}+v\frac{\partial u}{\partial y}+w\frac{\partial u}{\partial z} &= -\frac{1}{\rho}\frac{\partial p}{\partial x}+\nu\nabla^2 u, \\
\frac{\partial v}{\partial t}+u\frac{\partial v}{\partial x}+v\frac{\partial v}{\partial y}+w\frac{\partial v}{\partial z} &= -\frac{1}{\rho}\frac{\partial p}{\partial y}+\nu\nabla^2 v, \\
\frac{\partial w}{\partial t}+u\frac{\partial w}{\partial x}+v\frac{\partial w}{\partial y}+w\frac{\partial w}{\partial z} &= -\frac{1}{\rho}\frac{\partial p}{\partial z}+\nu\nabla^2 w,
\end{aligned} \tag{29}$$

while (23) becomes

$$\frac{\partial \mathbf{v}}{\partial t}-\mathbf{v}\times\boldsymbol{\omega} = -\operatorname{grad}\!\left(\frac{p}{\rho}+\tfrac{1}{2}\mathbf{v}^2\right)-\nu\operatorname{curl}\boldsymbol{\omega}. \tag{30}$$

The equations of motion will henceforward be taken in this form, so that p will mean the difference of the actual pressure from the hydrostatic.

Although the following arguments are quite general, it is best, for definiteness, to consider a particular system; we shall consider the flow of an otherwise unbounded fluid past a fixed obstacle, of a given shape at a given orientation to the stream, which is assumed uniform apart from the disturbance due to the obstacle. We may take the axis of x in the direction of the undisturbed velocity of the stream, the magnitude of this velocity being U. Let d be a typical length of the obstacle, and write

$$u' = u/U, \qquad v' = v/U, \qquad w' = w/U, \qquad \mathbf{v}' = \mathbf{v}/U,$$
$$x' = x/d, \qquad y' = y/d, \qquad z' = z/d, \qquad t' = Ut/d,$$

and

$$p' = p/\rho U^2:$$

then the equations (29) become, after division by U^2/d,

$$\frac{\partial u'}{\partial t'}+u'\frac{\partial u'}{\partial x'}+v'\frac{\partial u'}{\partial y'}+w'\frac{\partial u'}{\partial z'} = -\frac{\partial p'}{\partial x'}+\frac{1}{R}\left(\frac{\partial^2 u'}{\partial x'^2}+\frac{\partial^2 u'}{\partial y'^2}+\frac{\partial^2 u'}{\partial z'^2}\right) \tag{31}$$

and two similar equations, where

$$R = Ud/\nu. \tag{32}$$

Further, the equation of continuity becomes simply

$$\operatorname{div}\mathbf{v}' = 0, \tag{33}$$

and the boundary conditions, $u = U$, $v = 0$, $w = 0$ at infinity, and $u = v = w = 0$ at the boundary of the solid obstacle, become $u' = 1$, $v' = 0$, $w' = 0$ at infinity, and $u' = v' = w' = 0$ at a fixed surface, independent of d, in the (x', y', z') space. These boundary conditions, together with (33) and the equations of type (31), determine u', v', w', and p'; and we see that, for fluids of different densities and kinematic viscosities, for streams of different speeds and obstacles of different sizes, so long as R is the same, u/U, v/U, w/U, and $p/\rho U^2$ will be functions of x/d, y/d, and z/d only. Since

$$p_{xx} = -p + 2\mu \frac{\partial u}{\partial x} = \rho U^2 \left(-p' + \frac{2}{R} \frac{\partial u'}{\partial x'} \right),$$

$$p_{yz} = \mu \left(\frac{\partial w}{\partial y} + \frac{\partial v}{\partial z} \right) = \frac{\rho U^2}{R} \left(\frac{\partial w'}{\partial y'} + \frac{\partial v'}{\partial z'} \right),$$

the same is true for any stress component divided by ρU^2. In other words, any velocity component divided by U, and any stress component divided by ρU^2, is a function of x/d, y/d, z/d, and R only. Again, the component along the axis of x, for example, of the force on the obstacle (apart from the force of buoyancy) is $\int p_{nx} dS$, and since, for a given value of R, p_{nx} varies as ρU^2, this force component will vary as $\rho U^2 S$, where S is some representative area associated with the obstacle. The same is true for any other force component; so that any force component divided by $\rho U^2 S$ depends on R only, i.e. it is a function of R alone.

Similar results hold in the case of any set of geometrically similar systems; and so we recover, by a somewhat clearer and more logical method, the results obtained by considerations of dimensions in Chap. I, § 5 (pp. 12 et seq.). The application of the results, and the precautions to be observed in applying them, were there considered, and need not be repeated here.†

39. General orthogonal coordinates.

It will be convenient at this stage to write out, for purposes of reference, the formulae giving the divergence, curl, etc. of a vector in general orthogonal coordinates α, β, γ. Let the elements of length at (α, β, γ) in the directions of α increasing, β increasing, and γ increasing, respectively, be $h_1 d\alpha$, $h_2 d\beta$, and $h_3 d\gamma$, so that

$$(ds)^2 = h_1^2 (d\alpha)^2 + h_2^2 (d\beta)^2 + h_3^2 (d\gamma)^2.$$

† The theory of dynamical similarity was first applied to hydrodynamical systems by Stokes, *Trans. Camb. Phil. Soc.* 9 (1851), 19; *Math. and Phys. Papers*, 3, 16, 17; and more fully by Helmholtz, *Monatsberichte der königl. Akademie der Wissenschaften zu Berlin* (1873), 501–514; *Wissenschaftliche Abhandlungen*, 1, 158–171.

Let (u, v, w) be used generally for the components of $\mathbf{v}$ in the directions of α increasing, β increasing, and γ increasing, respectively, and let (ξ, η, ζ) be so used for the components of $\boldsymbol{\omega}$ or curl $\mathbf{v}$. Then†

$$\operatorname{div} \mathbf{v} = \frac{1}{h_1 h_2 h_3} \left\{ \frac{\partial}{\partial \alpha} (h_2 h_3 u) + \frac{\partial}{\partial \beta} (h_3 h_1 v) + \frac{\partial}{\partial \gamma} (h_1 h_2 w) \right\}, \qquad (34)$$

$$\left. \begin{aligned} \xi &= \frac{1}{h_2 h_3} \left\{ \frac{\partial}{\partial \beta} (h_3 w) - \frac{\partial}{\partial \gamma} (h_2 v) \right\}, \\[2mm] \eta &= \frac{1}{h_3 h_1} \left\{ \frac{\partial}{\partial \gamma} (h_1 u) - \frac{\partial}{\partial \alpha} (h_3 w) \right\}, \\[2mm] \zeta &= \frac{1}{h_1 h_2} \left\{ \frac{\partial}{\partial \alpha} (h_2 v) - \frac{\partial}{\partial \beta} (h_1 u) \right\}. \end{aligned} \right\} \qquad (35)$$

Since curl $\boldsymbol{\omega}$ is related to $\boldsymbol{\omega}$ in the same way as $\boldsymbol{\omega}$ is related to $\mathbf{v}$, while the components of a gradient are

$$\frac{1}{h_1} \frac{\partial}{\partial \alpha}, \qquad \frac{1}{h_2} \frac{\partial}{\partial \beta}, \qquad \frac{1}{h_3} \frac{\partial}{\partial \gamma},$$

and the components of $\mathbf{v} \times \boldsymbol{\omega}$ are still

$$v\zeta - w\eta, \qquad w\xi - u\zeta, \qquad u\eta - v\xi,$$

the three components of equation (30) may be written down in any set of coordinates. For an incompressible fluid div $\mathbf{v} = 0$, and this introduces an indeterminateness into the equations, since expressions involving div $\mathbf{v}$ may be added. It is, in fact, usual to retain the form

$$\nu(\operatorname{grad} \operatorname{div} \mathbf{v} - \operatorname{curl} \boldsymbol{\omega})$$

in working out the last term in (30), since this has components $\nu \nabla^2 u$, $\nu \nabla^2 v$, $\nu \nabla^2 w$ in Cartesian coordinates without further transformation.

As regards the rate-of-strain components, $\frac{1}{2} e_{\alpha\alpha}$ is still the rate of extension of a line element in the direction of α increasing at the point (α, β, γ), and $e_{\beta\gamma}$ is still the rate of change of the angle between two lines, moving with the fluid, drawn through (α, β, γ) in the directions of β increasing and γ increasing, respectively; but the directions of α increasing, β increasing, and γ increasing are different at (α, β, γ) and at any neighbouring point, and this introduces extra terms into the expressions for the rate-of-strain components. These

† See Love, *Treatise on the Mathematical Theory of Elasticity* (Cambridge, 1927), pp. 54, 55, where other references are given. The h_1, h_2, h_3 used by Love are the reciprocals of those employed here.

expressions are†

$$
\begin{aligned}
\tfrac{1}{2}e_{\alpha\alpha} &= \frac{1}{h_1}\frac{\partial u}{\partial \alpha} + \frac{v}{h_1 h_2}\frac{\partial h_1}{\partial \beta} + \frac{w}{h_3 h_1}\frac{\partial h_1}{\partial \gamma}, \\
\tfrac{1}{2}e_{\beta\beta} &= \frac{1}{h_2}\frac{\partial v}{\partial \beta} + \frac{w}{h_2 h_3}\frac{\partial h_2}{\partial \gamma} + \frac{u}{h_1 h_2}\frac{\partial h_2}{\partial \alpha}, \\
\tfrac{1}{2}e_{\gamma\gamma} &= \frac{1}{h_3}\frac{\partial w}{\partial \gamma} + \frac{u}{h_3 h_1}\frac{\partial h_3}{\partial \alpha} + \frac{v}{h_2 h_3}\frac{\partial h_3}{\partial \beta}, \\
e_{\beta\gamma} &= \frac{h_3}{h_2}\frac{\partial}{\partial \beta}\left(\frac{w}{h_3}\right) + \frac{h_2}{h_3}\frac{\partial}{\partial \gamma}\left(\frac{v}{h_2}\right), \\
e_{\gamma\alpha} &= \frac{h_1}{h_3}\frac{\partial}{\partial \gamma}\left(\frac{u}{h_1}\right) + \frac{h_3}{h_1}\frac{\partial}{\partial \alpha}\left(\frac{w}{h_3}\right), \\
e_{\alpha\beta} &= \frac{h_2}{h_1}\frac{\partial}{\partial \alpha}\left(\frac{v}{h_2}\right) + \frac{h_1}{h_2}\frac{\partial}{\partial \beta}\left(\frac{u}{h_1}\right).
\end{aligned}
\tag{36}
$$

The stress components are still given by

$$
\begin{aligned}
p_{\alpha\alpha} &= -p + \mu e_{\alpha\alpha}, & p_{\beta\gamma} &= p_{\gamma\beta} = \mu e_{\beta\gamma}, \\
p_{\beta\beta} &= -p + \mu e_{\beta\beta}, & p_{\gamma\alpha} &= p_{\alpha\gamma} = \mu e_{\gamma\alpha}, \\
p_{\gamma\gamma} &= -p + \mu e_{\gamma\gamma}, & p_{\alpha\beta} &= p_{\beta\alpha} = \mu e_{\alpha\beta},
\end{aligned}
\tag{37}
$$

where $p_{\beta\gamma}$, for example, is the component in the direction of γ increasing of the stress exerted at (α, β, γ) across the surface $\beta =$ constant.

In the special cases when the motion is two-dimensional, or is symmetrical about an axis, the velocities may be expressed in terms of a stream-function. The equations for the stream-functions in general orthogonal coordinates in the two cases are not required in their generality for the further purposes of this chapter, and are given in an appendix at the end.

40. Cylindrical polar coordinates.

With cylindrical polar coordinates r, ϕ, z, such that

$$
x = r\cos\phi, \qquad y = r\sin\phi,
$$

if r, ϕ, z are taken as α, β, γ, respectively, then $h_1 = 1$, $h_2 = r$, and $h_3 = 1$. Hence

$$
\operatorname{div}\mathbf{v} = \frac{1}{r}\frac{\partial}{\partial r}(ru) + \frac{1}{r}\frac{\partial v}{\partial \phi} + \frac{\partial w}{\partial z},
\tag{38}
$$

$$
\xi = \frac{1}{r}\frac{\partial w}{\partial \phi} - \frac{\partial v}{\partial z}, \qquad \eta = \frac{\partial u}{\partial z} - \frac{\partial w}{\partial r}, \qquad \zeta = \frac{1}{r}\frac{\partial}{\partial r}(rv) - \frac{1}{r}\frac{\partial u}{\partial \phi}, \tag{39}
$$

† Cp. Love, *op. cit.*, pp. 53, 54, 628–632.

$$\tfrac{1}{2}e_{rr} = \frac{\partial u}{\partial r}, \qquad \tfrac{1}{2}e_{\phi\phi} = \frac{1}{r}\frac{\partial v}{\partial \phi} + \frac{u}{r}, \qquad \tfrac{1}{2}e_{zz} = \frac{\partial w}{\partial z},$$

$$e_{\phi z} = \frac{1}{r}\frac{\partial w}{\partial \phi} + \frac{\partial v}{\partial z}, \qquad e_{zr} = \frac{\partial u}{\partial z} + \frac{\partial w}{\partial r}, \qquad e_{r\phi} = r\frac{\partial}{\partial r}\left(\frac{v}{r}\right) + \frac{1}{r}\frac{\partial u}{\partial \phi}, \tag{40}$$

and the equations of motion are

$$\frac{\partial u}{\partial t} + u\frac{\partial u}{\partial r} + \frac{v}{r}\frac{\partial u}{\partial \phi} + w\frac{\partial u}{\partial z} - \frac{v^2}{r} = -\frac{1}{\rho}\frac{\partial p}{\partial r} + \nu\left(\nabla^2 u - \frac{u}{r^2} - \frac{2}{r^2}\frac{\partial v}{\partial \phi}\right),$$

$$\frac{\partial v}{\partial t} + u\frac{\partial v}{\partial r} + \frac{v}{r}\frac{\partial v}{\partial \phi} + w\frac{\partial v}{\partial z} + \frac{uv}{r} = -\frac{1}{\rho}\frac{1}{r}\frac{\partial p}{\partial \phi} + \nu\left(\nabla^2 v + \frac{2}{r^2}\frac{\partial u}{\partial \phi} - \frac{v}{r^2}\right), \tag{41}$$

$$\frac{\partial w}{\partial t} + u\frac{\partial w}{\partial r} + \frac{v}{r}\frac{\partial w}{\partial \phi} + w\frac{\partial w}{\partial z} = -\frac{1}{\rho}\frac{\partial p}{\partial z} + \nu\nabla^2 w,$$

where

$$\nabla^2 \equiv \frac{\partial^2}{\partial r^2} + \frac{1}{r}\frac{\partial}{\partial r} + \frac{1}{r^2}\frac{\partial^2}{\partial \phi^2} + \frac{\partial^2}{\partial z^2}.$$

41. Spherical polar coordinates.

With spherical polar coordinates R, θ, ϕ, such that

$$x = R\sin\theta\cos\phi, \qquad y = R\sin\theta\sin\phi, \qquad z = R\cos\theta,$$

if R, θ, ϕ are taken as α, β, γ respectively, then

$$h_1 = 1, \qquad h_2 = R, \qquad h_3 = R\sin\theta.$$

Hence

$$\operatorname{div}\mathbf{v} = \frac{1}{R^2}\frac{\partial}{\partial R}(R^2 u) + \frac{1}{R\sin\theta}\frac{\partial}{\partial \theta}(v\sin\theta) + \frac{1}{R\sin\theta}\frac{\partial w}{\partial \phi}, \tag{42}$$

$$\xi = \frac{1}{R\sin\theta}\left\{\frac{\partial}{\partial \theta}(w\sin\theta) - \frac{\partial v}{\partial \phi}\right\},$$

$$\eta = \frac{1}{R\sin\theta}\frac{\partial u}{\partial \phi} - \frac{1}{R}\frac{\partial}{\partial R}(Rw), \tag{43}$$

$$\zeta = \frac{1}{R}\frac{\partial}{\partial R}(Rv) - \frac{1}{R}\frac{\partial u}{\partial \theta},$$

$$\tfrac{1}{2}e_{RR} = \frac{\partial u}{\partial R}, \qquad \tfrac{1}{2}e_{\theta\theta} = \frac{1}{R}\frac{\partial v}{\partial \theta} + \frac{u}{R},$$

$$\tfrac{1}{2}e_{\phi\phi} = \frac{1}{R\sin\theta}\frac{\partial w}{\partial \phi} + \frac{u}{R} + \frac{v\cot\theta}{R},$$

$$e_{\theta\phi} = \frac{\sin\theta}{R}\frac{\partial}{\partial \theta}\left(\frac{w}{\sin\theta}\right) + \frac{1}{R\sin\theta}\frac{\partial v}{\partial \phi}, \tag{44}$$

$$e_{\phi R} = \frac{1}{R\sin\theta}\frac{\partial u}{\partial \phi} + R\frac{\partial}{\partial R}\left(\frac{w}{R}\right),$$

$$e_{R\theta} = R\frac{\partial}{\partial R}\left(\frac{v}{R}\right) + \frac{1}{R}\frac{\partial u}{\partial \theta},$$

and the equations of motion are

$$
\begin{aligned}
&\frac{\partial u}{\partial t}+u\frac{\partial u}{\partial R}+\frac{v}{R}\frac{\partial u}{\partial\theta}+\frac{w}{R\sin\theta}\frac{\partial u}{\partial\phi}-\frac{v^2+w^2}{R} \\
&\quad=-\frac{1}{\rho}\frac{\partial p}{\partial R}+\nu\left(\nabla^2u-\frac{2u}{R^2}-\frac{2}{R^2}\frac{\partial v}{\partial\theta}-\frac{2v\cot\theta}{R^2}-\frac{2}{R^2\sin\theta}\frac{\partial w}{\partial\phi}\right), \\
&\frac{\partial v}{\partial t}+u\frac{\partial v}{\partial R}+\frac{v}{R}\frac{\partial v}{\partial\theta}+\frac{w}{R\sin\theta}\frac{\partial v}{\partial\phi}+\frac{uv}{R}-\frac{w^2\cot\theta}{R} \\
&\quad=-\frac{1}{\rho}\frac{1}{R}\frac{\partial p}{\partial\theta}+\nu\left(\nabla^2v+\frac{2}{R^2}\frac{\partial u}{\partial\theta}-\frac{v}{R^2\sin^2\theta}-\frac{2\cos\theta}{R^2\sin^2\theta}\frac{\partial w}{\partial\phi}\right), \\
&\frac{\partial w}{\partial t}+u\frac{\partial w}{\partial R}+\frac{v}{R}\frac{\partial w}{\partial\theta}+\frac{w}{R\sin\theta}\frac{\partial w}{\partial\phi}+\frac{wu}{R}+\frac{vw\cot\theta}{R} \\
&\quad=-\frac{1}{\rho}\frac{1}{R\sin\theta}\frac{\partial p}{\partial\phi}+\nu\left(\nabla^2w-\frac{w}{R^2\sin^2\theta}+\frac{2}{R^2\sin\theta}\frac{\partial u}{\partial\phi}\right. \\
&\qquad\qquad\qquad\qquad\qquad\left.+\frac{2\cos\theta}{R^2\sin^2\theta}\frac{\partial v}{\partial\phi}\right),
\end{aligned}
\tag{45}
$$

where

$$
\nabla^2=\frac{1}{R^2}\frac{\partial}{\partial R}\left(R^2\frac{\partial}{\partial R}\right)+\frac{1}{R^2\sin\theta}\frac{\partial}{\partial\theta}\left(\sin\theta\frac{\partial}{\partial\theta}\right)+\frac{1}{R^2\sin^2\theta}\frac{\partial^2}{\partial\phi^2}.
$$

42. Examples of exact solutions of the equations of motion. Two-dimensional steady flow between non-parallel plane walls.

To discuss mathematically the steady flow of viscous fluid between two non-parallel plane walls, take a system of cylindrical polar coordinates r, ϕ, z in which the axis of z is the line of intersection of the planes of the walls, r is distance from this line, and the walls lie in the planes $\phi=\pm\alpha$. Then, in the notation of § 40, if the motion is purely radial $v=w=0$, and the equation of continuity is satisfied if

$$
u=\frac{f(\phi)}{r}.
\tag{46}
$$

The equations of motion then reduce to

$$
\begin{aligned}
-\frac{f^2}{r^3}&=-\frac{1}{\rho}\frac{\partial p}{\partial r}+\nu\frac{f''}{r^3}, \\
0&=-\frac{1}{\rho}\frac{1}{r}\frac{\partial p}{\partial\phi}+2\nu\frac{f'}{r^3}.
\end{aligned}
\right\}
\tag{47}
$$

P

From the first of these two equations it follows that $r^3 \partial p/\partial r$ is a function of ϕ only, and the second equation then gives

$$p = 2\mu\frac{f(\phi)}{r^2} + \frac{k\mu}{2r^2} + \text{constant}, \qquad (48)$$

where k is a constant. Hence, and from the first of equations (47), we find that
$$f'' + 4f + f^2/\nu + k = 0,$$

whence, after multiplication by $2f'$ and integration,

$$f'^2 = \frac{2}{3\nu}\{h - 3\nu kf - 6\nu f^2 - f^3\}, \qquad (49)$$

h being a second constant of integration. The problem is to integrate this equation and so to choose the constants that, with f zero at the walls, the total flux (per unit breadth) across a section has a given value. If the flow is purely divergent, f is positive; if it is purely convergent, f is negative. In either case f is symmetrical about $\phi = 0$; and in such cases the value of f when $\phi = 0$ may be given instead of the total flux. The equation may be integrated in terms of elliptic functions, and has been considered by several authors,† though it appears that the discussion is hardly yet complete.

As Reynolds number we may take the product of r and the average value of the velocity, divided by ν; or, for purely divergent or purely convergent flow, we may use the maximum instead of the average value of the velocity.

It appears that there is a very great difference between the cases of convergent and divergent flow. With increasing speed the velocity distribution, which at small Reynolds numbers and for small values of α is approximately parabolic, becomes, for convergent flow, flatter and flatter in the middle of the channel, the drop of the velocity to zero taking place in layers near the walls which become narrower and narrower as the Reynolds number is increased. For divergent flow, on the other hand, the velocity distribution alters

† Jeffery, *Phil. Mag.* (6), **29** (1915), 455–465; Hamel, *Jahresbericht der Deutschen Mathematiker-Vereinigung*, **25** (1916), 34–60; Harrison, *Proc. Camb. Phil. Soc.* **19** (1919), 307–312; Kármán, *Vorträge aus dem Gebiete der Hydro- und Aerodynamik, Innsbruck,* 1922 (Berlin, 1924), pp. 150, 151; Tollmien, *Handbuch der Experimentalphysik,* **4,** part 1 (Leipzig, 1931), 257–260; Noether, *Handbuch der physikalischen und technischen Mechanik,* **5** (Leipzig, 1931), 733–736; Dean, *Phil. Mag.* (7), **18** (1934), 759–777. See also the references in the footnote on p. 110.

with increasing Reynolds number in the opposite manner, the flux becoming more and more concentrated in the middle of the channel, until a Reynolds number is reached at which $f'(\phi)$, and therefore $\partial u/\partial \phi$, vanish at the walls.† If the Reynolds number is further increased, purely divergent flow becomes impossible. When a larger outward flux than the critical one is forced through the channel, there are regions of backward flow; and for the same flux it would appear that three solutions are possible, with the backward flow near one wall or the other, or near both walls. This critical flux, that may just be forced through a divergent channel without the occurrence of backward flow, increases as the angle between the walls decreases. It seems probable, but does not appear to have been demonstrated, that if the flux and the Reynolds number are still further increased, the number of possible regions of backward flow, and the number of possible solutions, also increase.

The analysis for the two cases may be illustrated in the following manner. Consider first the case of purely divergent flow, for which f is positive. Then (49) may be written in the form

$$f'^2 = \frac{2}{3\nu}\{(f_1-f)(f_2-f)(f_3-f)\}, \tag{50}$$

where f_1, f_2, f_3 are the zeros of the right-hand side. f_1, f_2 and f_3 may all be real, in which case we assume $f_1 \geqslant f_2 \geqslant f_3$; or one of them (f_1) may be real, and the other two (f_2, f_3) conjugate complex quantities. In either case

$$f_1+f_2+f_3 = -6\nu, \qquad f_1f_2+f_2f_3+f_3f_1 = 3k\nu, \qquad f_1f_2f_3 = h. \tag{51}$$

The sum of f_1, f_2, f_3 is negative. The range of possible variation of f is restricted by the fact that f'^2 must be positive; and, since f must vanish at the walls, $f = 0$ must occur in the range of values so determined. Also the value of f in the middle of the channel, where $f' = 0$, must be f_1, f_2, or f_3; for purely divergent flow it must be positive. These conditions are sufficient to prove that f_1 is positive and $0 \leqslant f \leqslant f_1$, and that f_2 and f_3 are negative or zero, or conjugate complex quantities, so that their product is positive or zero. Hence h is positive or zero. Then, since $f = 0$ when $\phi = \alpha$ and $f = f_1$ when $\phi = 0$,

$$\alpha = \sqrt{\left(\frac{3\nu}{2}\right)} \int_0^{f_1} \frac{df}{\{[f_1-f][f^2+f(6\nu+f_1)+h/f_1]\}^{\frac{1}{2}}}. \tag{52}$$

Since h is not negative, α has its greatest permissible value for a given value

† For an attempt to consider, by a method of successive approximation (starting from the parabolic velocity distribution), the flow of viscous fluid along any channel of slowly increasing breadth, see Blasius, *Zeitschr. f. Math. u. Phys.* **58** (1910), 225–233. For an experimental investigation of the flow at small Reynolds numbers in a channel of small exponential divergence, see G. N. Patterson, *Canadian Journ. of Research*, **11** (1934), 770–779; **12** (1935), 676–685.

of f_1 when $h = 0$,—i.e. when $f_2 = 0$. Then $f' = 0$ when $f = 0$, at the walls. When this holds, if we write

$$f = f_1 w, \qquad R = \frac{f_1}{\nu} = \frac{r u_{\max}}{\nu}, \tag{53}$$

then
$$\alpha = \sqrt{\left(\frac{3}{2R}\right)} \int_0^1 \frac{dw}{\{[1-w][w^2+w(1+6/R)]\}^{\frac{1}{2}}}. \tag{54}$$

If we put
$$w = \cos^2\psi, \tag{55}$$

this reduces to
$$(R+3)^{\frac{1}{2}}\alpha = \sqrt{3} \int_0^{\frac{1}{2}\pi} \frac{d\psi}{[1-\frac{1}{2}(1+3/R)^{-1}\sin^2\psi]^{\frac{1}{2}}} \tag{56}$$

or, if R is large, to

$$R^{\frac{1}{2}}\alpha = \sqrt{3} \int_0^{\frac{1}{2}\pi} \frac{d\psi}{(1-\frac{1}{2}\sin^2\psi)^{\frac{1}{2}}} = 3{\cdot}211.\dagger \tag{57}$$

This gives an upper limit to $R^{\frac{1}{2}}\alpha$ if R is large and α is small. A graph of $R^{\frac{1}{2}}\alpha$ against R, calculated from equation (56), is shown in Fig. 39 below.

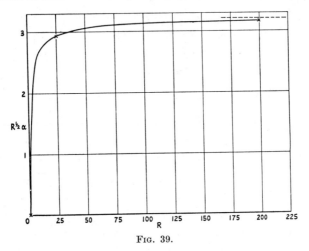

FIG. 39.

For convergent flow, on the other hand, f must be negative, and in order that the conditions may be satisfied f_1, f_2 and f_3 must all be real, with f_1 positive and f_2 and f_3 negative, and $f_2 \leqslant f \leqslant 0$. If we write

$$R = -\frac{f_2}{\nu} = \frac{r|u|_{\max}}{\nu}, \qquad \frac{f}{f_2} = w, \qquad \frac{f_3}{f_2} = w_3, \qquad -\frac{f_1}{f_2} = w_1, \tag{58}$$

then w, w_1, and w_3 are all positive, and, from (51),

$$1 - w_1 + w_3 = 6/R. \tag{59}$$

† The value of the integral is $1{\cdot}85407$. See, for example, Dale's *Mathematical Tables*, p. 76. The critical value for $R^{\frac{1}{2}}\alpha$ given by Tollmien, *loc. cit.*, was $3{\cdot}057$.

From (50)

$$\phi = \pm \sqrt{\left(\frac{3}{2R}\right)} \int_{w}^{1} \frac{dw}{\{(1-w)(w_3-w)(w_1+w)\}^{\frac{1}{2}}}, \tag{60}$$

so that

$$R^{\frac{1}{2}}\alpha = \sqrt{\frac{3}{2}} \int_{0}^{1} \frac{dw}{\{(1-w)(w_3-w)(w_1+w)\}^{\frac{1}{2}}}. \tag{61}$$

There is now no restriction on the possible values of $R^{\frac{1}{2}}\alpha$. But if $R^{\frac{1}{2}}\alpha$ is large, then, in order that the integral on the right may be large, w_3 must be

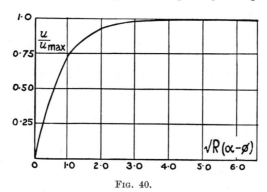

FIG. 40.

nearly equal to 1, so that, if $6/R$ is neglected, w_1 is nearly equal to 2. A more detailed examination shows, in fact, that w_3-1 must be of order $e^{-\sqrt{(2R)\alpha}}$, and that w is nearly equal to 1 and the velocity is nearly uniform, unless, with ϕ positive, $\alpha-\phi$ is small, of order $(2R)^{-\frac{1}{2}}$. With $w_3 = 1$, $w_1 = 2$, we find from (60), for ϕ positive, that

$$\alpha-\phi = \sqrt{\left(\frac{3}{2R}\right)} \int_{0}^{w} \frac{dw}{(1-w)(2+w)^{\frac{1}{2}}}, \tag{62}$$

and this leads to

$$w = \frac{f}{f_2} = \frac{u}{u_{\max}} = 3\tanh^2[\sqrt{(\tfrac{1}{2}R)}(\alpha-\phi)+\beta]-2, \tag{63}$$

where β is a constant (equal to $1\cdot146$), such that $\tanh^2\beta = \tfrac{2}{3}$.

Since the hyperbolic tangent is very nearly equal to 1 for large values of the argument, u is equal to $u_{\max}$ except in a narrow layer near each wall, of thickness proportional to $R^{-\frac{1}{2}}$. A graph of $u/u_{\max}$ against $\sqrt{R}(\alpha-\phi)$ is shown in Fig. 40.

Further, when $w_3 = 1$ and $w_1 = 2$, (51) shows that $k\nu = -f_2^2$; and then we see from (48) that

$$\frac{p}{\rho} = -\frac{f_2^2}{2r^2}\{1+O(R^{-1})\} \tag{64}$$

or

$$\frac{p}{\rho} + \tfrac{1}{2}u_{\max}^2 = O\left(\frac{u_{\max}^2}{R}\right). \tag{65}$$

In this example we see, then, that the assumptions and deductions of the boundary layer theory concerning motions at large Reynolds numbers, as set out in Chap. II, §15 (and more precisely in Chap. IV), are all satisfied.

It may not be out of place to state explicitly that these results apply only to steady, not to turbulent, flow. Convergence of a channel tends to stabilize the flow, divergence to make it unstable. To a large extent the results are theoretical only, especially for diverging channels; but they are nevertheless interesting. The experimental results for turbulent flow, which bear a strong qualitative resemblance to those given by theory for laminar flow, are considered in Chap. VIII, § 166.

Hamel, in the work referred to on p. 106, discussed the flow between non-parallel straight walls as a special case of flow in which the stream-lines are equiangular spirals, which he showed to be the only possible form if, for a two-dimensional motion, they are to coincide with the stream-lines of a potential flow without the actual motion itself being irrotational. When the more general spiral motion takes place between solid walls, the results are analogous to those obtained above. Hamel's results have formed the starting point for a number of researches by other authors.†

43. Examples of exact solutions of the equations of motion. The flow due to a rotating disk.

An infinite plane lamina, coinciding with the plane $z = 0$, rotates with constant angular velocity Ω about the axis $r = 0$ in viscous fluid. We consider the motion of the fluid on the side of the plane for which z is positive, the fluid being supposed infinite in extent and bounded only by the plane $z = 0$. In the notation of § 40, the boundary conditions are

$$u = 0, \quad v = \Omega r, \quad w = 0 \quad \text{at} \quad z = 0,$$
$$u = 0, \quad v = 0 \qquad\qquad \text{at} \quad z = \infty.$$

The axial velocity w will not vanish at $z = \infty$, but must tend to a finite negative limit, which can be determined from the equations. There is, in fact, a steady axial flow towards the rotating lamina:

† Olsson and Faxen, *Zeitschr. f. angew. Math. u. Mech.* **7** (1927), 496–498; Oseen, *Ark. f. mat. astr. och fys.* **20** A (1927), Nos. 14 and 22; Rosenblatt, *Bulletin des Sciences Math.* (2), **55** (1931), 1–18; *Bulletin de l'Académie Polonaise des Sciences et des Lettres* (1931), 438–459; *Sur Certains Mouvements des Liquides Visqueux Incompressibles* (Paris, 1933).

this is necessary to preserve continuity, since the rotating lamina acts as a kind of centrifugal fan, the fluid moving radially outwards, especially near the lamina.

With these boundary conditions, the equations of motion and continuity may be satisfied by taking†

$$u = rf(z), \qquad v = rg(z), \qquad w = h(z), \qquad p = p(z). \qquad (66)$$

If we further write

$$z = (\nu/\Omega)^{\frac{1}{2}}z_1, \qquad f = \Omega F(z_1), \qquad g = \Omega G(z_1), \\ h = (\nu\Omega)^{\frac{1}{2}}H(z_1), \qquad p = -\rho\nu\Omega P(z_1), \qquad \Bigg\} \qquad (67)$$

so that

$$u = r\Omega F(z_1), \qquad v = r\Omega G(z_1), \qquad w = (\nu\Omega)^{\frac{1}{2}}H(z_1), \qquad (68)$$

we obtain the equations of motion in the following non-dimensional form (dashes denoting differentiations with respect to z_1):

$$\left. \begin{array}{c} F^2-G^2+F'H = F'', \\ 2FG+G'H = G'', \\ HH' = P'+H''. \end{array} \right\} \qquad (69)$$

The equation of continuity becomes

$$2F+H' = 0, \qquad (70)$$

and the boundary conditions are

$$\left. \begin{array}{ll} F = 0, \quad G = 1, \quad H = 0 \quad \text{at} \quad z_1 = 0, \\ F \to 0, \quad G \to 0, \qquad\qquad \text{when} \quad z_1 \to \infty. \end{array} \right\} \qquad (71)$$

The first two of equations (69), together with (70), give F, G and H, whilst the third of equations (69) gives P.

If $H \to -c$ when $z_1 \to \infty$, there are formal expansions of F, G, H in powers of e^{-cz_1}, satisfying the differential equations and the conditions at infinity, of which the first few terms are

$$\left. \begin{array}{l} F = Ae^{-cz_1} - \dfrac{A^2+B^2}{2c^2}e^{-2cz_1} + \dfrac{A(A^2+B^2)}{4c^4}e^{-3cz_1} + \dots, \\[2mm] G = Be^{-cz_1} \qquad\qquad\qquad\quad - \dfrac{B(A^2+B^2)}{12c^4}e^{-3cz_1} + \dots, \\[2mm] H = -c + \dfrac{2A}{c}e^{-cz_1} - \dfrac{A^2+B^2}{2c^3}e^{-2cz_1} + \dfrac{A(A^2+B^2)}{6c^5}e^{-3cz_1} + \dots. \end{array} \right\} \qquad (72)$$

A, B, and c are constants to be determined.

† These substitutions, and the resulting equations, are due to Kármán, *Zeitschr. f. angew. Math. u. Mech.* **1** (1921), 244–247.

There are also formal expansions of F, G and H in powers of z_1 which satisfy the differential equations and the conditions at the origin,—namely,

$$\left.\begin{aligned}
F &= a_0 z_1 - \tfrac{1}{2}z_1^2 - \tfrac{1}{3}b_0 z_1^3 - \tfrac{1}{12}b_0^2 z_1^4 - \cdots, \\
G &= 1 + b_0 z_1 + \tfrac{1}{3}a_0 z_1^3 + \tfrac{1}{12}(a_0 b_0 - 1)z_1^4 - \cdots, \\
H &= -a_0 z_1^2 + \tfrac{1}{3}z_1^3 + \tfrac{1}{6}b_0 z_1^4 + \cdots,
\end{aligned}\right\} \tag{73}$$

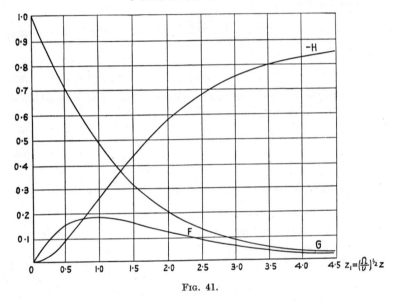

FIG. 41.

where a_0 and b_0 are constants to be determined. The constants a_0, b_0, c, A and B have to be chosen so that F, G, H, F' and G' are continuous; and it will then follow from the differential equations that all the other derivatives are continuous. The computation has been carried out by Cochran,[†] who integrated the differential equations numerically, found that

$$\left.\begin{aligned}
a_0 &= 0\cdot510, \quad b_0 = -0\cdot616, \quad c = 0\cdot886, \\
A &= 0\cdot934, \quad B = 1\cdot208,
\end{aligned}\right\} \tag{74}$$

and gave tables and graphs of F, G, H, F' and G'. The graphs of F, G and H are reproduced in Fig. 41.

F and G tend to zero exponentially, and become indistinguishable from zero for some finite value of z_1. Hence, if ν/Ω is small, $u/(\Omega r)$ and

† *Proc. Camb. Phil. Soc.* **30** (1934), 365–375.

$v/(\Omega r)$ are appreciable only in a thin layer near the disk whose thickness is of order $(\nu/\Omega)^{\frac{1}{2}}$. Also, if P_0 is the value of P at the plate,

$$P - P_0 = \tfrac{1}{2}H^2 - H' = \tfrac{1}{2}H^2 + 2F, \tag{75}$$

and the differences of the pressure p throughout the layer in which $u/(\Omega r)$ and $v/(\Omega r)$ are sensible are of order $\rho\nu\Omega$. In this example, then, the assumptions and results of the boundary layer theory are again confirmed, as they were in the last example. There is, however, this difference between the two examples, that in this case the terms in the equations that would be neglected according to the mathematical theory of the boundary layer (see Chap. IV) are identically zero. The equations solved are, in fact, boundary layer equations, even though the solution in this particular case applies for all Reynolds numbers. In the example of the preceding section the equations solved were not the same as those of the boundary layer theory, but contained terms neglected in that theory, as we shall see more clearly later (Chap. IV, § 56).

The solution we have just obtained applies strictly only to an infinite disk; but if we neglect edge effect we can find the frictional moment on a rotating disk of radius a. The shearing stress is given by

$$p_{z\phi} = \rho\nu\frac{\partial v}{\partial z} = \rho(\nu\Omega^3)^{\frac{1}{2}}rG'(0) \tag{76}$$

at the disk, so that the moment is

$$-\int_0^a 2\pi r^2 p_{z\phi}\,dr = -\tfrac{1}{2}\pi a^4\rho(\nu\Omega^3)^{\frac{1}{2}}G'(0). \tag{77}$$

This is the moment for one side only: for both sides the result must be doubled. Hence, in terms of the Reynolds number

$$R = a^2\Omega/\nu, \tag{78}$$

the moment is given by

$$M = -\pi G'(0)\rho a^5\Omega^2/R^{\frac{1}{2}}, \tag{79}$$

and, with $S = \pi a^2$, a non-dimensional moment coefficient is given by

$$C_M = \frac{M}{\tfrac{1}{2}\rho a^3\Omega^2 S} = -\frac{2G'(0)}{R^{\frac{1}{2}}} = \frac{1\cdot 232}{R^{\frac{1}{2}}}. \tag{80}$$

The neglect of edge effect is probably justified if the radius is large compared with the thickness of the boundary layer. If R is too large (greater than about 5.10^5), the motion is turbulent. (For a discussion of the turbulent motion, and for experimental results, see Chap. VIII, § 164.)

APPENDIX

THE EQUATIONS FOR THE STREAM-FUNCTION IN GENERAL ORTHOGONAL COORDINATES

Two-dimensional motion.—For two-dimensional motion, if α and β are general orthogonal coordinates in the plane of the motion, then, in the notation of § 39, the equation of continuity is

$$\frac{\partial}{\partial \alpha}(h_2 u) + \frac{\partial}{\partial \beta}(h_1 v) = 0,$$

and there is a stream-function ψ such that

$$u = \frac{1}{h_2}\frac{\partial \psi}{\partial \beta}, \qquad v = -\frac{1}{h_1}\frac{\partial \psi}{\partial \alpha}.$$

$\xi = \eta = 0$, and

$$\zeta = -\frac{1}{h_1 h_2}\left[\frac{\partial}{\partial \alpha}\left(\frac{h_2}{h_1}\frac{\partial \psi}{\partial \alpha}\right) + \frac{\partial}{\partial \beta}\left(\frac{h_1}{h_2}\frac{\partial \psi}{\partial \beta}\right)\right] = -\nabla^2 \psi.$$

The equation satisfied by ψ is the equation for the vorticity, which may be written

$$\frac{\partial \boldsymbol{\omega}}{\partial t} - \operatorname{curl}(\mathbf{v} \times \boldsymbol{\omega}) = -\nu \operatorname{curl}\operatorname{curl} \boldsymbol{\omega}.$$

The third component of this equation gives us the equation required. It is

$$\frac{\partial}{\partial t}(\nabla^2 \psi) - \frac{1}{h_1 h_2}\frac{\partial(\psi, \nabla^2 \psi)}{\partial(\alpha, \beta)} = \nu \nabla^4 \psi.$$

In Cartesian coordinates

$$u = \frac{\partial \psi}{\partial y}, \qquad v = -\frac{\partial \psi}{\partial x}, \qquad \nabla^2 \equiv \frac{\partial^2}{\partial x^2} + \frac{\partial^2}{\partial y^2}, \qquad h_1 = h_2 = 1.$$

In polar coordinates, with α as r and β as ϕ, and u and v as the velocity components in the directions of r and ϕ increasing, respectively,

$$u = \frac{1}{r}\frac{\partial \psi}{\partial \phi}, \qquad v = -\frac{\partial \psi}{\partial r}, \qquad \nabla^2 \equiv \frac{\partial^2}{\partial r^2} + \frac{1}{r}\frac{\partial}{\partial r} + \frac{1}{r^2}\frac{\partial^2}{\partial \phi^2}, \qquad h_1 = 1, \qquad h_2 = r.$$

Motion symmetrical about an axis.—For motion symmetrical about an axis let α and β be general orthogonal coordinates in a meridian plane and let γ be the azimuthal angle ϕ: then h_3 will be the distance from the axis of revolution. All quantities are supposed independent of ϕ. In the notation of § 39 the equation of continuity is

$$\frac{\partial}{\partial \alpha}(h_2 h_3 u) + \frac{\partial}{\partial \beta}(h_3 h_1 v) = 0,$$

and so there is a stream-function ψ such that

$$h_3 u = \frac{1}{h_2}\frac{\partial \psi}{\partial \beta}, \qquad h_3 v = -\frac{1}{h_1}\frac{\partial \psi}{\partial \alpha}.$$

This is true whether the velocity w round the axis is zero or not, so long as it is independent of ϕ. If it is not zero, put

$$h_3 w = \Omega.$$

Then
$$\xi = \frac{1}{h_2 h_3}\frac{\partial\Omega}{\partial\beta}, \qquad \eta = -\frac{1}{h_3 h_1}\frac{\partial\Omega}{\partial\alpha},$$

and
$$\zeta = -\frac{1}{h_1 h_2}\left[\frac{\partial}{\partial\alpha}\left(\frac{h_2}{h_3 h_1}\frac{\partial\psi}{\partial\alpha}\right) + \frac{\partial}{\partial\beta}\left(\frac{h_1}{h_2 h_3}\frac{\partial\psi}{\partial\beta}\right)\right] = -\frac{1}{h_3}D^2\psi,$$

where
$$D^2 \equiv \frac{h_3}{h_1 h_2}\left[\frac{\partial}{\partial\alpha}\left(\frac{h_2}{h_3 h_1}\frac{\partial}{\partial\alpha}\right) + \frac{\partial}{\partial\beta}\left(\frac{h_1}{h_2 h_3}\frac{\partial}{\partial\beta}\right)\right].$$

The third (γ or ϕ) component of the equation for the vorticity is

$$\frac{\partial}{\partial t}(D^2\psi) + \frac{2\Omega}{h_1 h_2 h_3^2}\frac{\partial(\Omega, h_3)}{\partial(\alpha,\beta)} - \frac{1}{h_1 h_2 h_3}\frac{\partial(\psi, D^2\psi)}{\partial(\alpha,\beta)} + \frac{2D^2\psi}{h_1 h_2 h_3^2}\frac{\partial(\psi, h_3)}{\partial(\alpha,\beta)} = \nu D^4\psi.$$

If $w = 0$, then $\Omega = 0$, and this is the equation for ψ. Otherwise we require another equation, which is provided by the third (γ or ϕ) component of the vector equation of motion. This gives

$$\frac{\partial\Omega}{\partial t} - \frac{1}{h_1 h_2 h_3}\frac{\partial(\psi,\Omega)}{\partial(\alpha,\beta)} = \nu D^2\Omega.$$

The direction of γ, or ϕ, increasing must correspond with a right-handed screw from the direction of α increasing to that of β increasing. Hence, for cylindrical polar coordinates r, ϕ, z, we must take α as z and β as r. Then $h_1 = h_2 = 1$, $h_3 = r$, and the equations reduce to

$$u = \frac{1}{r}\frac{\partial\psi}{\partial r}, \qquad v = -\frac{1}{r}\frac{\partial\psi}{\partial z}, \qquad w = \frac{\Omega}{r},$$

$$D^2 \equiv \frac{\partial^2}{\partial r^2} - \frac{1}{r}\frac{\partial}{\partial r} + \frac{\partial^2}{\partial z^2},$$

$$\frac{\partial}{\partial t}(D^2\psi) + \frac{2\Omega}{r^2}\frac{\partial\Omega}{\partial z} + \frac{1}{r}\frac{\partial(\psi, D^2\psi)}{\partial(r, z)} + \frac{2}{r^2}\frac{\partial\psi}{\partial z}D^2\psi = \nu D^4\psi,$$

$$\frac{\partial\Omega}{\partial t} + \frac{1}{r}\frac{\partial(\psi,\Omega)}{\partial(r, z)} = \nu D^2\Omega,$$

u, v and w being the velocity components along z, r and ϕ increasing, respectively.

For spherical polar coordinates R, θ, ϕ, we take α as R and β as θ: then $h_1 = 1$, $h_2 = R$, $h_3 = R\sin\theta$. If u, v, and w are the velocity components in the directions of R, θ, and ϕ increasing,

$$u = \frac{1}{R^2\sin\theta}\frac{\partial\psi}{\partial\theta}, \qquad v = -\frac{1}{R\sin\theta}\frac{\partial\psi}{\partial R}, \qquad w = \frac{\Omega}{R\sin\theta},$$

$$D^2 \equiv \frac{\partial^2}{\partial R^2} + \frac{\sin\theta}{R^2}\frac{\partial}{\partial\theta}\left(\frac{1}{\sin\theta}\frac{\partial}{\partial\theta}\right),$$

$$\frac{\partial}{\partial t}(D^2\psi) + \frac{2\Omega}{R^2\sin^2\theta}\left(\frac{\partial\Omega}{\partial R}\cos\theta - \frac{1}{R}\frac{\partial\Omega}{\partial\theta}\sin\theta\right) - \frac{1}{R^2\sin\theta}\frac{\partial(\psi, D^2\psi)}{\partial(R, \theta)}$$
$$+ \frac{2D^2\psi}{R^2\sin^2\theta}\left(\frac{\partial\psi}{\partial R}\cos\theta - \frac{1}{R}\frac{\partial\psi}{\partial\theta}\sin\theta\right) = \nu D^4\psi,$$

$$\frac{\partial\Omega}{\partial t} - \frac{1}{R^2\sin\theta}\frac{\partial(\psi,\Omega)}{\partial(R, \theta)} = \nu D^2\Omega.$$

THE MATHEMATICAL THEORY OF MOTION
IN A BOUNDARY LAYER

44. Boundary layer theory. Two-dimensional motion. Flow along a plane wall.

THERE is no reason to doubt that the general dynamical equations discussed in the preceding chapter give a correct representation of the flow; but except for a few special problems they are exceedingly difficult to solve, and the solutions are often subject to serious limitations.

Perhaps the greatest limitation arises from the fact that solutions representing steady motion, even when obtained, would give an accurate representation of the observed phenomena only at Reynolds numbers below certain values, since at higher Reynolds numbers the actual motion would become quasi-periodic or turbulent, the unsteadiness arising presumably from instability of the theoretical steady flow. This unsteadiness, already mentioned in Chap. II, will form the main subject of Chap. V and will be a prominent feature of the discussion in most of the subsequent chapters; for the present we are concerned with less fundamental difficulties.

One of the main mathematical difficulties lies in the fact that the equations are not linear. In many of the exact solutions the quadratic terms are identically zero,—e.g. for the flow under pressure through a pipe, or for the flow between rotating cylinders. There are other problems in which the quadratic terms may be neglected, e.g. in the theory of lubrication. For the flow past an obstacle also, solutions may be obtained if the inertia terms are omitted, after the manner of Stokes, or taken only partly into account, after the manner of Oseen. But such approximate solutions have validity only at quite small Reynolds numbers.†

On the other hand, if the viscous terms are neglected, the equations relate to the theory of inviscid fluids, the results of which were compared with observation in a fluid of small viscosity in a general way in Chap. I.

It appears then that even in a fluid of small viscosity there must be regions where the inertia terms and the viscous terms are of the

† These various problems are discussed in Lamb's *Hydrodynamics* (Cambridge, 1932), pp. 581 *et seq.*

same order of magnitude. The number of exact solutions that have so far been found in which both sets of terms have been taken into account is very small; in fact, the solutions in §§ 42 and 43 of Chap. III seem to be the only ones with much physical significance. In those solutions (except for flow in a diverging channel, when the fluid is moving against a pressure gradient and backward flow sets in) the velocity changes rapidly at high Reynolds numbers from its value at a solid wall to its value in the body of the fluid, the transition taking place in a very narrow layer near the wall. This is in agreement with common observation, which suggests that whenever a fluid of small viscosity flows past a solid surface the transition from the velocity of the surface to that of the stream is accomplished in a narrow layer near the surface. In such a layer the space rate of change of the shearing stress may be very large, and consequently the viscous terms in the equations of motion may be comparable with the inertia terms even when the viscosity is very low. It is therefore appropriate to look first to such layers for the regions where the inertia terms and the viscous terms are of the same order of magnitude. For this reason the method of approximation, first suggested by Prandtl† in 1904 and developed below, is called boundary layer theory, and the simplified equations so obtained are called boundary layer equations. The method applies equally well, however, to certain other regions and phenomena where solid boundaries are absent,—notably to the surface layer of a jet of fluid or to the wake behind an obstacle.

We begin by establishing the equations for the two-dimensional flow of a fluid of small viscosity along a plane wall. The equations of motion and continuity are

$$
\left.\begin{array}{c}
\dfrac{\partial u}{\partial t}+u\dfrac{\partial u}{\partial x}+v\dfrac{\partial u}{\partial y}=-\dfrac{1}{\rho}\dfrac{\partial p}{\partial x}+\nu\left(\dfrac{\partial^{2}u}{\partial x^{2}}+\dfrac{\partial^{2}u}{\partial y^{2}}\right), \\[2mm]
\dfrac{\partial v}{\partial t}+u\dfrac{\partial v}{\partial x}+v\dfrac{\partial v}{\partial y}=-\dfrac{1}{\rho}\dfrac{\partial p}{\partial y}+\nu\left(\dfrac{\partial^{2}v}{\partial x^{2}}+\dfrac{\partial^{2}v}{\partial y^{2}}\right), \\[2mm]
\dfrac{\partial u}{\partial x}+\dfrac{\partial v}{\partial y}=0,
\end{array}\right\}
\tag{1}
$$

where the plane of (x, y) is the plane of the motion. We take the axis of x along and the axis of y perpendicular to the wall. Then u and v vanish at $y = 0$. If δ is the thickness of the boundary layer,

† *Verhandlungen des dritten internationalen Mathematiker-Kongresses, Heidelberg,* 1904 (Leipzig, 1905), pp. 484–491; reprinted in *Vier Abhandlungen zur Hydrodynamik und Aerodynamik* by Prandtl and Betz (Göttingen, 1927).

u changes from zero to its value u_1 in the main stream in a length δ, and, u_1 being taken as a magnitude of standard order and δ as small, $\partial u/\partial y$ will be $O(\delta^{-1})$ and $\partial^2 u/\partial y^2$ will be $O(\delta^{-2})$ in the boundary layer. Also u, $\partial u/\partial t$, $\partial u/\partial x$, $\partial^2 u/\partial x^2$ will all be $O(1)$. The equation of continuity then shows that $\partial v/\partial y$ is $O(1)$, and since v is zero when y is zero, v will be $O(\delta)$. Also $\partial v/\partial t$, $\partial v/\partial x$, and $\partial^2 v/\partial x^2$ will be $O(\delta)$, and $\partial^2 v/\partial y^2$ will be $O(\delta^{-1})$.

In the first equation $\partial^2 u/\partial x^2$ may be neglected in comparison with $\partial^2 u/\partial y^2$, and then the equation becomes

$$\frac{\partial u}{\partial t}+u\frac{\partial u}{\partial x}+v\frac{\partial u}{\partial y}=-\frac{1}{\rho}\frac{\partial p}{\partial x}+v\frac{\partial^2 u}{\partial y^2}. \tag{2}$$

The viscous term is now supposed to be of the same order as the inertia terms. Hence $v\delta^{-2}$ is $O(1)$, and δ is $O(v^{\frac{1}{2}})$. The second equation then gives

$$-\frac{1}{\rho}\frac{\partial p}{\partial y}=O(\delta). \tag{3}$$

The total change of pressure throughout the boundary layer along a normal to the wall is therefore of order δ^2, and may be neglected. Hence the pressure may be taken as constant along any such normal, and equal to its value just outside the boundary layer in the main stream. The influence of viscosity being very slight in the main stream, we may therefore write

$$-\frac{1}{\rho}\frac{\partial p}{\partial x}=\frac{\partial u_1}{\partial t}+u_1\frac{\partial u_1}{\partial x}, \tag{4}$$

where u_1 is the velocity in the main stream just outside the boundary layer.

The equation of continuity must be satisfied, so there is a streamfunction ψ such that

$$u=\frac{\partial \psi}{\partial y}, \qquad v=-\frac{\partial \psi}{\partial x}; \tag{5}$$

and the substitution of these values in (2) gives an equation for ψ in which the highest derivative occurring is $\partial^3\psi/\partial y^3$, whereas in the full equation of motion derivatives of the fourth order occur. (See the Appendix to Chap. III, p. 114.) On the other hand, $\partial p/\partial x$ must be supposed known.†

† This method of establishing the equations, due to Prandtl, is given more fully by Blasius, *Zeitschr. f. Math. u. Phys.* 56 (1908), 1–4. For the derivation of the equations reference may also be made to Kármán, *Zeitschr. f. angew. Math. u. Mech.* 1 (1921), 233–235; Pohlhausen, *ibid.* 252–255; Bairstow, *Journ. Roy. Aero. Soc.* 29 (1925), 3–8; Mises, *Zeitschr. f. angew. Math. u. Mech.* 7 (1927), 425–427.

45. Flow along a curved wall.

To establish the equations for two-dimensional flow along a curved surface, as in flow past a cylindrical obstacle, for example, we return to Chap. III, § 39, and use general orthogonal coordinates. The motion being two-dimensional, we may take γ as the coordinate z at right angles to the plane of the motion: then w is zero and all quantities are independent of γ. For the curves $\alpha = $ constant we take the normals to the wall, and for the curves $\beta = $ constant we take the curves parallel to the wall, each of which intersects the normals at a constant distance from the wall. Then α is the distance measured along the wall from a fixed point, which, for flow past a cylinder, is taken as the forward stagnation point; while β is the normal distance from the wall. It will cause no confusion, and will allow us to treat plane and curved walls together, if we use x and y for α and β; so that, quite generally, x and y are distances along and perpendicular to the wall. If κ is the curvature of the wall (so that κ is a function of x), the elements of length along the parallel curves and along the normals are $(1+\kappa y)\,dx$ and dy respectively. Hence $h_1 = 1+\kappa y$ and $h_2 = 1$. Then $\xi = \eta = 0$ and

$$\zeta = \frac{1}{1+\kappa y}\frac{\partial v}{\partial x} - \frac{\partial u}{\partial y} - \frac{\kappa}{1+\kappa y}u, \tag{6}$$

where u and v are the velocity components parallel and perpendicular to the wall. If we now work out the components of the vector equation of motion (equation (30), Chap. III, p. 100), and write down the equation of continuity (equation (2), Chap. III, p. 90), we find

$$
\begin{aligned}
&\frac{\partial u}{\partial t} + \frac{1}{1+\kappa y}u\frac{\partial u}{\partial x} + v\frac{\partial u}{\partial y} + \frac{\kappa}{1+\kappa y}uv \\
&= -\frac{1}{\rho}\frac{1}{1+\kappa y}\frac{\partial p}{\partial x} + \nu\left[\frac{1}{(1+\kappa y)^2}\frac{\partial^2 u}{\partial x^2} + \frac{\partial^2 u}{\partial y^2} - \frac{y}{(1+\kappa y)^3}\frac{\partial \kappa}{\partial x}\frac{\partial u}{\partial x}\right.\\
&\left.\quad + \frac{\kappa}{1+\kappa y}\frac{\partial u}{\partial y} - \frac{\kappa^2}{(1+\kappa y)^2}u + \frac{1}{(1+\kappa y)^3}\frac{\partial \kappa}{\partial x}v + \frac{2\kappa}{(1+\kappa y)^2}\frac{\partial v}{\partial x}\right], \\
&\frac{\partial v}{\partial t} + \frac{1}{1+\kappa y}u\frac{\partial v}{\partial x} + v\frac{\partial v}{\partial y} - \frac{\kappa}{1+\kappa y}u^2 \\
&= -\frac{1}{\rho}\frac{\partial p}{\partial y} + \nu\left[\frac{1}{(1+\kappa y)^2}\frac{\partial^2 v}{\partial x^2} + \frac{\partial^2 v}{\partial y^2} - \frac{y}{(1+\kappa y)^3}\frac{\partial \kappa}{\partial x}\frac{\partial v}{\partial x}\right.\\
&\left.\quad + \frac{\kappa}{1+\kappa y}\frac{\partial v}{\partial y} - \frac{\kappa^2}{(1+\kappa y)^2}v - \frac{1}{(1+\kappa y)^3}\frac{\partial \kappa}{\partial x}u - \frac{2\kappa}{(1+\kappa y)^2}\frac{\partial u}{\partial x}\right], \\
&\frac{\partial u}{\partial x} + \frac{\partial}{\partial y}[(1+\kappa y)v] = 0.
\end{aligned}
\tag{7}
$$

These equations are exact. If we carry out a process of approximation (similar to that in §44) for flow in a boundary layer of thickness
δ, they reduce approximately to

$$\left.\begin{array}{c}
\dfrac{\partial u}{\partial t}+u\dfrac{\partial u}{\partial x}+v\dfrac{\partial u}{\partial y}=-\dfrac{1}{\rho}\dfrac{\partial p}{\partial x}+\nu\dfrac{\partial^2 u}{\partial y^2}, \\[2mm]
-\kappa u^2=-\dfrac{1}{\rho}\dfrac{\partial p}{\partial y}, \\[2mm]
\dfrac{\partial u}{\partial x}+\dfrac{\partial v}{\partial y}=0,
\end{array}\right\} \tag{8}$$

terms of order δ being neglected. It is assumed that $\kappa\delta$ and $\delta^2\partial\kappa/\partial x$
are small, so at any point at which κ becomes infinite (as at a salient
point), or at which κ changes abruptly, the equations break down.
In order that the inertia and the viscous terms may be of the same
order of magnitude, δ must again be $O(\nu^{\frac12})$.

It appears from (8) that the only difference between the equations
for plane and curved walls lies in the second equation, $\partial p/\partial y$ being
$O(1)$ for a curved wall instead of $O(\delta)$ as for a plane wall, since a pressure gradient is necessary to balance the centrifugal force. But the
total change of pressure throughout the boundary layer along a
normal to the wall will still be small, of order δ, and may be neglected;
so that, the normal component of the fluid velocity being negligibly
small just outside the boundary layer, we shall still have

$$-\frac{1}{\rho}\frac{\partial p}{\partial x}=\frac{\partial u_1}{\partial t}+u_1\frac{\partial u_1}{\partial x},$$

where u_1 is the velocity in the main stream parallel to the wall just
outside the boundary layer. The equations to be solved are then
exactly the same, namely (2) and (5), whether the boundary is plane
or curved.

46. Non-dimensional form of the theory.

The theory may now be expressed in non-dimensional form. If
u_0 is a typical velocity and d a typical length, and if R is $u_0 d/\nu$, then
expressed non-dimensionally the relation $\delta = O(\nu^{\frac12})$ becomes

$$\frac{\delta}{d} = O(R^{-\frac12}). \tag{9}$$

Thus as R increases the thickness of the boundary layer diminishes
as $R^{-\frac12}$, and to get a true representation of what happens in the limit,
when $R \to \infty$, the scale of distances normal to the wall must be

multiplied by $R^{\frac{1}{2}}$, as also must the velocity normal to the wall. Hence we are led to write

$$x' = \frac{x}{d}, \qquad y' = R^{\frac{1}{2}}\frac{y}{d}, \qquad u' = \frac{u}{u_0}, \qquad v' = R^{\frac{1}{2}}\frac{v}{u_0}, \Bigg\}$$
$$t' = \frac{tu_0}{d}, \qquad p' = \frac{p}{\rho u_0^2}. \tag{10}$$

If we make these substitutions in equations (1), the equations become

$$\frac{\partial u'}{\partial t'} + u'\frac{\partial u'}{\partial x'} + v'\frac{\partial u'}{\partial y'} = -\frac{\partial p'}{\partial x'} + \frac{1}{R}\frac{\partial^2 u'}{\partial x'^2} + \frac{\partial^2 u'}{\partial y'^2},$$

$$\frac{1}{R}\left[\frac{\partial v'}{\partial t'} + u'\frac{\partial v'}{\partial x'} + v'\frac{\partial v'}{\partial y'}\right] = -\frac{\partial p'}{\partial y'} + \frac{1}{R^2}\frac{\partial^2 v'}{\partial x'^2} + \frac{1}{R}\frac{\partial^2 v'}{\partial y'^2},$$

$$\frac{\partial u'}{\partial x'} + \frac{\partial v'}{\partial y'} = 0.$$

On the assumption that the derivatives occurring explicitly remain finite when $R \to \infty$, the limiting form of these equations is

$$\frac{\partial u'}{\partial t'} + u'\frac{\partial u'}{\partial x'} + v'\frac{\partial u'}{\partial y'} = -\frac{\partial p'}{\partial x'} + \frac{\partial^2 u'}{\partial y'^2},$$
$$0 = -\frac{\partial p'}{\partial y'}, \Bigg\} \tag{11}$$
$$\frac{\partial u'}{\partial x'} + \frac{\partial v'}{\partial y'} = 0,$$

which are the non-dimensional forms of (2), (3) and the equation of continuity. The error in each of the first two equations is $O(R^{-1})$: the third is exact.

If we make the substitutions (10), together with $\kappa' = \kappa d$, in (7), and take the limit as $R \to \infty$, we arrive at the same equations (11): the errors are now of orders $\kappa' R^{-\frac{1}{2}}$, R^{-1} and $R^{-\frac{1}{2}}\partial\kappa'/\partial x'$ in each of the first two, and of order $\kappa' R^{-\frac{1}{2}}$ in the third.

This method of obtaining the equations is fundamentally the same as that given previously. It is mathematically more elegant, but less clear physically.

We now summarize the conditions for the validity of the approximations. For definiteness we have considered the flow along a solid wall: this is not necessary; the trace of the wall in the plane of the motion may be replaced by any stream-line, so long as the assumed conditions hold. Expressed non-dimensionally, they require u/u_0 to change rapidly from one finite value to another over a length, normal to the basic stream-line, of order $R^{-\frac{1}{2}}d$, while changes in the direction of the stream-line are not rapid—i.e. $(d/u_0)\partial u/\partial x$, and so on, are of the same order as u/u_0. (u_0 is a typical velocity, d a typical length, and R is $u_0 d/\nu$.) The equations cease to be valid at any point where the curvature of the basic stream-line, or the rate of change of that curvature along the stream-line, becomes infinite.

47. Vorticity. Stress components. Dissipation of energy.

Equations (7) have been written out in full, only in order to make clear the error involved in passing to (8). Once it is assumed that δ, $\kappa\delta$, and $\delta^2\partial\kappa/\partial x$ are small, we may write

$$\zeta = -\frac{\partial u}{\partial y} \tag{12}$$

approximately, ζ being large of order $\nu^{-\frac{1}{2}}$; and it suffices to substitute $-\partial\zeta/\partial y$ and $\partial\zeta/\partial x$ for the terms in square brackets in the first two of equations (7), respectively. Equations (8) then follow as before.

According to equations (36) and (37) of Chap. III (p. 103), the normal tractions over surfaces parallel and perpendicular to the wall differ from $-p$ by quantities of order R^{-1}, which may generally be neglected; whilst the shearing stress over surfaces parallel to the wall is of order $R^{-\frac{1}{2}}$, and may be taken as

$$p_{xy} = \mu\frac{\partial u}{\partial y} \tag{13}$$

simply.

Further, the rate of dissipation of energy per unit time per unit volume in the boundary layer (see equation (28), Chap. III, p. 99) is approximately given by

$$\Phi = \mu\left(\frac{\partial u}{\partial y}\right)^2, \tag{14}$$

and has a finite limit when $R \to \infty$. In fact the order of magnitude of the thickness of the boundary layer could have been determined by imposing this requirement.

48. Boundary conditions. Boundary layer thickness. Displacement thickness.

We must now consider the boundary conditions under which the first and third of equations (8) are to be integrated, more particularly for steady motion. First, u and v must vanish at $y = 0$. Then, in general, u is given for $x = 0$ or for some other value of x. Finally, the fluid velocity must pass over smoothly into the velocity in the main stream, so that u must become equal to u_1, and $\partial u/\partial y$ equal to zero, as we pass into the main stream. (It appears indeed from (2) and (4) that if $\partial u/\partial y$ and $\partial^2 u/\partial y^2$ become zero and u becomes equal to u_1 for some value of x, then u will be equal to u_1 just outside the boundary layer in the main stream for all subsequent values of x.) Solutions may be obtained only if v is neglected in the boundary conditions at $x = 0$ (or at the section where u is given if this is not at $x = 0$) and also where the velocity passes over into that of the main stream. In general an error of order $R^{-\frac{1}{2}}$ is thus introduced.

If the motion is not steady, u must be given at $t = 0$.

The equations are such that the conditions $u = u_1$, $\partial u/\partial y = 0$, where the velocity passes over into that of the main stream, cannot be satisfied for a finite value of y, but must be taken to be asymptotic conditions for $y = \infty$. It follows that there is some difficulty in defining the thickness δ of the boundary layer. Experimentally the boundary layer may be defined as the region in which a loss of total head may be observed: analytically the limit of the layer may be defined by requiring u to be equal to u_1 to a prescribed degree of accuracy (e.g. 1 or $\frac{1}{2}$ per cent.), and this is attained for a finite value of $R^{\frac{1}{2}}y$. Actually the solutions have the property that the difference of u from u_1 is quite small for moderate values of $R^{\frac{1}{2}}y$; and, in spite of the uncertainty of its definition, it is convenient to regard the boundary layer as having a thickness δ. In cases where it is desired to specify a length characteristic of the boundary layer and capable of precise definition, this may be done by specifying what is known as the displacement thickness δ_1, defined by

$$u_1 \delta_1 = \int (u_1 - u)\, dy, \tag{15}$$

the integral being taken along a normal right across the boundary layer. $u_1 \delta_1$ gives the diminution of flux due to frictional retardation; the stream-lines of the external flow are therefore displaced outwards by an amount δ_1.

49. Some general deductions and remarks for flow against a pressure gradient and flow past obstacles.

When fluid is flowing along a wall, u vanishes at the wall and increases to u_1 as we go through the boundary layer. If u increases steadily, $\partial u/\partial y$ is everywhere positive, and in particular is positive at the wall. If, as we go along the wall, a position is reached at which $\partial u/\partial y$ vanishes and changes sign, then, as explained in Chap. II, § 18 (p. 57), this means that the forward flow separates from the wall and that a backward flow (usually slow) takes place. The point of separation is given by $(\partial u/\partial y)_{y=0} = 0$, or, with the non-dimensional symbols of equation (10), by $(\partial u'/\partial y')_{y'=0} = 0$. If now, in a steady motion, the reduced velocity u_1/u_0 just outside the boundary layer is the same function of x/d for all Reynolds numbers, then $\partial p'/\partial x'$ is independent of R and the equations (11) are completely independent of R. If, furthermore, the given value of u/u_0 at $x = 0$ is independent of R, so are all the boundary conditions for u' and v'. (For flow past a cylinder $x = 0$ is the front stagnation point, and $u = 0$ there.) Hence the value of x' for which $(\partial u'/\partial y')_{y'=0}$ vanishes will be independent of the Reynolds number. Thus in geometrically similar systems the points of separation will be corresponding points if u_1/u_0 or $p/(\rho u_0^2)$ remains the same at corresponding points. Theoretically it is important to notice that even in the limit, for a fluid of vanishingly small viscosity ($R \to \infty$), separation still takes place. Practically, we may notice that the point of separation should be changed by change of velocity or scale only in so far as the pressure distribution along the wall or round the cylinder is changed. On the other hand, as R increases, the scale of the boundary layer normal to the wall and the normal velocity component v decrease as $R^{-\frac{1}{2}}$, and therefore the angle made with the wall by the streamline through the point of separation becomes smaller and smaller.

We have seen in Chap. II, § 18 that separation is to be expected if the pressure increases in the direction of the flow, i.e. if $\partial p/\partial x$ is positive. Calculations by which the position of the point of separation is determined in such circumstances will be mentioned later; but one consequence of the equations, which has a bearing on this matter and also on the stability of flow in the boundary layer (see footnote †, p. 200), may be mentioned at once. Since u and v vanish at the wall, it follows from (8) that

$$\nu\left(\frac{\partial^2 u}{\partial y^2}\right)_{y=0} = \frac{1}{\rho}\frac{\partial p}{\partial x}. \tag{16}$$

Hence if $\partial p/\partial x$ is positive, $\partial^2 u/\partial y^2$ is positive at $y = 0$. Now upstream of the point of separation $\partial u/\partial y$ is positive at the wall, and if $\partial p/\partial x$ is positive, $\partial u/\partial y$ begins to increase. But at the outside of the boundary layer $\partial u/\partial y$ vanishes; it must therefore eventually decrease and

$\partial^2 u/\partial y^2$ must become negative. Hence $\partial^2 u/\partial y^2$ must change sign, and the graph of u against y must have a point of inflexion. (Cf. Fig. 22, p. 57.)

Once separation of the flow has taken place, the boundary layer thickens rapidly and the equations cease to provide a good approximation to the actual circumstances; or perhaps it may be preferable to say that the layer in which the rate of shearing is large is no longer at the surface. Immediately downstream of the point of separation the circumstances in the actual flow, which have been to some extent described in Chap. II, §§ 19 and 20 and are further discussed in Chap. XIII, § 241, are too complicated to admit of accurate mathematical treatment in the present state of the theory.

In a general way we may say that in flow past an obstacle vorticity is practically confined to the boundary layer and the wake, and that outside these regions the motion is practically irrotational. The motion in the boundary layer up to the point of separation, together with the position of the point of separation itself, may be calculated from the boundary layer equations of previous sections if, and only if, the pressure distribution just outside the boundary layer is known. The equations may also be used to calculate the motion in the wake at some distance downstream of a body if the drag of the body is known (see Chap. XIII, § 248); but no satisfactory calculations have been published of either the drag or the pressure distribution when separation takes place.†

The limitations of steady motion solutions should be emphasized again, in that actually the motions at high Reynolds numbers are turbulent. Thus if, in a given fluid, the velocity and dimensions of the system are sufficiently large, the flow in the boundary layer along a wall is in practice turbulent at a sufficient distance downstream. The Reynolds numbers at which the transitions to turbulent motion take place are, however, large enough to allow of the steady motion being calculated from the approximate equations (2)–(5) for a considerable range of values of the Reynolds number. On the other hand, calculations of steady motion in a wake at large Reynolds numbers are of very limited application in fluids of small viscosity, and for bluff obstacles are not applicable at all.

The details of the irrotational motion outside the boundary layer

† For the attempts that have been made reference may be made to the works cited in the footnotes on pp. 36 and 49.

and the wake are also beyond the reach of mathematical calculation at present,—at any rate for flow past bluff obstacles. (Otherwise we could, of course, calculate the pressure distribution round an obstacle, at any rate up to the point of separation.) At large distances the flow approximates to the general streaming plus the flow due to a source in the neighbourhood of the obstacle, of strength $D/(\rho u_0)$, where D is the drag on the obstacle and u_0 the undisturbed velocity of the stream.†

If no separation occurs, the vorticity is confined entirely to the boundary layer and we may, at any rate for a first approximation, neglect the slight displacement of the stream-lines outward due to frictional retardation in the layer, and calculate the irrotational motion according to the usual theory, neglecting the boundary layer entirely, and applying only the condition of zero normal velocity at the boundary. The pressure distribution so calculated may then be taken as a datum for boundary layer calculations. Even for the flow past a stream-line body this procedure may be used as an approximation when the wake is narrow. But we require to know the circulation independently, or to calculate it by the method of Chap. I, § 9 (p. 34), or that of Chap. II, § 22. (See also Chap. X, § 212.)

50. Transformation of the equations for steady motion.

For steady motion the equations of § 44 or § 45 may be written

$$\left.\begin{aligned} u\frac{\partial u}{\partial x}+v\frac{\partial u}{\partial y} &= u_1\frac{du_1}{dx}+\nu\frac{\partial^2 u}{\partial y^2}, \\ u=\frac{\partial \psi}{\partial y}, \qquad v &= -\frac{\partial \psi}{\partial x}. \end{aligned}\right\} \tag{17}$$

If we take x and ψ as independent variables instead of x and y, and denote the derivative of u with respect to x when ψ is constant by $(\partial u/\partial x)_\psi$, with a similar notation for other derivatives, we have the transformation formulae

$$\left(\frac{\partial u}{\partial x}\right)_y = \left(\frac{\partial u}{\partial x}\right)_\psi + \left(\frac{\partial u}{\partial \psi}\right)_x \frac{\partial \psi}{\partial x} = \left(\frac{\partial u}{\partial x}\right)_\psi - v\left(\frac{\partial u}{\partial \psi}\right)_x,$$

$$\left(\frac{\partial u}{\partial y}\right)_x = \left(\frac{\partial u}{\partial \psi}\right)_x \frac{\partial \psi}{\partial y} = u\left(\frac{\partial u}{\partial \psi}\right)_x,$$

$$\left(\frac{\partial^2 u}{\partial y^2}\right)_x = u\frac{\partial}{\partial \psi}\left[u\left(\frac{\partial u}{\partial \psi}\right)_x\right]_x.$$

† See Chap. XIII, § 249 and Chap. VI, § 115.

Hence with the new variables the equation of motion is

$$u\frac{\partial u}{\partial x} = u_1\frac{du_1}{dx} + \nu u\frac{\partial}{\partial\psi}\left(u\frac{\partial u}{\partial\psi}\right),$$

where the subscripts have been dropped. If we now take

$$z = u_1^2 - u^2 \tag{18}$$

as dependent variable, this equation becomes†

$$\frac{\partial z}{\partial x} = \nu u\frac{\partial^2 z}{\partial\psi^2} = \nu\sqrt{(u_1^2 - z)}\frac{\partial^2 z}{\partial\psi^2}. \tag{19}$$

The boundary conditions are $z = u_1^2$ when $\psi = 0$, $z = 0$ when $\psi = \infty$, and (if the velocity is given at $x = 0$) z is given at $x = 0$. To return to the (x, y) system of coordinates after the equation has been solved, use must be made of the relation

$$y = \int_0^\psi \frac{d\psi}{u} = \int_0^\psi \frac{d\psi}{(u_1^2 - z)^{\frac{1}{2}}}. \tag{20}$$

Moreover,

$$\left(\frac{\partial u}{\partial y}\right)_x = u\left(\frac{\partial u}{\partial\psi}\right)_x = -\tfrac{1}{2}\frac{\partial z}{\partial\psi}, \tag{21}$$

so that the shear stress is $-\tfrac{1}{2}\mu\,\partial z/\partial\psi$, and the condition for separation of the forward flow from a wall is $(\partial z/\partial\psi)_{\psi=0} = 0$.

The equation (19) presents a certain formal analogy with the equation of heat conduction, but the equation is not linear, the quantity $\nu u = \nu(u_1^2 - z)^{\frac{1}{2}}$, which depends both on z and x, taking the place of the thermometric conductivity. This quantity vanishes at the walls, and the equation has a singularity there. Beyond the point where the forward flow separates from the wall this also happens in the interior of the fluid.

The applications so far made of this form of the equations will be referred to in §59, (pp. 154, 155), §62, (p. 165 *et seq.*) and Chap. XIII, §248 (pp. 573, 574). But we may notice here that if z is known as a function of ψ for any value of x, then according to (19) $\partial z/\partial x$ is known, and, apart from the difficulty due to the singularity, z could be found numerically by a step-by-step process, were it not for the difficulty involved in the numerical double differentiation necessary on the

---

† Mises, *Zeitschr. f. angew. Math. u. Mech.* 7 (1927), 425–431; in particular 427, 428.

right. This objection applies to all such transformations. For example, in place of (19) we can prove† that

$$\frac{\partial u}{\partial x} = \frac{\partial u}{\partial y} \int_0^y \frac{v\partial^2 u/\partial y^2 + u_1\, du_1/dx}{u^2}\, dy + \frac{v\partial^2 u/\partial y^2 + u_1\, du_1/dx}{u}. \quad (22)$$

This equation, which gives $\partial u/\partial x$ in terms of u, $\partial u/\partial y$, and $\partial^2 u/\partial y^2$, also solves our problem theoretically. It may be proved by writing (17) in the form

$$-\frac{\partial}{\partial y}\left(\frac{v}{u}\right) = \frac{v\partial^2 u/\partial y^2 + u_1\, du_1/dx}{u^2}, \quad (23)$$

and noticing that, since u and $\partial u/\partial x$ both vanish at the wall and v has a double zero there $(\partial v/\partial y = -\partial u/\partial x)$, each side of (23) stays finite at the wall. On integrating, multiplying by u, and then again differentiating with respect to y, we obtain (22).

51. Motion symmetrical about an axis.

Let us consider first the boundary layer at the surface of a blunt-nosed body of revolution fixed in a stream with its axis in the direction of the undisturbed velocity. The motion is symmetrical about this axis, and there is no component of velocity about the axis. In the notation of Chap. III, § 39, we may take γ to be the azimuthal angle ϕ about the axis, so that $w = 0$ and all quantities are independent of γ. The surfaces $\alpha = $ constant and $\beta = $ constant are taken as surfaces of revolution about the axis, and are such that, if Γ is the curve of intersection of the surface of the body by a meridian plane, then the sections of the surfaces $\alpha = $ constant and $\beta = $ constant are normals to Γ and parallel curves to Γ, respectively. Hence α may be taken as the distance x from the forward stagnation point measured along Γ, and β as the normal distance y from the surface. We denote by δ the thickness of the boundary layer and by κ the curvature of Γ. If $\kappa\delta$ and $\delta^2\partial\kappa/\partial x$ are small, h_1 and h_2 may be put equal to 1, exactly as for two-dimensional motion. But h_3 is equal to the distance from the axis of revolution. This distance we denote, in general, by r; for points on the surface of the body we denote it by r_0. Then if ϑ is the angle made by a tangent to a curve $y = $ constant with the axis of revolution,

$$\frac{\partial r}{\partial x} = \sin\vartheta, \qquad \frac{\partial r}{\partial y} = \cos\vartheta. \quad (24)$$

† Goldstein, *Proc. Camb. Phil. Soc.* **26** (1930), 18, footnote.

ϑ is the same at points on the same normal for all such curves, and may be taken as the value for Γ (Fig. 42).

$\xi = \eta = 0$, and with the same approximations as in § 45

$$\zeta = -\frac{\partial u}{\partial y}. \tag{25}$$

The components of curl $\boldsymbol{\omega}$ are then

$$\frac{1}{r}\frac{\partial}{\partial y}(r\zeta), \qquad -\frac{1}{r}\frac{\partial}{\partial x}(r\zeta), \qquad 0. \tag{26}$$

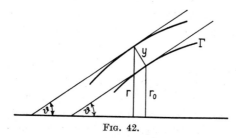

FIG. 42.

The first component is

$$-\frac{\partial^2 u}{\partial y^2} - \frac{\cos\vartheta}{r}\frac{\partial u}{\partial y}. \tag{27}$$

Now $|\cos\vartheta|/r$ is less than $1/r_0$; and this is finite except at the front stagnation point. At the front stagnation point, where $\cos\vartheta$ and r_0 both vanish, their quotient remains finite, and is, in fact, the curvature at the nose. Since $\partial u/\partial y$ is small compared with $\partial^2 u/\partial y^2$, the second term in (27) may therefore be neglected compared with the first.

The second component of curl $\boldsymbol{\omega}$ is

$$\frac{\partial^2 u}{\partial x\partial y} + \frac{\sin\vartheta}{r}\frac{\partial u}{\partial y}. \tag{28}$$

Near the front stagnation point r may be $O(\delta)$, otherwise it is $O(1)$; whilst $\partial u/\partial y$ and $\partial^2 u/\partial x\partial y$ are $O(\delta^{-1})$ (in the notation of § 44). Hence this component may be $O(\delta^{-2})$ near the front stagnation point; otherwise it is $O(\delta^{-1})$.

Then, exactly as in § 44, δ must be $O(\nu^{\frac{1}{2}})$, and we arrive finally at the equations

$$\left.\begin{array}{c} \dfrac{\partial u}{\partial t} + u\dfrac{\partial u}{\partial x} + v\dfrac{\partial u}{\partial y} = -\dfrac{1}{\rho}\dfrac{\partial p}{\partial x} + \nu\dfrac{\partial^2 u}{\partial y^2}, \\[2mm] \dfrac{\partial p}{\partial y} = O(1); \end{array}\right\} \tag{29}$$

and these equations are exactly the same as for two dimensions. But the equation of continuity is

$$\frac{\partial}{\partial x}(ru) + \frac{\partial}{\partial y}(rv) = 0, \tag{30}$$

or
$$\frac{\partial u}{\partial x} + \frac{\partial v}{\partial y} + \frac{u}{r}\frac{\partial r}{\partial x} + \frac{v}{r}\frac{\partial r}{\partial y} = 0.$$

v is small compared with u, and the last term, which is equal to $(v\cos\vartheta)/r$, may be neglected. But the term $(u/r)(\partial r/\partial x)$ cannot be neglected, so that the equation of continuity must be taken either in the form (30) or in the form

$$\frac{\partial u}{\partial x} + \frac{\partial v}{\partial y} + \frac{u}{r}\frac{\partial r}{\partial x} = 0. \tag{31}$$

For a blunt-nosed body u/r remains finite at the front stagnation point and may be replaced by u/r_0, whilst $\partial r/\partial x$ may be replaced by dr_0/dx. Hence also r may be replaced by r_0 in (30).†

In one case, and in one case only, the equation of continuity is approximately the same as for two dimensions, namely, if r_0 is constant so that dr_0/dx is zero. Hence for flow along the surface of a circular cylinder with its generators parallel to the flow the equations may be put in the same form as for flow along a flat wall. This is easily verified directly from equations (38) and (41) of Chap. III (pp. 103, 104).

If instead of considering flow along a wall we consider flow in a jet or in the wake behind a body of revolution, the axis of revolution is in the fluid. The second term in (27) cannot then be neglected. In such cases, however, it is sufficient to use cylindrical polar coordinates, so that $\vartheta = 0$ and $r = y$; and we have the equations

$$\left.\begin{array}{l}\dfrac{\partial u}{\partial t} + u\dfrac{\partial u}{\partial x} + v\dfrac{\partial u}{\partial r} = -\dfrac{1}{\rho}\dfrac{\partial p}{\partial x} + \dfrac{v}{r}\dfrac{\partial}{\partial r}\left(r\dfrac{\partial u}{\partial r}\right), \\[3mm] \dfrac{\partial}{\partial x}(ru) + \dfrac{\partial}{\partial r}(rv) = 0, \end{array}\right\} \tag{32}$$

as may easily be verified directly from equations (38) and (41) of

---

† Cf. Boltze, *Göttingen Dissertation*, 1908; Millikan, *Trans. Amer. Soc. Mechanical Engineers*, Applied Mechanics Section, **54** (1932), 29, 30.

Chap. III, with the necessary changes in notation (u and x for w and z, and v for u).

52. The momentum equation of the boundary layer.

We assume that the boundary layer has a definite thickness δ. Then, considering first two-dimensional flow, let BD be a section of its outer limit, AC being a section of the wall, and AB, CD normals to the wall. Let AC be of length dx, and consider a stratum of fluid of unit breadth perpendicular to the

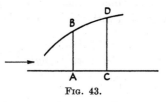

Fig. 43.

plane of the motion. Then the flux of fluid across CD per unit time exceeds that across AB by

$$dx \frac{\partial}{\partial x} \int_0^\delta \rho u \, dy,$$

and this must be the inward flux across BD. The fluid crossing BD has velocity u_1 in the x-direction, and so the inward flux of momentum across BD is

$$u_1 \, dx \frac{\partial}{\partial x} \int_0^\delta \rho u \, dy.$$

But the flux of momentum across CD exceeds that across AB by

$$dx \frac{\partial}{\partial x} \int_0^\delta \rho u^2 \, dy,$$

so that the net outward flux of momentum is

$$dx \left[\frac{\partial}{\partial x} \int_0^\delta \rho u^2 \, dy - u_1 \frac{\partial}{\partial x} \int_0^\delta \rho u \, dy \right].$$

The rate of change of momentum inside $ACDB$, considered as a fixed surface, is

$$dx \int_0^\delta \rho \frac{\partial u}{\partial t} \, dy,$$

whilst the forces acting on the fluid in the x-direction are the skin-friction, $-\mu \, dx (\partial u / \partial y)_{y=0}$, and the difference of the pressures on AB and CD, $-\delta (\partial p / \partial x) \, dx$. Hence[†]

$$\int_0^\delta \rho \frac{\partial u}{\partial t} \, dy + \frac{\partial}{\partial x} \int_0^\delta \rho u^2 \, dy - u_1 \frac{\partial}{\partial x} \int_0^\delta \rho u \, dy = -\delta \frac{\partial p}{\partial x} - \mu \left(\frac{\partial u}{\partial y} \right)_{y=0}. \quad (33)$$

This equation may also be obtained by integrating the equation of motion with respect to y between the limits 0 and δ. Thus

$$\int_0^\delta \left(u \frac{\partial u}{\partial x} + v \frac{\partial u}{\partial y} \right) dy = \int_0^\delta u \frac{\partial u}{\partial x} \, dy + [uv]_0^\delta - \int_0^\delta u \frac{\partial v}{\partial y} \, dy.$$

But
$$\frac{\partial v}{\partial y} = - \frac{\partial u}{\partial x},$$

and hence also
$$(v)_{y=\delta} = - \int_0^\delta \frac{\partial u}{\partial x} \, dy.$$

It follows that

$$\int_0^\delta \left(u \frac{\partial u}{\partial x} + v \frac{\partial u}{\partial y} \right) dy = \int_0^\delta \frac{\partial}{\partial x} (u^2) \, dy - u_1 \int_0^\delta \frac{\partial u}{\partial x} \, dy,$$

which is equivalent to

$$\frac{\partial}{\partial x} \int_0^\delta u^2 \, dy - u_1 \frac{\partial}{\partial x} \int_0^\delta u \, dy,$$

since the extra terms arising from the variability of the upper limit with x cancel out. Equation (33) then follows.[‡]

Equation (33) may be put in a different form, which is more convenient for some purposes. In place of $\mu (\partial u / \partial y)_{y=0}$, which is the shearing stress at the wall, we write τ_0, so that

$$\tau_0 = u_1 \frac{\partial}{\partial x} \int_0^\delta \rho u \, dy - \frac{\partial}{\partial x} \int_0^\delta \rho u^2 \, dy - \int_0^\delta \rho \frac{\partial u}{\partial t} \, dy - \delta \frac{\partial p}{\partial x}. \quad (34)$$

For steady flow along a flat plate in unlimited fluid, or for any case of steady flow in which u_1 is independent of x, this equation reduces to

$$\tau_0 = \frac{\partial}{\partial x} \int_0^\delta \rho (u_1 - u) u \, dy, \quad (35)$$

and the difference in the values of the integral at any two sections

† Kármán, *Zeitschr. f. angew. Math. u. Mech.* **1** (1921), 235, 236.
‡ Cf. Pohlhausen, *ibid.* **1** (1921), 256, 257.

represents the rate at which unit breadth of the fluid between the two sections is losing momentum. We can now express the general equation (34) in terms of this integral and of the displacement thickness δ_1, defined by

$$u_1\delta_1 = \int_0^\delta (u_1-u)\,dy, \tag{36}$$

as in equation (15). We first define a new length ϑ by the equation

$$\int_0^\delta (u_1-u)u\,dy = u_1^2\,\vartheta. \tag{37}$$

Then since

$$-\frac{\partial p}{\partial x} = \rho\left(\frac{\partial u_1}{\partial t}+u_1\frac{\partial u_1}{\partial x}\right),$$

as in equation (4), and

$$-\delta\frac{\partial p}{\partial x} = \rho\int_0^\delta \frac{\partial u_1}{\partial t}\,dy +\rho\frac{\partial u_1}{\partial x}\int_0^\delta u_1\,dy,$$

we find that

$$\tau_0 = \frac{\partial}{\partial x}(\rho u_1^2\vartheta)-\rho\frac{\partial u_1}{\partial x}\int_0^\delta u\,dy -\rho\int_0^\delta \frac{\partial u}{\partial t}\,dy +\rho\int_0^\delta \frac{\partial u_1}{\partial t}\,dy +\rho\frac{\partial u_1}{\partial x}\int_0^\delta u_1\,dy$$

$$= \frac{\partial}{\partial x}(\rho u_1^2\vartheta)+\rho u_1\frac{\partial u_1}{\partial x}\delta_1+\rho\frac{\partial}{\partial t}(u_1\delta_1),$$

so that

$$\frac{\tau_0}{\rho u_1^2} = \frac{\partial\vartheta}{\partial x}+\frac{1}{u_1}\frac{\partial u_1}{\partial x}(2\vartheta+\delta_1)+\frac{1}{u_1^2}\frac{\partial}{\partial t}(u_1\delta_1). \tag{38}$$

For laminar motion τ_0 is $\mu(\partial u/\partial y)_{y=0}$. With a general symbol for the shearing stress at the wall, the equation has also been used for turbulent motion. (See, for example, Chap. VIII, § 163.)

Methods similar to those used in finding equation (33) may be used to find the momentum equation for the boundary layer at the surface of a solid of revolution. In the notation of § 51 this equation may be written

$$\int_0^\delta \rho r\frac{\partial u}{\partial t}\,dy +\frac{\partial}{\partial x}\int_0^\delta \rho ru^2\,dy -u_1\frac{\partial}{\partial x}\int_0^\delta \rho ru\,dy$$

$$= -\frac{\partial p}{\partial x}\int_0^\delta r\,dy -\mu r_0\left(\frac{\partial u}{\partial y}\right)_{y=0}, \tag{39}$$

which for a blunt-nosed body may be simplified to†

$$\int_0^\delta \rho \frac{\partial u}{\partial t}\, dy + \frac{\partial}{\partial x} \int_0^\delta \rho u^2\, dy - u_1 \frac{\partial}{\partial x} \int_0^\delta \rho u\, dy$$

$$-\frac{1}{r_0}\frac{dr_0}{dx}\left[u_1 \int_0^\delta \rho u\, dy - \int_0^\delta \rho u^2\, dy \right] = -\delta \frac{\partial p}{\partial x} - \mu \left(\frac{\partial u}{\partial y}\right)_{y=0}. \quad (40)$$

This equation differs from (33) only by the term containing r_0'/r_0. It may also be found by integrating the equation of motion (29) with respect to y between the limits 0 and δ, and using the equation of continuity in the form (31) with r_0 in place of r.

The equations (33) and (40), as they stand, can tell us nothing about the values of δ or $(\partial u/\partial y)_{y=0}$, or their variation with x. To obtain these values it is necessary to make some more or less plausible assumptions concerning the distribution of the velocity u, satisfying as many of the boundary conditions as is convenient. These boundary conditions are

$$\left.\begin{array}{ll} u = u_1, & \dfrac{\partial u}{\partial y} = \dfrac{\partial^2 u}{\partial y^2} = \dfrac{\partial^3 u}{\partial y^3} = \ldots = 0 \quad \text{at } y = \delta, \\[2ex] \text{and} \quad u = 0, & \nu\dfrac{\partial^2 u}{\partial y^2} = \dfrac{1}{\rho}\dfrac{\partial p}{\partial x}, \quad \nu\dfrac{\partial^3 u}{\partial y^3} = \dfrac{\partial^2 u}{\partial t \partial y}, \ldots \text{at } y = 0, \end{array}\right\} \quad (41)$$

the last two conditions being obtained by putting $y = 0$ in the equation of motion (see (8) and (29)) and in the equation derived from it by differentiation with respect to y. Further conditions at $y = 0$ may be obtained by repeated differentiation with respect to y before making y vanish. Substitution in (33) or (40) then gives an equation which for steady motion is an ordinary differential equation, and for variable motion a partial differential equation, for δ in terms of x and t. The boundary layer thickness δ is itself a somewhat indefinite parameter, and the values so obtained vary rather wildly with varying assumptions about the form of u; hence it is better to regard the method as a method of determining δ_1 or ϑ, or $(\partial u/\partial y)_{y=0}$. Details of the practical application of the method will be considered in § 60.

With the substitution of a general symbol for the shearing stress at the wall in place of $\mu(\partial u/\partial y)_{y=0}$, the equation (40) also has been used for turbulent motion (see Chap. XI, § 226).

† Millikan, *Trans. Amer. Soc. Mechanical Engineers*, Applied Mechanics Section, **54** (1932), 31, 32.

53. The flow along a flat plate.

The problem of determining, according to the boundary layer equations, the steady two-dimensional motion along a plate placed edgeways to the stream, was considered roughly by Prandtl in his original paper referred to on p. 117, and was investigated in detail by Blasius.† The fluid being supposed unlimited in extent, the velocity u_1 outside the boundary layer is taken as constant, and with the origin in the forward edge, the equations reduce to

$$\left.\begin{aligned} u\frac{\partial u}{\partial x}+v\frac{\partial u}{\partial y} &= \nu\frac{\partial^2 u}{\partial y^2}, \\ u=\frac{\partial \psi}{\partial y}, \qquad v &= -\frac{\partial \psi}{\partial x}, \end{aligned}\right\} \tag{42}$$

with the boundary conditions $u = v = 0$ at $y = 0$, $u = u_1$ at $y = \infty$ and at $x = 0$. If we put

$$\eta = \tfrac{1}{2}(u_1/\nu x)^{\frac{1}{2}}y, \qquad \psi = (\nu u_1 x)^{\frac{1}{2}}f, \tag{43}$$

a solution may be found in which f is a function of η only. We have

$$u = \tfrac{1}{2}u_1 f', \qquad v = \tfrac{1}{2}(u_1\nu/x)^{\frac{1}{2}}(\eta f'-f),$$

$$\left.\frac{\partial u}{\partial y} = \frac{u_1}{4}\left(\frac{u_1}{\nu x}\right)^{\frac{1}{2}}f'', \qquad \frac{\partial u}{\partial x} = -\frac{1}{4}\frac{u_1}{x}\eta f'', \qquad \frac{\partial^2 u}{\partial y^2} = \frac{u_1}{8}\left(\frac{u_1}{\nu x}\right)f''', \right\} \tag{44}$$

and (42) reduces to
$$f'''+ff'' = 0. \tag{45}$$

(Dashes denote differentiations with respect to η.) The boundary conditions are $f = f' = 0$ at $\eta = 0$, and $f' = 2$ at $\eta = \infty$. If $f''(0) = \alpha$, the solution of (45) may be expanded in a series

$$f = \frac{\alpha\eta^2}{2!}-\frac{\alpha^2\eta^5}{5!}+\frac{11\alpha^3\eta^8}{8!}-\frac{375\alpha^4\eta^{11}}{11!}+\frac{27897\alpha^5\eta^{14}}{14!}-..., \tag{46}$$

in which the conditions at the origin are satisfied. If $F(\eta)$ is the solution when $\alpha = 1$, then (46) may be written in the form

$$f = \alpha^{\frac{1}{3}}F(\alpha^{\frac{1}{3}}\eta). \tag{47}$$

Hence
$$\lim_{\eta\to\infty} f' = \alpha^{\frac{2}{3}}\lim_{\eta\to\infty} F'(\alpha^{\frac{1}{3}}\eta) = \alpha^{\frac{2}{3}}\lim_{\eta\to\infty} F'(\eta), \tag{48}$$

and this must be 2, so that

$$\alpha = \left\{\frac{2}{\lim\limits_{\eta\to\infty} F'(\eta)}\right\}^{\frac{3}{2}}. \tag{49}$$

The equation may be integrated numerically to give F, F', and F'', the integration being started from the origin and continued until

† *Zeitschr. f. Math. u. Physik*, **56** (1908), 4–13. For experimental results see § 145.

F' is constant to a sufficient approximation. In this way it is found that[†]

$$\alpha = 1\cdot32824. \tag{50}$$

If (45) is now integrated numerically with this value of α, f' should tend to 2, and this provides a check on the accuracy of the work. A table of u/u_1, which is equal to $\frac{1}{2}f'$, is given below.

TABLE 3

η	u/u_1	η	u/u_1	η	u/u_1	η	u/u_1
o	o	o·8	o·5168	1·6	o·8761	2·4	o·9878
o·1	o·0664	o·9	o·5748	1·7	o·9018	2·5	o·9915
o·2	o·1328	1·0	o·6298	1·8	o·9233	2·6	o·9942
o·3	o·1989	1·1	o·6813	1·9	o·9411	2·7	o·9962
o·4	o·2647	1·2	o·7290	2·0	o·9555	2·8	o·9975
o·5	o·3298	1·3	o·7725	2·1	o·9670	2·9	o·9984
o·6	o·3938	1·4	o·8115	2·2	o·9759	3·0	o·9990
o·7	o·4563	1·5	o·8460	2·3	o·9827		

When $y = 0$, $\partial u/\partial y$ is $\frac{1}{4}\alpha u_1(u_1/\nu x)^{\frac{1}{2}}$, and the shearing stress at the wall is $\frac{1}{4}\alpha\rho u_1(\nu u_1/x)^{\frac{1}{2}}$. Hence, for both sides of a plate of length l, the drag per unit breadth is

$$D = \frac{1}{2}\alpha\rho u_1 \int_0^l (\nu u_1/x)^{\frac{1}{2}}\, dx = \alpha\rho u_1^2 l(u_1 l/\nu)^{-\frac{1}{2}}, \tag{51}$$

so that the drag coefficient is given by

$$C_D = D/(\tfrac{1}{2}\rho u_1^2 l) = 2\alpha R^{-\frac{1}{2}} = 2\cdot656R^{-\frac{1}{2}}, \tag{52}$$

where $R = u_1 l/\nu$.

For the displacement thickness δ_1 (equation (15)) we have the result

$$\delta_1 = \int_0^\infty (1 - u/u_1)\, dy = (\nu x/u_1)^{\frac{1}{2}} \int_0^\infty (2 - f')\, d\eta$$

$$= (\nu x/u_1)^{\frac{1}{2}} \lim_{\eta\to\infty} (2\eta - f) = 1\cdot7208(\nu x/u_1)^{\frac{1}{2}}, \tag{53}$$

the numerical value being obtained from the numerical solution of (45).

That a solution could be found in which u is a function of $y/\sqrt{x}$ only was noticed by Prandtl. The argument given by Blasius to prove this may be summarized as follows:—We inquire what must be the relation between m and n if, when $u = f(x, y)$ is a solution of (42), $u = f(mx, ny)$ is also to be a solution. The equation of con-

---

† This method of integration was first given by Töpfer, *Zeitschr. f. Math. u. Physik*, **60** (1912), 397, 398. The numerical value is from Goldstein, *Proc. Camb. Phil. Soc.* **26** (1930), 19. See also Howarth, *Proc. Roy. Soc.* A, **164** (1938), 551. Another method of integration was given by Bairstow, *Journ. Roy. Aero. Soc.* **29** (1925), 7–11. [A revised value for α is 1·32823 (Hoskins, unpublished).]

tinuity shows that if $v_1(x, y)$ is the value of v in the first case, then its value in the second is $(m/n)v_1(mx, ny)$. The first of equations (42) then shows that the required condition is $m = n^2$; and the boundary conditions are also satisfied. It follows that there is a solution in which u is a function of $y/\sqrt{x}$ only. This argument may be generalized to test whether, in more general circumstances, there is a solution of the form $u = x^p f(y/x^q)$, and to find the values of p and q.

The substitutions (43) are also in accordance with the general theory of the boundary layer given in § 46. For the motion at a distance x from the leading edge is unaffected by the state of affairs farther downstream, and in particular, therefore, cannot depend on the length of the plate. Hence as the 'representative length' of the system we must take, not l, but x; as the Reynolds number of § 46, not $u_1 l/\nu$, but $u_1 x/\nu$. The substitutions (43) are then seen to be in accordance with the substitutions in (10). From this point of view it immediately appears that the solution cannot be expected to be a good approximation very near the leading edge, when x is very small; an examination of the solution verifies this, since there is a singularity at the leading edge, v/u and $(\partial u/\partial x)/(\partial u/\partial y)$ being infinite there. Thus even for an unlimited fluid and an infinitely thin plate, some discrepancy from the actual state of affairs is to be expected very near the forward edge. (Actually in experiment a plate of finite thickness, usually sharpened at the forward edge, has to be used.) On the other hand, as x increases $u_1 x/\nu$ increases, so we should expect the solution to become a better and better approximation to the accurate solution of the full equations of motion as we go farther and farther downstream from the forward edge. (Actually if $u_1 x/\nu$ is too large the motion becomes turbulent. There is always a portion of the plate near the front where the motion in the boundary layer is laminar; the position of transition to turbulence depends considerably on external circumstances, such as the degree of turbulence in the external flow.)

Although a formula of the type (51), with a rough value ($1 \cdot 1$) of α, was given by Prandtl in 1904, and a corrected value by Blasius in 1908, an independent investigation by Rayleigh in 1911,† though much less exact, has considerable interest in that the analysis is simple and a similar method may perhaps be used with advantage

† *Phil. Mag.* (6), **21** (1911), 697–711; *Scientific Papers*, **6**, 39, 40.

in more complicated cases. If an infinite plane (infinite in both directions) is initially at rest in a fluid and is then (at time $t = 0$) moved with a constant velocity u_1 in its own plane, the velocity of the fluid is given, for positive values of y, by

$$u = u_1 \left[1 - \operatorname{erf} \frac{y}{2\sqrt{(\nu t)}} \right], \tag{54}$$

where
$$\operatorname{erf} x = \frac{2}{\sqrt{\pi}} \int_0^x e^{-\xi^2} d\xi. \tag{55}$$

Hence the stress at the wall is

$$-\mu \left(\frac{\partial u}{\partial y} \right)_{y=0} = \rho u_1 \left(\frac{\nu}{\pi t} \right)^{\frac{1}{2}}. \tag{56}$$

The supposition made by Rayleigh is that, for a fluid of small viscosity, this formula may be applied to the case previously under consideration on taking t equal to x/u_1. This leads to a formula of the type (51), but with α equal to $4\pi^{-\frac{1}{2}}$, or 2·26. Low[†] has given an argument to show that the true value must lie between $1/\sqrt{2}$ and $\frac{1}{2}$ of this.

It has previously been noted (p. 130) that the equations of flow in the boundary layer along a circular cylinder with its generators parallel to the stream are the same as for two-dimensional flow, so long as the thickness of the boundary layer is small compared with the radius of the cylinder. It follows that if a hollow cylinder (a tube), open at its ends, is placed in a stream with its axis parallel to the flow, then the velocity in the boundary layer should also be given by the table on p. 136; and the drag on a cylinder of length l and radius r_0 is

$$D = 1\cdot328\rho u_1^2 (2\pi r_0 l)(u_1 l/\nu)^{-\frac{1}{2}}, \tag{57}$$

so that the drag coefficient is given by

$$C_D = \frac{D}{\frac{1}{2}\rho u_1^2 (2\pi r_0 l)} = 2\cdot656 R^{-\frac{1}{2}}, \tag{58}$$

where R is $u_1 l/\nu$, exactly as in (52). There is, however, an important difference between the flows along a cylindrical and along a plane surface. In the latter case the approximation becomes better as x increases; in the former, since δ/r_0 is assumed small, this is not true. The approximation then holds, in fact, only if x is very small compared with a fraction (about 1/20th or 1/30th) of $u_1 r_0^2/\nu$, since δ^2 will

† *Journ. Roy. Aero. Soc.* **29** (1925), 16.

be about $20\nu x/u_1$. For the flow inside the tube the mathematical problem is, for longer tubes, the same as that of determining the flow in the inlet length of a circular pipe, which is considered in more detail in Chap. VII, § 139.

Finally, it may be remarked that to solve the problem of flow along a flat plate from the transformed equation (19) we should take $\psi/(\nu u_1 x)^{\frac{1}{2}}$ as independent variable, and z/u_1^2 as dependent variable; and that this is practically equivalent to the usual text-book method of reducing by one the order of an equation such as (45) in which the independent variable does not occur explicitly, which is to take f as the independent and f' as the dependent variable. This relation is the usual one in cases in which the problem may be reduced to the solution of an ordinary differential equation. No advantage is gained for the numerical solution.

54. Steady flow in the boundary layer along a cylinder near the forward stagnation point. Solution when $u_1 = cx^m$.

Very near the forward stagnation point in two-dimensional flow past an obstacle the velocity, u_1, just outside the boundary layer is proportional to the distance x from that point, so that we may put $u_1 = \beta_1 x$, where β_1 is a constant. The equations for steady motion in the boundary layer are

$$\left.\begin{aligned} u\frac{\partial u}{\partial x}+v\frac{\partial u}{\partial y} &= \beta_1^2 x+\nu\frac{\partial^2 u}{\partial y^2}, \\ u=\frac{\partial\psi}{\partial y}, \qquad v &= -\frac{\partial\psi}{\partial x}, \end{aligned}\right\} \tag{59}$$

with the boundary conditions $u = v = 0$ at $y = 0$, $u = 0$ at $x = 0$, $u = \beta_1 x$ at $y = \infty$. These equations may be satisfied by taking

$$\left.\begin{aligned} \psi &= (\nu\beta_1)^{\frac{1}{2}}xf(\eta), \\ \eta &= (\beta_1/\nu)^{\frac{1}{2}}y. \end{aligned}\right\} \tag{60}$$

where

Then

$$u = \beta_1 xf'(\eta), \qquad v = -(\nu\beta_1)^{\frac{1}{2}}f(\eta), \tag{61}$$

and the equation for f is

$$f'^2-ff'' = 1+f'''. \tag{62}$$

The boundary conditions are $f(0) = 0$, $f'(0) = 0$, $f'(\infty) = 1$. The equation was given by Blasius,[†] and integrated numerically by Hiemenz.[‡] The numerical integration has been repeated and

---

† *Zeitschr. f. Math u. Physik*, **56** (1908), 13–17.

‡ *Göttingen Dissertation*, 1911; *Dingler's Polytech. Journal*, **326** (1911), 321–324.

improved by Howarth[†] and Bickley:[‡] the results will be given in Table 4 on p. 151 (where f is denoted by f_1).

For the general calculation of steady flow in the boundary layer along the surface of a cylindrical obstacle in a stream, if u_1 can be expanded in a series of powers of x, a solution may be sought in which ψ is a series of powers of x whose coefficients are functions of y. Then the solution above will represent the first term of this series. The development of this method of calculation will be considered in § 58.

Meanwhile we may notice that the result obtained above as a solution of the approximate boundary layer equations is, as a matter of fact, a solution of the full equations of motion (1) if x and y are Cartesian coordinates, so that the fluid is flowing along a plane surface.[||] For the solution makes $\partial^2 u/\partial x^2$ vanish, so that the first equation is satisfied if

$$-\frac{1}{\rho}\frac{\partial p}{\partial x} = u_1\frac{du_1}{dx} = \beta_1^2 x. \tag{63}$$

Since $\partial v/\partial x$ is zero, the second equation of motion reduces to

$$v\frac{\partial v}{\partial y} = -\frac{1}{\rho}\frac{\partial p}{\partial y}+\nu\frac{\partial^2 v}{\partial y^2}, \tag{64}$$

and so

$$\frac{p}{\rho} = \text{constant}-\tfrac{1}{2}(u_1^2+v^2)+\nu\frac{\partial v}{\partial y}, \tag{65}$$

together with the values of u and v in (61), satisfy the full equations of motion. Moreover $u = v = 0$ when $y = 0$.

The solutions found in this and the preceding sections are special cases of a more general solution given by Falkner and Skan,[††] in which u_1 is taken to be cx^m, where c is a constant. With this value of u_1, if we put

$$\left.\begin{array}{l}\psi = c^{\frac{1}{2}}x^{\frac{1}{2}(m+1)}\nu^{\frac{1}{2}}f(\eta) = (u_1\nu x)^{\frac{1}{2}}f(\eta), \\ \eta = c^{\frac{1}{2}}x^{\frac{1}{2}(m-1)}\nu^{-\frac{1}{2}}y = (u_1/\nu x)^{\frac{1}{2}}y,\end{array}\right\} \tag{66}$$

where

the equation to be satisfied by f is

$$mf'^2-\tfrac{1}{2}(m+1)ff'' = m+f'''. \tag{67}$$

If m is 1, this equation is (62) above; if m is 0, it becomes the same as (45) if $\tfrac{1}{2}\eta$ is taken as the independent variable instead of η.

† A.R.C. Reports and Memoranda, No. 1632 (1935), 7–14.
‡ Unpublished.
|| Tollmien, Handbuch der Experimentalphysik, 4, part 1 (Leipzig, 1931), 255.
†† A.R.C. Reports and Memoranda, No. 1314 (1930). See particularly pp. 1–8.

Since we must have $u = v = 0$ at $y = 0$ and $u = u_1$ at $y = \infty$, the boundary conditions for f are $f(0) = 0$, $f'(0) = 0$, $f'(\infty) = 1$. Moreover, $u = cx^m f'(\eta)$, and so $u = 0$ at $x = 0$ if $m > 0$. If $m = 0$, then $u = u_1$ at $x = 0$. But if $m < 0$, both u and u_1 are infinite at $x = 0$, so that the initial section must correspond to some finite value of x, and the value of u at that section must be determined *a posteriori*. To this extent the solution for negative m is artificial. If we put

$$[\tfrac{1}{2}(m+1)]^{\frac{1}{2}}\eta = Y, \qquad [\tfrac{1}{2}(m+1)]^{\frac{1}{2}}f = F, \qquad \beta = \frac{2m}{m+1}, \qquad (68)$$

the equation for F is

$$\frac{d^3F}{dY^3} + F\frac{d^2F}{dY^2} = \beta\left[\left(\frac{dF}{dY}\right)^2 - 1\right], \qquad (69)$$

and the boundary conditions are

$$F = 0, \qquad \frac{dF}{dY} = 0 \quad \text{at } Y = 0, \qquad \frac{dF}{dY} \to 1 \quad \text{as } Y \to \infty. \qquad (70)$$

The equation in this form has been studied by Hartree.† If $m > 0$, then $\beta > 0$; if $-1 < m < 0$, then $\beta < 0$. For positive values of β the solution is unique; but for negative values this is not so, and the value of d^2F/dY^2 at the origin required to satisfy the condition at infinity, when F and dF/dY vanish at the origin, is indeterminate. There is, however, one value of d^2F/dY^2 at the origin which, as $Y \to \infty$, makes $dF/dY \to 1$ from below more rapidly than with any other value. (It seems probable that this is the only value which makes $dF/dY \to 1$ *exponentially*, all other solutions being such that for large values of Y the difference $1 - dF/dY$ is approximately equal to a multiple of a negative power of Y.) When β is negative, it is the solution which makes $dF/dY \to 1$ as rapidly as possible when $Y \to \infty$ which has been computed.

The solution was found numerically for $\beta = -0\cdot1988$, $-0\cdot19$, $-0\cdot18$, $-0\cdot16$, $-0\cdot14$, $-0\cdot10$, 0, $0\cdot1$, $0\cdot2$, $0\cdot3$, $0\cdot4$, $0\cdot5$, $0\cdot6$, $0\cdot8$, $1\cdot0$, $1\cdot2$, $1\cdot6$, $2\cdot0$, $2\cdot4$. When $\beta = -0\cdot1988$, $m = -0\cdot0904$, d^2F/dY^2 vanishes at the origin, so that $\partial u/\partial y$ vanishes when $y = 0$ for all x. The solution then represents a flow taking place against a pressure gradient which is continually diminishing in such a way that separation of the forward flow does not occur, though it would occur for any increase, however slight, in the adverse pressure gradient.

† *Proc. Camb. Phil. Soc.* **33** (1937), 223–239.

Falkner and Skan made the general solution of (67) the basis of an approximate method of calculation with an arbitrarily given distribution of velocity or pressure outside the boundary layer (see § 64, pp. 178–180).

55. Steady flow in the boundary layer along a surface of revolution near the forward stagnation point.

Very near the forward stagnation point in flow past a body of revolution the velocity, u_1, just outside the boundary layer may be put equal to $\beta_1 x$, where x is distance from the stagnation point along a meridian curve and β_1 is a constant. For a blunt-nosed body the distance, r_0, of a point on the surface of the body from the axis of revolution is, very near the stagnation point, equal to x. The approximate equation of continuity (equation (30) with r_0 in place of r) is then satisfied, very near the stagnation point, by

$$u = \frac{1}{x}\frac{\partial\psi}{\partial y}, \qquad v = -\frac{1}{x}\frac{\partial\psi}{\partial x}. \tag{71}$$

The equation for steady motion in the boundary layer is

$$u\frac{\partial u}{\partial x} + v\frac{\partial u}{\partial y} = \beta_1^2 x + \nu\frac{\partial^2 u}{\partial y^2}. \tag{72}$$

A solution is obtained by putting

$$\eta = (\beta_1/\nu)^{\frac{1}{2}}y, \qquad \psi = (\beta_1\nu)^{\frac{1}{2}}x^2 f(\eta), \tag{73}$$

so that
$$u = \beta_1 x f'(\eta), \qquad v = -2(\beta_1\nu)^{\frac{1}{2}}f(\eta), \tag{74}$$

and the equation for f is

$$f'^2 - 2ff'' = 1 + f'''. \tag{75}$$

Since $u = v = 0$ at $y = 0$, $u = \beta_1 x$ at $y = \infty$, the boundary conditions for f are $f(0) = 0$, $f'(0) = 0$, $f'(\infty) = 1$. A table of values of f has been obtained by Homann† by joining a solution of the differential equation in ascending powers of η to an asymptotic solution for large η. [With $F = \sqrt{2}f, Y = \sqrt{2}\eta$, eqn. (75) reduces to eqn. (69) with $\beta = \frac{1}{2}$, and the boundary conditions are eqns. (70). Hence Hartree's solution may be used.]

For the general calculation of steady flow in a boundary layer along a surface of revolution, if u_1 is expanded in a series of powers of x a solution may be sought in which the stream-function ψ is a series of

† *Zeitschr. f. angew. Math. u. Mech.* **16** (1936), 153–164, especially 155–159.

powers of x whose coefficients are functions of y. The solution above will represent the first term of this series. In the further development of the method we should, however, have to write

$$u = \frac{1}{r_0}\frac{\partial \psi}{\partial y}, \qquad v = -\frac{1}{r_0}\frac{\partial \psi}{\partial x} \tag{76}$$

in place of (71), and to expand r_0^{-1} in powers of x.

Just as for two-dimensional flow in the previous section, the solution obtained above as a solution of the approximate boundary layer equations is a solution of the full equations of motion if the surface is a plane surface at right angles to the direction of the incident stream. The exact equations of motion are then equations (41) of Chap. III (p. 104) with r and z replaced by x and y respectively, w replaced by v, all quantities independent of ϕ, and the v of the original equations equal to zero. The equations thus become

$$\left.\begin{aligned}
u\frac{\partial u}{\partial x}+v\frac{\partial u}{\partial y} &= -\frac{1}{\rho}\frac{\partial p}{\partial x}+\nu\left(\frac{\partial^2 u}{\partial x^2}+\frac{1}{x}\frac{\partial u}{\partial x}-\frac{u}{x^2}+\frac{\partial^2 u}{\partial y^2}\right), \\
u\frac{\partial v}{\partial x}+v\frac{\partial v}{\partial y} &= -\frac{1}{\rho}\frac{\partial p}{\partial y}+\nu\left(\frac{\partial^2 v}{\partial x^2}+\frac{1}{x}\frac{\partial v}{\partial x}+\frac{\partial^2 v}{\partial y^2}\right).
\end{aligned}\right\} \tag{77}$$

The equation of continuity (cf. equations (2) and (38) of Chap. III) becomes

$$\frac{\partial}{\partial x}(xu)+\frac{\partial}{\partial y}(xv) = 0, \tag{78}$$

and is satisfied exactly by the values of u and v derived above. Since $\partial^2 u/\partial x^2 = 0$ and $x^{-1}\partial u/\partial x = u/x^2$, the first equation of motion is satisfied if

$$-\frac{1}{\rho}\frac{\partial p}{\partial x} = u_1\frac{\partial u_1}{\partial x} = \beta_1^2 x. \tag{79}$$

Since $\partial v/\partial x = 0$, the second equation of motion is satisfied if

$$v\frac{\partial v}{\partial y} = -\frac{1}{\rho}\frac{\partial p}{\partial y}+\nu\frac{\partial^2 v}{\partial y^2}. \tag{80}$$

Hence $$\frac{p}{\rho} = \text{constant}-\tfrac{1}{2}(u_1^2+v^2)+\nu\frac{\partial v}{\partial y}, \tag{81}$$

together with the values of u and v in (74), satisfy the full equations of motion. Moreover, $u = v = 0$ at $y = 0$.

56. Steady two-dimensional flow along a wall in a converging canal.

To calculate the steady two-dimensional motion in the boundary layer along either of two non-parallel plane walls forming a converging canal, we denote by x the distance from the line of intersection of the planes of the two walls, and we write

$$u_1 = -c/x, \tag{82}$$

c being positive, since for converging flow the velocity is in the direction of x decreasing. Then the equations to be solved are

$$\left.\begin{aligned} u\frac{\partial u}{\partial x}+v\frac{\partial u}{\partial y} &= -\frac{c^2}{x^3}+v\frac{\partial^2 u}{\partial y^2}, \\ \frac{\partial u}{\partial x}+\frac{\partial v}{\partial y} &= 0. \end{aligned}\right\} \tag{83}$$

A solution may be obtained in which†

$$\left.\begin{aligned} u &= f(\theta)/x, \\ \theta &= y/x. \end{aligned}\right\} \tag{84}$$

where

Then
$$\frac{\partial u}{\partial x} = -\frac{1}{x^2}(f+\theta f') = -\frac{\partial v}{\partial y} = -\frac{1}{x}\frac{\partial v}{\partial\theta},$$

and so
$$v = \theta f/x. \tag{85}$$

The equation satisfied by f becomes, on substitution in (83) and multiplication by $-x^3$,

$$f^2 = c^2 - vf''. \tag{86}$$

Multiply by f' and integrate. Then

$$\tfrac{1}{3}f^3 = c^2 f - \tfrac{1}{2}vf'^2 + A, \tag{87}$$

where A is a constant of integration. When $u = u_1$, $\partial u/\partial y = 0$. Hence $f = -c$ and $f' = 0$ together, and $A = \tfrac{2}{3}c^3$. Since u_1 is negative, $\partial u/\partial y$ is negative and f' is negative. Hence

$$\left(\frac{3v}{2}\right)^{\frac{1}{2}}\frac{df}{d\theta} = -(c+f)(2c-f)^{\frac{1}{2}}. \tag{88}$$

If we put $(2c-f)^{\frac{1}{2}} = (3c)^{\frac{1}{2}}\tanh\xi,$

(88) becomes $d\xi = (c/2v)^{\frac{1}{2}}\,d\theta,$

and since $f = 0$ when $\theta = 0$, the integral of (88) is

$$-\frac{f}{c} = \frac{u}{u_1} = 3\tanh^2\!\left[\left(\frac{c}{2v}\right)^{\frac{1}{2}}\theta+\beta\right]-2, \tag{89}$$

where $\tanh^2\beta = \tfrac{2}{3}$, so that $\beta = 1{\cdot}146$. This solution should be compared with the solution of the full equations in Chap. III, § 42. To compare we must put $u_1 = u_{\max}$, and write r for x and $r|u|_{\max}$ for c,

† Pohlhausen, Zeitschr. f. angew. Math. u. Mech. 1 (1921), 267, 268.

so that R is c/ν. Also $\alpha-\phi$ is here called θ. Hence (89) is the same as (63), Chap. III, p. 109. The altered meaning of c being remembered, (87) should be compared with (49), Chap. III, p. 106.

57. The spread of a jet.

As an example of the application of the approximations of the boundary layer theory to flow where no wall is present, we may set out calculations for the spread of a jet when the motion is laminar. This example has been worked out by Schlichting, both for two-dimensional motion and for motion symmetrical about an axis.† (In practice the motion in such cases is usually turbulent: calculations for turbulent motion are discussed in Chap. XIII, § 255.)

For the two-dimensional motion we may suppose that a jet of air flows through a narrow slit in a wall, and then mixes with the surrounding air. Our calculations will give the distribution of velocity across the jet at some distance from the slit.

The axis of x is taken along the axis of the jet, and the axis of y perpendicular thereto. $\partial^2 u/\partial x^2$ is assumed small in comparison with $\partial^2 u/\partial y^2$, and is neglected. The variation of pressure across the jet is neglected, so that, the fluid being unlimited laterally, the pressure is taken as constant everywhere. (These assumptions may be justified *a posteriori*.) The equations of motion then take the same form as in § 53 (equations (42)), but the boundary conditions are $u = 0$ when $y = \infty$, and (on account of the symmetry of the jet) $v = 0$ and $\partial u/\partial y = 0$ when $y = 0$. Further, the pressure being constant and the motion steady, the rate, M, at which momentum flows across a section of the jet must be the same for all sections, where

$$M = 2\rho \int_0^\infty u^2 \, dy. \qquad (90)$$

If we seek for a solution of the form $\psi = x^p f(y/x^q)$, we find that, in order that M may be constant and $u \, \partial u/\partial x$ of the same degree in x as $\partial^2 u/\partial y^2$, we must have $p = \frac{1}{3}$, $q = \frac{2}{3}$.‡ This will make the breadth of the jet increase as $x^{\frac{2}{3}}$, and the maximum velocity fall off as $x^{\frac{1}{3}}$. We proceed to put

$$\eta = \frac{1}{3\nu^{\frac{1}{2}}} \frac{y}{x^{\frac{2}{3}}}, \qquad \psi = \nu^{\frac{1}{2}} x^{\frac{1}{3}} f(\eta). \qquad (91)$$

---

† *Zeitschr. f. angew. Math. u. Mech.* **13** (1933), 260–263. For an experimental confirmation in the latter case see Andrade and Tsien, *Proc. Phys. Soc. London,* **49** (1937), 381–391.

‡ The same results follow from taking $\eta = y/\chi(x)$, $\psi = \phi(x)f(\eta)$. It is found that $\phi \propto x^{\frac{1}{3}}$, $\chi \propto x^{\frac{2}{3}}$.

Then $$u = \frac{1}{3x^{\frac{2}{3}}}f'(\eta), \qquad v = -\frac{\nu^{\frac{1}{3}}}{3x^{\frac{1}{3}}}(f - 2\eta f'), \tag{92}$$

and on substitution into (42) we find the following equation for f:

$$\frac{d}{d\eta}(ff') + f''' = 0. \tag{93}$$

The boundary conditions require $f(0) = 0$, $f''(0) = 0$, and $f'(\infty) = 0$. Since f and f'' vanish together, (93) may be immediately integrated to give $$ff' + f'' = 0. \tag{94}$$

If α is any constant and we write

$$\xi = \alpha\eta = \frac{\alpha}{3\nu^{\frac{1}{3}}}\frac{y}{x^{\frac{2}{3}}}, \qquad f = 2\alpha F(\xi), \tag{95}$$

then $$F'' + 2FF' = 0, \tag{96}$$

where dashes now denote differentiations with respect to ξ. The boundary conditions require $F(0) = 0$, $F''(0) = 0$, $F'(\infty) = 0$, and since we have already introduced an arbitrary constant (α), we may take the solution for which $F'(0) = 1$. Then

$$F = \tanh\xi \tag{97}$$

satisfies all the required conditions† and makes

$$u = \frac{2\alpha^2}{3x^{\frac{2}{3}}}\,\mathrm{sech}^2\xi.$$

α is determined in terms of M from (90), which reduces to

$$\frac{3M}{8\rho\nu^{\frac{1}{3}}} = \alpha^3 \int_0^\infty \mathrm{sech}^4\xi\, d\xi = \tfrac{2}{3}\alpha^3.$$

Hence $$\alpha^3 = \frac{9}{16}\frac{M}{\rho\nu^{\frac{1}{3}}}, \qquad \alpha = 0{\cdot}82548(M/\rho\nu^{\frac{1}{3}})^{\frac{1}{3}}, \tag{98}$$

and so, from (91), (92), (95), and (97),

$$\left.\begin{array}{l} \psi = 1{\cdot}6510(M\nu x/\rho)^{\frac{1}{3}}\tanh\xi, \\[4pt] u = 0{\cdot}4543(M^2/\rho^2\nu x)^{\frac{1}{3}}\,\mathrm{sech}^2\xi, \\[4pt] v = 0{\cdot}5503(M\nu/\rho x^2)^{\frac{1}{3}}(2\xi\,\mathrm{sech}^2\xi - \tanh\xi), \end{array}\right\} \tag{99}$$

where $$\xi = 0{\cdot}2752(M/\rho\nu^2)^{\frac{1}{3}}y/x^{\frac{2}{3}}.$$

The approximations are seen to be adequate so long as $Mx/\rho\nu^2$ is large. (There is a singularity at $x = 0$.)

† The solution in the text is due to Bickley, *Phil. Mag.* (7), **23** (1937), 727–731. Schlichting connected a series in ascending powers with an asymptotic solution, and obtained different numerical results.

The flux of mass, Q, across any section of the jet is given by

$$Q/\rho = 2 \int_0^\infty u \, dy = 2 \int_0^\infty \frac{\partial \psi}{\partial y} \, dy = 2[\psi]_0^\infty$$

$$= 3 \cdot 3019 (M\nu x/\rho)^{\frac{1}{2}}. \tag{100}$$

In the case of fluid issuing from a small hole in a wall, when the motion is symmetrical about an axis, then, with the axis of x along the axis of the jet and with r denoting distance from that axis, as before, the equations of motion and continuity may be written (cf. (32)),

$$\left. \begin{aligned} u\frac{\partial u}{\partial x} + v\frac{\partial u}{\partial r} &= \frac{\nu}{r}\frac{\partial}{\partial r}\left(r\frac{\partial u}{\partial r}\right), \\ u = \frac{1}{r}\frac{\partial \psi}{\partial r}, \qquad v &= -\frac{1}{r}\frac{\partial \psi}{\partial x}, \end{aligned} \right\} \tag{101}$$

with

$$M = 2\pi\rho \int_0^\infty u^2 r \, dr, \tag{102}$$

the assumptions and meanings of the symbols being the same as before. The boundary conditions are $u = 0$ at $r = \infty$, $v = 0$ and $\partial u/\partial r = 0$ at $r = 0$. In addition M is constant. The solution may be obtained in the form

where

$$\left. \begin{aligned} \psi &= \nu x g(\eta), \\ \eta &= \frac{1}{\nu^{\frac{1}{2}}}\frac{r}{x}. \end{aligned} \right\} \tag{103}$$

This makes

$$\left. \begin{aligned} u &= \frac{g'}{\eta x}, \\ v &= \frac{\nu^{\frac{1}{2}}}{x}\left(g' - \frac{g}{\eta}\right). \end{aligned} \right\} \tag{104}$$

The equation for g is

$$-\frac{d}{d\eta}\left(\frac{gg'}{\eta}\right) = \frac{d}{d\eta}\left(g'' - \frac{g'}{\eta}\right), \tag{105}$$

and as boundary conditions we have that $g'(\infty) = 0$, whilst at $\eta = 0$, g'/η must stay finite and both $g' - g/\eta$ and $\dfrac{d}{d\eta}(g'/\eta)$, i.e. $g''/\eta - g'/\eta^2$, must vanish. Hence $g(0) = 0$ and $g'(0) = 0$; and, since $g'' - g'/\eta$ and gg'/η both vanish at the origin, (105) may be immediately integrated in the form

$$\eta g'' - g' + gg' = 0. \tag{106}$$

The required solution is $\quad g = \dfrac{\xi^2}{1+\frac{1}{4}\xi^2}$, $\qquad$ (107)

where $\qquad\qquad\qquad \xi = \alpha\eta$, $\qquad\qquad\qquad$ (108)

α being an arbitrary constant. This makes

$$u = \frac{2\alpha^2}{x(1+\frac{1}{4}\xi^2)^2}, \qquad (109)$$

so that $\qquad\qquad M = \dfrac{16}{3}\pi\mu\alpha^2.$ $\qquad\qquad$ (110)

Hence

$$\left.\begin{aligned} u &= \frac{3M}{8\pi\mu}\frac{1}{x}\frac{1}{(1+\frac{1}{4}\xi^2)^2}, \\[1mm] v &= \frac{1}{4}\left(\frac{3M}{\pi\rho}\right)^{\frac{1}{2}}\frac{1}{x}\frac{\xi(1-\frac{1}{4}\xi^2)}{(1+\frac{1}{4}\xi^2)^2}, \end{aligned}\right\} \qquad (111)$$

where $\qquad\qquad \xi = \dfrac{1}{4\nu}\left(\dfrac{3M}{\pi\rho}\right)^{\frac{1}{2}}\dfrac{r}{x}.$ $\qquad\qquad$ (112)

The approximations are adequate so long as $M/\rho\nu^2$ is large.

The flux of mass, Q, across any section of the jet is given by

$$Q/\rho = 2\pi \int_0^\infty ur\, dr = 8\pi\nu x, \qquad (113)$$

and is therefore independent of the flow of momentum in the jet, i.e. of the pressure under which the fluid is forced through the opening in the wall. If this is large, the jet remains relatively narrow; if this is smaller, the jet broadens out more, setting more undisturbed fluid in motion, and in this case the effects just balance.

Examples of the application of boundary layer theory to flow in wakes, where again no solid surfaces are immediately present, will be given in Chap. XIII. Turbulent flow both in wakes and in jets will also be considered.

58. Approximate methods of calculating steady two-dimensional boundary layer flow. Expansion in series.

We proceed to consider methods of general application for the calculation of steady two-dimensional flow in a boundary layer. Foundations for several of these methods have been laid in previous sections.

The pressure, p, or the velocity, u_1, just outside the boundary layer is required as a datum for these calculations. In some cases (when there is no separation of the forward flow, or in flow past a stream-line body when the wake is very narrow) it may be profitable to carry through the calculations with values or formulae for p or u_1 derived from ideal fluid theory; but more generally the values must be obtained by experiment. We have therefore to contemplate calculations in which p and u_1 are not given analytically, but by graphs or numerical tables of values. Even when analytical solutions for p and u_1 from ideal fluid theory are being used, the formulae will almost always be so complicated as to necessitate recourse to the methods below.

In flow past a cylindrical obstacle fixed in a stream of fluid we measure x along the surface of the cylinder from the forward stagnation point. If u_1 can be expanded in a series of powers of x, or if a polynomial can be fitted to the experimental values for a range of values of x from $x = 0$, then the stream-function ψ may be expanded in a series of powers of x whose coefficients are functions of y, the normal distance from the surface of the cylinder. If the section of the cylinder is symmetrical about a line in the direction of the undisturbed stream, the expansion of u_1 will contain only odd powers of x, and we shall have

$$u_1 = \beta_1 x + \beta_3 x^3 + \beta_5 x^5 + \ldots. \qquad (114)$$

We then assume an expansion for ψ,

$$\psi = F_1 x + F_3 x^3 + F_5 x^5 + \ldots, \qquad (115)$$

where the F's are functions of y. With

$$u = \frac{\partial \psi}{\partial y}, \qquad v = -\frac{\partial \psi}{\partial x}, \qquad (116)$$

we then substitute in the equation of motion (equation (17)), and equate coefficients of the several powers of x on the two sides of the equation. In this way a series of ordinary differential equations for the F's is obtained. The boundary conditions for the F's are similarly obtained from the conditions $u = v = 0$ at $y = 0$, $u \to u_1$ as $y \to \infty$. These boundary conditions are $F_n(0) = 0$, $F_n'(0) = 0$, $F_n'(\infty) = \beta_n$ for $n = 1, 3, 5, \ldots$, dashes denoting differentiation with respect to y. Inspection of the differential equations and of the boundary conditions then shows that it is possible, by changing both the independent variable (y) and the dependent variables (the F's), to transform the equations and boundary conditions into forms which are independent of the kinematic viscosity ν and of the coefficients

β_1, β_3, etc., in the expansion of u_1, so that the solutions of these equations may be applied to all cases. To reduce the equations to this non-dimensional form it is, however, necessary to express F_5 as the sum of two functions, F_7 as the sum of three functions, F_9 as the sum of five functions, and so on. In this way it is found that

$$u = \beta_1 f_1' x + 4\beta_3 f_3' x^3 + 6\left(\beta_5 g_5' + \frac{\beta_3^2}{\beta_1} h_5'\right)x^5$$

$$+ 8\left(\beta_7 g_7' + \frac{\beta_3 \beta_5}{\beta_1} h_7' + \frac{\beta_3^3}{\beta_1^2} k_7'\right)x^7 + ..., \quad (117)$$

where the functions $f_1, f_3, g_5, h_5,...$ are functions of

$$\eta = (\beta_1/\nu)^{\frac{1}{2}} y, \quad (118)$$

and dashes denote differentiation with respect to η. It follows that

$$\frac{\partial u}{\partial y} = (\beta_1/\nu)^{\frac{1}{2}} \frac{\partial u}{\partial \eta}, \quad (119)$$

so that the skin-friction can be found as a multiple of $\partial u/\partial \eta$ at $\eta = 0$. Its determination involves the knowledge of f_1'', f_3'', etc., at $\eta = 0$. Separation of the forward flow will occur when $\partial u/\partial \eta = 0$ at $\eta = 0$.

Tables of f_1, f_3, g_5, h_5, and k_7, and of their first two derivatives, are reproduced in Table 4 below. (f_1 is the same as the function f which satisfies the equation (62).) g_7 and h_7 have not been tabulated, and the tabulation of k_7' determines the coefficient of x^7 in u only when β_5 and β_7 are zero.

This series solution will always give reliable values of u and $\partial u/\partial y$ for sufficiently small values of x, but it must not be used for values of x large enough to make the neglected terms in the series of importance. For flow past a bluff obstacle, such as a circular cylinder, the pressure distribution is such that the method can be applied with success for a very considerable range of values of x, probably up to the point of separation. Thus Hiemenz† found that his experimentally obtained values of u_1 for a circular cylinder of diameter d equal to 9·74 cm. in a stream of velocity u_0 equal to 19·2 cm./sec. (the Reynolds number $u_0 d/\nu$ being $1·85 \times 10^4$) could be represented sufficiently accurately by three terms of (114), with $\beta_1 = 7·151$, $\beta_3 = -0·04497$, $\beta_5 = -0·0003300$, x being measured in cm.; and Howarth‡ has shown that the values in Table 4 are sufficient to

---

† *Göttingen Dissertation*, 1911; *Dingler's Polytech. Journal*, **326** (1911), 321–324.
‡ *A.R.C. Reports and Memoranda*, No. 1632 (1935), 47.

TABLE 4

η	f_1	f_1'	f_1''	f_3	f_3'	f_3''	g_3	g_5'	g_5''	h_5	h_5'	h_5''	k_7	k_7'	k_7''
0·0	0·0000	0·0000	1·23258766	0·0000	0·000	0·7246	0·00	0·00	0·637	0·00	0·00	0·12	0·00	0·00	0·012
0·1	0·0060	0·1183	1·1328	0·004	0·068	0·625	0·00	0·06	0·54	0·00	0·01	0·07	0·00	0·00	0·01
0·2	0·0233	0·2266	1·0345	0·013	0·125	0·529	0·01	0·11	0·44	0·00	0·01	+0·03	0·00	0·00	0·02
0·3	0·0510	0·3252	0·9386	0·028	0·174	0·438	0·03	0·15	0·35	0·00	0·02	−0·01	0·00	0·00	0·02
0·4	0·0881	0·4145	0·8463	0·048	0·213	0·354	0·04	0·18	0·27	0·01	+0·01	−0·04	0·00	0·01	0·02
0·5	0·1336	0·4946	0·7583	0·071	0·245	0·278	0·06	0·20	0·20	0·01	0·01	−0·07	0·00	0·01	0·03
0·6	0·1867	0·5663	0·6752	0·096	0·272	0·211	0·08	0·22	0·14	0·01	0·00	−0·08	0·00	0·01	0·04
0·7	0·2466	0·6299	0·5974	0·124	0·287	0·153	0·10	0·23	0·09	0·00	−0·01	−0·08	0·00	0·01	0·05
0·8	0·3124	0·6859	0·5251	0·154	0·308	0·104	0·13	0·24	0·05	+0·00	−0·02	−0·08	0·00	0·02	0·05
0·9	0·3835	0·7351	0·4587	0·184	0·308	0·063	0·15	0·24	0·02	−0·00	−0·03	−0·07	0·00	0·02	0·05
1·0	0·4592	0·7779	0·3980	0·215	0·313	0·029	0·17	0·24	+0·02	−0·01	−0·04	−0·06	0·01	0·03	0·05
1·1	0·5389	0·8149	0·3431	0·246	0·314	+0·003	0·20	0·24	−0·01	−0·02	−0·05	−0·04	0·01	0·03	0·04
1·2	0·6220	0·8467	0·2938	0·277	0·313	−0·017	0·22	0·23	−0·03	−0·03	−0·05	−0·03	0·01	0·04	0·03
1·3	0·7067	0·8738	0·2498	0·309	0·311	−0·031	0·25	0·23	−0·04	−0·04	−0·05	−0·02	0·01	0·04	0·02
1·4	0·7967	0·8968	0·2110	0·340	0·307	−0·041	0·27	0·22	−0·05	−0·04	−0·05	−0·01	0·02	0·05	0·02
1·5	0·8873	0·9162	0·1770	0·370	0·302	−0·048	0·29	0·21	−0·06	−0·05	−0·05	+0·01	0·02	0·05	0·01
1·6	0·9798	0·9323	0·1474	0·400	0·293	−0·051	0·31	0·21	−0·06	−0·05	−0·04	0·02	0·03	0·05	+0·01
1·7	1·0738	0·9458	0·1218	0·429	0·288	−0·052	0·34	0·20	−0·07	−0·05	−0·04	0·02	0·03	0·05	0·00
1·8	1·1689	0·9568	0·1000	0·458	0·283	−0·051	0·36	0·19	−0·06	−0·05	−0·03	0·03	0·04	0·05	−0·01
1·9	1·2650	0·9659	0·0814	0·487	0·278	−0·048	0·38	0·19	−0·06	−0·05	−0·03	0·03	0·04	0·05	−0·02
2·0	1·3620	0·9732	0·0658	0·515	0·273	−0·045	0·39	0·18	−0·06	−0·05	−0·02	0·02	0·05	0·04	−0·03
2·1	1·4596	0·9791	0·0528	0·543	0·269	−0·040	0·41	0·18	−0·05	−0·05	−0·01	0·02	0·05	0·04	−0·04
2·2	1·5578	0·9839	0·0420	0·570	0·266	−0·036	0·43	0·18	−0·05	−0·05	0·00	0·02	0·06	0·03	−0·05
2·3	1·6563	0·9876	0·0332	0·597	0·263	−0·032	0·45	0·18	−0·04	−0·05	0·00	0·01	0·07	0·02	−0·05
2·4	1·7553	0·9905	0·0260	0·623	0·259	−0·028	0·46	0·18	−0·04	−0·05	0·00	0·01	0·08	0·01	−0·04
2·5	1·8544	0·9929	0·0202	0·649	0·258	−0·023	0·48	0·17	−0·03	−0·05		0·00	0·09	0·00	−0·03
2·6	1·9538	0·9946	0·0156	0·676	0·257	−0·020	0·49	0·17	−0·03	−0·05		0·00	0·09	0·00	−0·02
2·7	2·0533	0·9960	0·0119	0·701	0·256	−0·017	0·51	0·17	−0·02	−0·05			0·09	0·00	−0·01
2·8	2·1527	0·9970	0·0090	0·726	0·254	−0·013	0·53	0·17	−0·01	−0·05			0·09	0·00	−0·01
2·9	2·2527	0·9978	0·0068	0·751	0·253	−0·011	0·54		−0·01	−0·05			0·09	0·00	0·00
3·0	2·3524	0·9984	0·0051	0·777	0·252	−0·010	0·56		0·00	−0·05					0·00
3·1	2·4524	0·9989	0·0038	0·802	0·251	−0·008	0·58		0·00	−0·05					0·00
3·2	2·5523	0·9992	0·0028	0·828	0·251	−0·007									
3·3	2·6523	0·9994	0·0020	0·853	0·251	−0·005									
3·4	2·7522	0·9996	0·0014	0·879	0·250	−0·004									
3·5	2·8522	0·9997	0·0010	0·904	0·250	−0·003									
3·6	2·9521	0·9998	0·0007	0·929	0·250	−0·002									
3·7	3·0521	0·9999	0·0004	0·954	0·250	−0·002									
3·8	3·1521	0·9999	0·0002	0·979	0·250	−0·001									
3·9	3·2521	0·9999	0·0002	1·004	0·250	−0·001									
4·0	3·3521	1·0000	0·0001	1·029	0·250	−0·001									
4·1	3·4521	1·0000	0·0001	1·054	0·250	−0·000									
4·2	3·5521	1·0000	0·0001	1·079	0·250	0·000									
4·3	3·6521	1·0000	0·0001	1·104	0·250	0·000									

determine that separation takes place between $81°$ and $83°$ from the forward stagnation point.† For less bluff obstacles, however, more terms in the expansion (or polynomial expression) for u_1 are required to proceed far from the forward stagnation point; for a stream-line body it is found to be impracticable to proceed far by this method, in spite of the fact that for any special case more terms in the series could be found by *ad hoc* integrations, since then F_7, F_9, F_{11}, and so on, could be found by solving one equation, instead of three, five, seven, and so on, respectively.

If the section of the cylindrical obstacle is not symmetrical about a line in the direction of the undisturbed flow, the expression for u_1 in either direction along the surface from the forward stagnation point will be of the form

$$u_1 = \beta_1 x + \beta_2 x^2 + \beta_3 x^3 + \dots . \tag{120}$$

The expansion for ψ will also involve both odd and even powers of x; if we proceed in a similar way as for the symmetrical case we find

$$u = \beta_1 f_1' x + 3\beta_2 f_2' x^2 + 4\left(\beta_3 g_3' + \frac{\beta_2^2}{\beta_1} h_3'\right)x^3 + 5\left(\beta_4 g_4' + \frac{\beta_2\beta_3}{\beta_1} h_4' + \frac{\beta_2^3}{\beta_1^2} k_4'\right)x^4 + \dots , \tag{121}$$

where f_1, f_2, g_3, h_3,... are functions of $\eta = (\beta_1/\nu)^{\frac{1}{2}}y$ and dashes denote differentiation as before. f_1 is the same function as in equation (117) and Table 4. The functions f_2, g_3, h_3, and k_4, and their first two derivatives, are tabulated in Table 5.‡

---

† The position of the point of separation, as determined both experimentally and by calculation by Hiemenz, was at $82°$ from the forward stagnation point. Hiemenz did not express F_5 non-dimensionally, but found it by an *ad hoc* integration with his special values of ν, β_1, β_3, β_5. The terms of (115) after the first three were neglected.

‡ The method of expansion in series, for the symmetrical case only, was first used by Blasius, who reduced F_1 and F_3 to non-dimensional form, and found approximate values of f_1 and f_3 (*Zeitschr. f. Math. u. Physik*, **56** (1908), 13–19). The equations for f_1 and f_3 were integrated numerically by Hiemenz, *loc. cit.* The integration was repeated and improved by Howarth, who also showed how F_5, F_7, etc., could be reduced to non-dimensional form, and considered the asymmetrical case (*A.R.C. Reports and Memoranda*, No. 1632 (1935)). Tables 4 and 5 are reproduced from Howarth's report (which also contains a critical survey, with extensions, of the methods of calculation of steady boundary layer flow which had been proposed before 1934). In Table 4 the value of $f_1''(0)$ is an improved value due to W. G. Bickley (private communication), the error being not more than one unit in the eighth place; and the values of f_1, f_1', f_1'' have been checked against Bickley's table.

TABLE 5

η	f_2	f_2'	f_2''	g_3	g_3'	g_3''	h_2	h_2'	h_2''	k_4	k_4'	k_4''
0·0	0·000	0·000	0·7982	0·000	0·000	0·725	0·00	0·00	0·166	0·00	0·00	−0·019
0·1	0·004	0·075	0·699	0·004	0·068	0·625	0·00	0·01	0·12	0·00	0·00	−0·02
0·2	0·015	0·140	0·602	0·013	0·125	0·529	0·00	0·02	0·07	0·00	0·00	−0·02
0·3	0·032	0·195	0·509	0·028	0·174	0·438	0·01	0·03	+0·03	0·00	−0·01	−0·01
0·4	0·054	0·242	0·423	0·048	0·213	0·354	0·01	0·03	−0·01	0·00	−0·01	−0·01
0·5	0·080	0·280	0·344	0·071	0·245	0·278	0·01	0·03	−0·04	0·00	−0·01	0·00
0·6	0·109	0·311	0·273	0·096	0·269	0·211	0·01	0·02	−0·05	0·00	−0·01	0·00
0·7	0·142	0·336	0·210	0·124	0·287	0·153	0·02	0·02	−0·07	−0·01	0·00	+0·01
0·8	0·175	0·353	0·156	0·154	0·300	0·104	0·02	+0·01	−0·07	−0·01	0·00	0·02
0·9	0·212	0·367	0·109	0·184	0·308	0·063	0·02	0·00	−0·07	−0·01	0·00	0·03
1·0	0·249	0·375	0·070	0·215	0·313	0·029	0·02	−0·01	−0·07	−0·01	0·00	0·03
1·1	0·287	0·381	0·037	0·246	0·314	+0·003	0·02	−0·01	−0·06	−0·01	0·00	0·04
1·2	0·325	0·384	+0·012	0·277	0·313	−0·017	0·01	−0·02	−0·05	−0·01	+0·01	0·04
1·3	0·363	0·384	−0·007	0·309	0·311	−0·031	0·01	−0·02	−0·04	0·00	0·01	0·04
1·4	0·402	0·382	−0·021	0·340	0·307	−0·041	0·01	−0·03	−0·03	0·00	0·01	0·04
1·5	0·440	0·380	−0·032	0·370	0·302	−0·048	+0·01	−0·03	−0·02	0·00	0·02	0·03
1·6	0·477	0·377	−0·039	0·400	0·298	−0·051	0·00	−0·03	0·00	0·00	0·02	0·03
1·7	0·515	0·373	−0·042	0·429	0·293	−0·052	0·00	−0·03	0·00	0·00	0·02	0·02
1·8	0·552	0·368	−0·043	0·458	0·288	−0·051	0·00	−0·03	+0·01	+0·01	0·03	0·01
1·9	0·588	0·364	−0·043	0·487	0·283	−0·048	−0·01	−0·03	0·02	0·01	0·03	+0·01
2·0	0·625	0·361	−0·041	0·515	0·278	−0·045	−0·01	−0·03	0·03	0·01	0·03	0·00
2·1	0·661	0·357	−0·038	0·543	0·273	−0·040	−0·01	−0·02	0·03	0·02	0·03	−0·01
2·2	0·696	0·353	−0·034	0·570	0·269	−0·036	−0·01	−0·02	0·03	0·02	0·03	−0·01
2·3	0·731	0·350	−0·030	0·597	0·266	−0·032	−0·01	−0·02	0·03	0·02	0·02	−0·02
2·4	0·766	0·346	−0·026	0·623	0·263	−0·028	−0·01	−0·02	0·04	0·02	0·02	−0·02
2·5	0·801	0·344	−0·022	0·649	0·259	−0·023	−0·02	−0·01	0·03	0·03	0·02	−0·03
2·6	0·835	0·342	−0·019	0·676	0·258	−0·020	−0·02	−0·01	0·03	0·03	0·02	−0·03
2·7	0·870	0·340	−0·016	0·701	0·257	−0·017	−0·02	−0·01	0·02	0·03	0·02	−0·03
2·8	0·904	0·338	−0·014	0·726	0·256	−0·013	−0·02	−0·01	0·02	0·03	0·01	−0·02
2·9	0·938	0·337	−0·011	0·751	0·254	−0·011	−0·02	0·00	0·02	0·03	0·01	−0·02
3·0	0·972	0·336	−0·009	0·777	0·253	−0·010	−0·02	0·00	0·02	0·03	0·00	−0·01
3·1	1·006	0·335	−0·007	0·802	0·252	−0·008	−0·02	0·00	0·02	0·03	0·00	0·00
3·2	1·040	0·335	−0·006	0·828	0·251	−0·007	−0·02	0·00	0·01	0·03	0·00	0·00
3·3	1·073	0·335	−0·005	0·853	0·251	−0·005	−0·02	0·00	0·01	0·03	0·00	0·00
3·4	1·106	0·334	−0·003	0·879	0·251	−0·004	−0·02	0·00	0·00	0·03	0·00	0·00
3·5	1·139	0·334	−0·003	0·904	0·250	−0·003	−0·02	0·00	0·00	−0·03	0·00	0·00
3·6	1·172	0·334	−0·002	0·929	0·250	−0·002	−0·02	0·00	0·00	0·03	0·00	0·00
3·7	1·205	0·334	−0·001	0·954	0·250	−0·002	−0·02	0·00	0·00	0·03	0·00	0·00
3·8	1·238	0·333	−0·001	0·979	0·250	−0·001	−0·02	0·00	0·00	0·03	0·00	0·00
3·9	1·271	0·333	−0·001	1·004	0·250	−0·001	−0·02	0·00	0·00	0·03	0·00	0·00
4·0	1·304	0·333	−0·001	1·029	0·250	−0·001	−0·02	0·00	0·00	0·03	0·00	0·00
4·1	1·337	0·333	0·000	1·054	0·250	0·000	−0·02	0·00	0·00	0·03	0·00	0·00
4·2	1·370	0·333	0·000									
4·3	1·403	0·333	0·000									

59. Approximate methods of calculating steady two-dimensional boundary layer flow. Step-by-step methods.

Several methods of step-by-step calculation (i.e. of proceeding from the values of u for one value of x to the values for a slightly larger x) have been suggested. In the first place, the velocity distribution at the initial section may be supposed expressed as a power series in y, which, since $u = 0$ when $y = 0$, will begin with a multiple of y. To reduce the calculations to non-dimensional form, all lengths are expressed as multiples of a characteristic length d, all velocities as multiples of a characteristic velocity u_0, and the pressure as a multiple of ρu_0^2. Distances and velocity components normal to the wall are then multiplied by $R^{\frac{1}{2}}$ (where $R = u_0 d/\nu$ as in §46, equation (10)). If the velocity at the initial section is given by

$$u = \alpha_1 y + \alpha_2 \frac{y^2}{2!} + \alpha_3 \frac{y^3}{3!} + ..., \tag{122}$$

x

and the pressure gradient by

$$-\frac{\partial p}{\partial x} = \pi_0 + \pi_1 x + \cdots, \tag{123}$$

where x is measured from the initial section, the solution has a singularity at $x = 0$ unless the coefficients satisfy the conditions

$$\alpha_2 + \pi_0 = 0, \quad \alpha_3 = 0, \quad \alpha_5 + 2\alpha_1 \pi_1 = 0, \quad \alpha_6 = 2\pi_0 \pi_1, \ldots. \tag{124}$$

If we write

$$\xi = x^{\frac{1}{3}}, \qquad \eta = y/3x^{\frac{1}{3}}, \tag{125}$$

then the stream-function may be expanded in a series

$$\psi = \xi^2 \{ f_0(\eta) + \xi f_1(\eta) + \xi^2 f_2(\eta) + \cdots \}. \tag{126}$$

f_0 is $\frac{9}{2}\alpha_1 \eta^2$; f_1 can be expressed in finite form in terms of the incomplete gamma function; and the function f_2 has been determined by expansion in series, numerical integration, and asymptotic expansion.† For large values of η (126) is unsuitable on account of the rapid increase of f_r with r; a solution, valid for large η, can be found in the form

$$\psi = \psi_0(y) + \xi^2 \frac{\psi_2(y)}{2!} + \xi^3 \frac{\psi_3(y)}{3!} + \xi^3 \log \xi \frac{\psi_3^*(y)}{3!} + \xi^4 \frac{\psi_4(y)}{4!} + \cdots, \tag{127}$$

and from the determination of f_0, f_1, f_2 it is possible to determine $\psi_0, \psi_2, \psi_3, \psi_3^*$. The form of the solution for any power-series expansion of the initial values of u is thus found; the solution is useful in determining the nature of the singularity and allowing a short step to be taken from the value of x at which it occurs; but the convergence is poor, and only a very short step can be taken.

The solution will be invalidated by the singularity at the initial section $x = 0$, but will be valid a short distance from the initial section (the distance required being smaller the greater the speed or the smaller the kinematic viscosity), as in the simpler solution of § 53.

If the coefficients in the expansion of u at the initial section satisfy (124), so that

$$u = \alpha_1 y - \pi_0 \frac{y^2}{2!} + \alpha_4 \frac{y^4}{4!} - 2\alpha_1 \pi_1 \frac{y^5}{5!} + 2\pi_0 \pi_1 \frac{y^6}{6!} + \alpha_7 \frac{y^7}{7!} + \cdots, \tag{128}$$

a solution free from singularities may be obtained. In particular,‡

$$\left(\frac{\partial u}{\partial y} \right)_{y=0} = \alpha_1 + \frac{\alpha_4}{\alpha_1} x + \frac{\alpha_1 \alpha_7 + \alpha_4^2}{8\alpha_1^3} x^2 + \cdots, \tag{129}$$

so that if the expansion of u in the form (128) is known for any section, the skin-friction for a short distance downstream can be found by multiplying (129) by the viscosity μ.

Alternative step-by-step methods are provided by equations (19) and (22). In equation (19) z, equal to $u_1^2 - u^2$, where u_1 is the velocity just outside the

† Goldstein, *Proc. Camb. Phil. Soc.* **26** (1930), 1–18. The form of the solution if the expansion of u at the initial section begins with a constant term $(u = \alpha_0 + \alpha_1 y + \cdots)$, or with a multiple of $y^2 \left(u = \alpha_2 \frac{y^2}{2!} + \alpha_3 \frac{y^3}{3!} + \cdots \right)$, is also considered in the paper cited. In the former case a previously disturbed stream flows along a solid surface with a leading edge, such as the flat plate of § 53; in the latter case the initial section is taken at a position of separation of the forward flow.

‡ Goldstein, *op. cit.*, p. 4.

boundary layer, is expressed as a function of x and the stream-function ψ; and from the value of $\partial z/\partial x$ given by (19) it follows that

$$z(x+\Delta x,\psi)-z(x,\psi) = \nu\Delta x\{u_1^2(x)-z(x,\psi)\}^{\frac{1}{2}}\frac{\partial^2}{\partial\psi^2}z(x,\psi), \tag{130}$$

approximately. If z is known as a function of ψ for any value of x, the values at $x+\Delta x$ may theoretically be found by this formula; but the numerical double differentiation on the right presents difficulties because of the inaccuracy involved in the process. This difficulty can be avoided by taking the value of the right-hand side at $x+\Delta x$ instead of at x, when (130) becomes a non-linear second-order differential equation for $z(x+\Delta x,\psi)$. It is considerably easier, and probably not less accurate, to change x into $x+\Delta x$ only in $\partial^2 z/\partial\psi^2$ on the right-hand side, and to leave the expression in brackets unaltered. The equation to be solved for $z(x+\Delta x,\psi)$ is then the linear equation

$$z(x+\Delta x,\psi)-z(x,\psi) = \nu\Delta x\{u_1^2(x)-z(x,\psi)\}^{\frac{1}{2}}\frac{\partial^2}{\partial\psi^2}z(x+\Delta x,\psi), \tag{131}$$

the boundary conditions being $z(x+\Delta x,\psi) = 0$ when $\psi = \infty$ and

$$z(x+\Delta x,\psi) = u_1^2 \quad \text{when} \quad \psi = 0.$$

The difficulty connected with the fact that the equation has a singular point at $\psi = 0$ can be overcome by using the methods outlined above for an initial velocity distribution given by either (122) or (128). Corresponding values of ψ, z (equal to $u_1^2-u^2$), and $\partial z/\partial\psi$ (equal to $-2\partial u/\partial y$) in the neighbourhood of $\psi = 0$ at $x+\Delta x$ may thus be found. The method has been employed by Luckert[†] to calculate the velocity distribution in the wake downstream from the rear edge of a plate of finite length and at zero incidence: in this case, since u does not vanish along the middle line of the wake, the difficulty of the singularity at $\psi = 0$ does not enter.

When z, and therefore u, has been found as a function of x and ψ in this way, it is necessary, in order to express u as a function of x and y, to connect ψ and y by the relation

$$y = \int_0^\psi \frac{d\psi}{u}, \tag{132}$$

the lower limit of the integral being zero since y and ψ vanish together.

It is doubtful whether the actual numerical work involved in using (19) in this way is not greater than that involved in working direct from (22), although the theory of the method of using (19) may be expressed more neatly than that of using (22). One method of using (22) is first to find u, $\partial u/\partial y$, and $\partial^2 u/\partial y^2$ at $y = 0$ at $x+\Delta x$ by considering the initial velocity distributions to be given by either (122) or (128) above; and to find values of $\partial^2 u/\partial y^2$ at $x+\Delta x$ for various values of y by extrapolation of the values upstream, and hence $\partial u/\partial y$ and u at $x+\Delta x$ by integration. These extrapolated values can then be used in (22) to find $\dfrac{\partial}{\partial x}u(x+\Delta x,y)$. The extrapolated values of $\partial^2 u/\partial y^2$ are then varied until

$$u(x+\Delta x,y)-u(x,y) = \Delta x\frac{\partial}{\partial x}u(x+\Delta x,y). \tag{133}$$

[†] *Berlin Dissertation* (1933). (See also Chap. XIII, § 248.) An account of the method is given by Howarth *A.R.C. Reports and Memoranda*, No. 1632 (1935), 33–36.

The terms of these equations are sensitive to small variations in the extrapolated values of $\partial^2 u/\partial y^2$, and the required correction can usually be found at the first or second trial. The extrapolated values are corrected in steps for y ($y = \epsilon$, $y = 2\epsilon$, $y = 3\epsilon$, and so on, where ϵ is suitably chosen) in order.[†]

It may be added that the step-by-step method of solving partial differential equations, together with the method of correcting for the finite length of each step, which has been used by Hartree,[‡] may be applied to the equations of steady boundary layer motion; and the integrations may be performed on an integrating machine of Bush's type (a machine specially devised for obtaining solutions of differential equations).

60. Approximate methods of calculating steady two-dimensional boundary layer flow. Application of the momentum equation.

The method of using the momentum equation (33) or (38) has been described on p. 134. The boundary conditions (41) are (for steady flow) satisfied by

$$u/u_1 = f(\eta),$$

where

$$\eta = y/\delta, \qquad\qquad (134)$$

if

$$f(1) = 1, \qquad f'(1) = f''(1) = f'''(1) = \dots = 0,$$
$$f(0) = 0, \qquad f''(0) = -\Lambda, \qquad f'''(0) = 0,\dots \qquad (135)$$

where

$$\Lambda = -\frac{\delta^2}{\nu\rho u_1}\frac{\partial p}{\partial x} = \frac{\delta^2}{\nu}\frac{du_1}{dx}. \qquad (136)$$

The skin-friction, τ_0, displacement thickness, δ_1 (equation (36)), and momentum thickness, ϑ (equation (37)), are then given by

$$\frac{\tau_0}{\rho u_1^2} = \frac{\nu}{u_1\delta}f'(0),$$
$$\delta_1 = \delta \int_0^1 (1-f)\,d\eta, \qquad (137)$$
$$\vartheta = \delta \int_0^1 (f-f^2)\,d\eta.$$

If the pressure gradient is zero ($\partial p/\partial x = 0$, $du_1/dx = 0$), then $\Lambda = 0$ and f depends only on η. The momentum equation (38) becomes

$$\frac{\tau_0}{\rho u_1^2} = \frac{d\vartheta}{dx}, \qquad (138)$$

[†] Howarth, *op cit.*, pp. 27–33.
[‡] Hartree and Womersley, *Proc. Roy. Soc.* A, **161** (1937), 353–366.

or
$$\frac{\nu}{u_1 \delta} f'(0) = \frac{d\delta}{dx} \int_0^1 (f - f^2)\, d\eta. \tag{139}$$

If $\delta = 0$ when $x = 0$, the integral of this equation is

$$\frac{2\nu}{u_1} f'(0) x = \delta^2 \int_0^1 (f - f^2)\, d\eta. \tag{140}$$

Hence by assuming various forms for f consistent with (135), we have from (140) and (137) approximate values of δ, τ_0, δ_1, and ϑ for the flow along a flat plate at zero incidence, x being measured from the leading edge. An accurate solution of the boundary layer equations for this motion was obtained in § 53.

Following Pohlhausen,[†] we may take f to be a polynomial of degree one, two, three or four respectively. A polynomial of degree one can be taken to satisfy the conditions $f(1) = 1$, $f(0) = 0$ only; for a polynomial of degree two we may also impose the condition $f'(1) = 0$; and as the degree increases we may impose the additional conditions $f''(0) = 0$, $f''(1) = 0$ in turn. Another form for f has been suggested by Lamb,[‡] who takes $f = \sin \frac{1}{2}\pi\eta$. This form satisfies the conditions $f(1) = 1$, $f(0) = 0$, $f'(1) = 0$, $f''(0) = 0$.

Whatever the form assumed for f,

$$\frac{\tau_0}{\rho u_1^2}\left(\frac{u_1 x}{\nu}\right)^{\frac{1}{2}}, \qquad \delta\left(\frac{u_1}{\nu x}\right)^{\frac{1}{2}}, \qquad \delta_1\left(\frac{u_1}{\nu x}\right)^{\frac{1}{2}}, \qquad \vartheta\left(\frac{u_1}{\nu x}\right)^{\frac{1}{2}}$$

are numerical constants: the values of the first three, with the forms assumed for f, are shown below. It follows from (138) that

$$\vartheta(u_1/\nu x)^{\frac{1}{2}} = 2(\tau_0/\rho u_1^2)(u_1 x/\nu)^{\frac{1}{2}}. \tag{141}$$

f	$\dfrac{\tau_0}{\rho u_1^2}\left(\dfrac{u_1 x}{\nu}\right)^{\frac{1}{2}}$	$\delta\left(\dfrac{u_1}{\nu x}\right)^{\frac{1}{2}}$	$\delta_1\left(\dfrac{u_1}{\nu x}\right)^{\frac{1}{2}}$
η	0·289	3·46	1·73
$2\eta - \eta^2$	0·365	5·48	1·83
$\frac{3}{2}\eta - \frac{1}{2}\eta^3$	0·323	4·64	1·74
$2\eta - 2\eta^3 + \eta^4$	0·343	5·83	1·75
$\sin \frac{1}{2}\pi\eta$	0·328	4·79	1·74
Exact solution	0·332	..	1·72

The polynomials of degree three and four, and the trigonometric form, give good approximations to τ_0, the errors being 2·7 per cent.,

† *Zeitschr. f. angew. Math. u. Mech.* **1** (1921), 257–261.
‡ *Hydrodynamics* (Cambridge, 1932), p. 686.

3·3 per cent., 1·2 per cent. respectively.† The values of δ_1 are also satisfactory. No definite value of δ is given by the exact solution, and the values from the approximate solutions change considerably with the form assumed for f. In the approximate solution δ is to be regarded as a convenient parameter rather than as a dependent

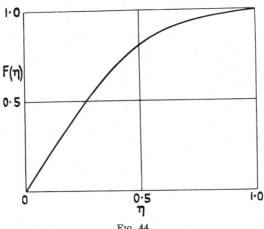

FIG. 44.

variable whose value is sought, the quantities regarded as being obtained from the approximate solution being τ_0, δ_1 and ϑ. The value of δ will be significant only as regards order of magnitude.

For the approximate solution of more general problems it has been usual to take f as a polynomial of degree four, since for zero pressure gradient it was found that no accuracy was gained by considering a polynomial of higher degree. With the boundary conditions $f(1) = 1$, $f(0) = 0$, $f'(1) = 0$, $f''(0) = -\Lambda$, $f''(1) = 0$, where Λ is the non-dimensional parameter defined in (136), we find that

$$u/u_1 = f = F(\eta) + \Lambda G(\eta), \qquad (142)$$

where $\qquad F(\eta) = 2\eta - 2\eta^3 + \eta^4, \qquad G(\eta) = \tfrac{1}{6}\eta(1-\eta)^3. \qquad (143)$

(See Figs. 44 and 45.)

† W. G. L. Sutton (*Phil. Mag.* (7), **23** (1937), 1146–1152) uses, in addition to the momentum equation, the integral relation obtained by multiplying the equation of motion by u and then integrating across the boundary layer. For zero pressure gradient, with a polynomial of degree four for u/u_1, the condition $\partial^2 u/\partial y^2 = 0$ at $y = 0$ is abandoned: so another parameter, in addition to δ, must be introduced, and both parameters are found by the use of the two integral relations. The resulting velocity distribution ($f = 1-(1-\eta)^3 - 1\cdot143\eta(1-\eta)^3$) is close to the exact solution, δ is $5\cdot603(\nu x/u_1)^{\frac{1}{2}}$ and $\tau_0/(\rho u_1^2)$ is $0\cdot3314(u_1 x/\nu)^{-\frac{1}{2}}$.

Thus, according to the approximations of this method, the velocity distributions across sections of the boundary layer, when expressed non-dimensionally, are all represented by a one-parameter family of curves. Moreover, the velocity distribution at any section depends on the velocity gradient just outside the boundary layer at that section only, being affected by the state of affairs upstream only in so far as this affects δ.

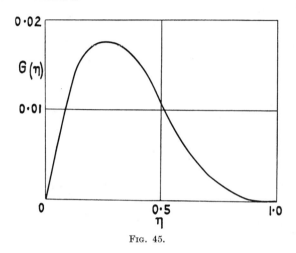

FIG. 45.

It follows from (137) and (142) that

$$
\left.
\begin{aligned}
\frac{\tau_0}{\rho u_1^2} &= \frac{\nu}{u_1 \delta}\,(2+\tfrac{1}{6}\Lambda), \\[2mm]
\delta_1 &= \frac{\delta}{120}\,(36-\Lambda), \\[2mm]
\vartheta &= \frac{\delta}{315}\left(37-\frac{\Lambda}{3}-\frac{5\Lambda^2}{144}\right).
\end{aligned}
\right\}
\tag{144}
$$

Separation of the forward flow occurs when τ_0 vanishes and changes sign. The value of Λ at the position of separation is therefore -12.

By substitution into the momentum equation (33) or (38) we finally arrive at the equation

$$
Z' = \frac{g(\Lambda)}{u_1} + Z^2 u_1'' h(\Lambda),
\tag{145}
$$

where dashes denote differentiation with respect to x,

$$
Z = \delta^2/\nu = \Lambda/u_1',
\tag{146}
$$

and

$$g(\Lambda) = \frac{15120 - 2784\Lambda + 79\Lambda^2 + \tfrac{5}{3}\Lambda^3}{(12-\Lambda)(37+\tfrac{25}{12}\Lambda)},$$

$$h(\Lambda) = \frac{8+\tfrac{5}{3}\Lambda}{(12-\Lambda)(37+\tfrac{25}{12}\Lambda)}.$$

$$\left.\begin{array}{r}\\ \\ \end{array}\right\} \qquad (147)$$

The functions $g(\Lambda)$ and $h(\Lambda)$ are tabulated below.†

TABLE 6

Λ	$g(\Lambda)$	$h(\Lambda)$
12·0	∞	∞
11·0	−62·20	0·4395
10·0	−27·25	0·2133
9·0	−13·88	0·1375
8·0	− 5·80	0·0994
7·8	− 4·46	0·0939
7·6	− 3·20	0·0889
7·4	− 1·99	0·0843
7·2	− 0·831	0·0801
7·052	0·00	0·0772
6·8	+ 1·37	0·0727
6·6	2·43	0·0693
6.4	3·46	0·0662
6·2	4·47	0·0633
6·0	5·45	0·0606
5·0	10·19	0·0492
4·0	14·76	0·0404
3·0	19·40	0·0334
2·0	24·00	0·0275
+ 1·0	28·88	0·0225
0·0	34·05	0·0180
− 1·0	39·61	0·0140
− 2·0	45·66	0·0102
− 3·0	52·33	0·0065
− 4·0	59·77	+0·0029
− 5·0	68·17	−0·00074
− 6·0	77·81	−0·0045
− 7·0	88·95	−0·0085
− 8·0	102·28	−0·0131
− 9·0	118·36	−0·0183
−10·0	138·31	−0·0244
−11·0	163·88	−0·0319
−12·0	198·00	−0·0417

For flow in a boundary layer at the surface of a cylindrical obstacle in a stream, u_1 vanishes at the forward stagnation point; and since

† Equation (145) may also be expressed as an equation for Λ:

$$\Lambda' = \frac{u_1'}{u_1}g(\Lambda) + \frac{u_1''}{u_1'}\{\Lambda^2 h(\Lambda) + \Lambda\}.$$

At the pressure minimum in flow past an obstacle $u_1' = 0$ and $\Lambda = 0$, and this equation has a singular point.

Z' must remain finite, $g(\Lambda)$ must vanish there. The zeros of $g(\Lambda)$ are 7·052, 17·75, and −70. Since u_1', and therefore Λ, is positive, the negative zero is irrelevant. It appears that the relevant zero is 7·052. If Λ were equal to 17·75 at the forward stagnation point, it would always pass through the value 12, where the denominator of $g(\Lambda)$ or $h(\Lambda)$ vanishes and Z' becomes infinite, before the position of minimum velocity ($u_1' = 0$, $\Lambda = 0$) is reached.

Moreover, x being measured from the forward stagnation point, the value of Z' at $x = 0$ is given by

$$Z' = \lim_{x \to 0}\left[\frac{g(\Lambda)}{u_1} + Z^2 u_1'' h(\Lambda)\right]$$

$$= \lim_{x \to 0}\left[\frac{g'(\Lambda)\Lambda'}{u_1'} + \frac{u_1''}{u_1'^2}\Lambda^2 h(\Lambda)\right]$$

$$= \lim_{x \to 0}\left[g'(\Lambda)\left\{Z' + \Lambda\frac{u_1''}{u_1'^2}\right\} + \frac{u_1''}{u_1'^2}\Lambda^2 h(\Lambda)\right],$$

whence $\qquad\qquad Z' = -5\cdot391 u_1''/u_1'^2 \qquad\qquad$ (148)

at the forward stagnation point. This value is required for the numerical or graphical integration of (145). Λ (and therefore Z) and Z' being known at $x = 0$, (145) can now be integrated numerically or graphically for any special case.†

Even with the value 7·052 for Λ at the forward stagnation point, Λ may become equal to 12. In such a case the method ceases to give results, and a modified method must be applied over a range of values of x commencing before the point where Λ becomes equal to 12. One such modification has been described by Dryden.‡ For details reference may be made to the original paper or to Howarth's report (*op. cit.*).

Pohlhausen applied his approximate method to Hiemenz's values of u_1 for a circular cylinder, as given by the formula (114) and the values of β_1, β_3, β_5 on p. 150, and found separation at 82° from the forward stagnation point. To the nearest degree this is the same value as Hiemenz found by the method of series: in fact, the difference between the two results for the position of separation is only 26'. It is to be remarked, however, that, according to the curves

---

† The method is due to Pohlhausen, *Zeitschr. f. angew. Math. u. Mech.* **1** (1921), 261–263. It is further considered and systematized in Howarth's report (*A.R.C. Reports and Memoranda*, No. 1632 (1935), 14–22), from which Table 6 is reproduced. $g(\Lambda)$ and $h(\Lambda)$ are denoted by $f(\lambda)$ and $g(\lambda)$ respectively in that report.

‡ *N.A.C.A. Report* No. 497 (1934).

of u/u_1 at various sections drawn by Howarth in his report (*op. cit.*), the velocity distributions given by this approximate method begin to depart quite substantially from the more accurate ones given by the method of series at about the pressure minimum, and depart more and more as the position of separation is approached. Moreover, the pressure minimum occurs about 70° from the forward stagnation point, and there is only about 12° before the position of separation is reached. Consequently this example is not a satisfactory test of the present approximate method even as regards locating the position of separation. A much more severe test was applied by Schubauer,† who measured the pressure distribution at an elliptic cylinder of fineness ratio 2·96:1, with its major axis in the direction of the undisturbed stream, and applied Pohlhausen's method to the observed pressure distribution. The distance from the forward stagnation point being expressed as a multiple x of the minor axis of the ellipse, the pressure minimum is at $x = 1·30$. Separation was observed at $x = 1·99$, whilst the calculations by Pohlhausen's method indicated no separation at all. The velocity distributions given by Pohlhausen's method agreed fairly well with experiment over about five-sevenths of the way between the pressure minimum and the observed point of separation, but thereafter diverged more and more. It must be added that in order to prevent a transition to turbulence in the boundary layer before the point of separation the Reynolds number of Schubauer's experiment was rather low; the boundary layer thickness was therefore fairly large, and the pressure gradient across the layer (needed to balance the centrifugal force) produced an appreciable pressure drop between the outside of the layer and the surface. Since this drop varied round the surface, a fundamental assumption of the boundary layer theory was to this extent violated, so that some discrepancy is to be expected between the experimental results and even an accurate solution of the boundary layer equations.‡ However, the comparison of observed values with those calculated by Pohlhausen's method leaves no doubt that that method is inadequate in a region of retarded flow, giving values of the skin-friction which are systematically too high, and consequently the calculated separation occurs either too late or not at all.

† *N.A.C.A. Report* No. 527 (1935).
‡ Howarth, *Proc. Roy. Soc.* A, **164** (1938), 575, 576.

It appears that the use of the momentum equation in the manner considered in this paragraph, which has the great merit of being comparatively easy, may be expected to give fairly satisfactory results in a region where the flow just outside the boundary layer is being accelerated. But in a region of retarded flow the results will get less and less reliable as the point of separation is approached; and the position of that point will not be obtained with anything approaching sufficient accuracy unless it occurs very shortly after the pressure minimum.

It remains to add that the momentum equation has been applied by Tollmien† to a case of variable flow (development of the boundary layer in flow past a rotating cylinder, when the motion is started from rest).

61. Application of the momentum equation for steady flow in the boundary layer at the surface of a solid of revolution.

The momentum equation for flow in a boundary layer at the surface of a solid of revolution with its axis in the direction of the undisturbed stream was given in equation (40), and it was remarked that it differed from the equation (33) for two-dimensional flow only by a term

$$\frac{r_0'}{r_0}\left[u_1 \int_0^\delta \rho u \, dy - \int_0^\delta \rho u^2 \, dy \right],$$

where r_0 is the distance of a point on the surface of the body from the axis of revolution, and the dash indicates differentiation with respect to x, which is measured from the forward stagnation point along a meridian curve. If ϑ is formally defined as in equation (37), this extra term is $(r_0'/r_0)(\rho u_1^2 \vartheta)$, so that the equation (38) may still formally be applied if $r_0' \vartheta/r_0$ is added to the right-hand side. Moreover, the boundary conditions to be applied to u are the same as in the two-dimensional case, so that if u is represented by a polynomial of the fourth degree, the equations (142), (143), and (144) will still apply. The value of Λ at the position of separation is again -12. On account of the extra term (145) is replaced by

$$Z' = \frac{g(\Lambda)}{u_1} + Z^2 u_1'' h(\Lambda) - \frac{r_0'}{r_0} \frac{1}{u_1} h^*(\Lambda), \qquad (149)$$

† *Göttingen Dissertation*, 1924.

where $g(\Lambda)$ and $h(\Lambda)$ are the same functions as before, and

$$h^*(\Lambda) = \frac{888\Lambda - 8\Lambda^2 - \frac{5}{6}\Lambda^3}{(12-\Lambda)(37+\frac{25}{12}\Lambda)} \qquad (150)$$

and is tabulated below.

TABLE 7

Λ	$h^*(\Lambda)$
5·0	12·46
4·71601	11·50
4·5	10·805
4·0	9·294
3·0	6·601
2·0	4·220
+ 1·0	+ 2·045
0·0	0·000
− 1·0	− 1·972
− 2·0	− 3·919
− 3·0	− 5·883
− 4·0	− 7·907
− 5·0	−10·037
− 6·0	−12·33
− 7·0	−14·84
− 8·0	−17·68
− 9·0	−20·96
−10·0	−24·87
−11·0	−29·72
−12·0	−36·00

At the forward stagnation point u_1 and r_0 vanish. For a blunt-nosed body r_0' is equal to 1 (cf. eq. (24)), and u_1/r_0 stays finite and is equal in the limit, when u_1 and r_0 both tend to zero, to u_1'. Hence $r_0' u_1/r_0 u_1' \to 1$; and in order that Z' may stay finite, $g(\Lambda) - h^*(\Lambda) = 0$ at the forward stagnation point. This cubic equation has one negative root, which is irrelevant since Λ must be positive, and two positive roots, 4·71601 and 21·14, of which the smaller is selected for the same reason as in the case of two-dimensional flow. The limiting value of Z' at $x = 0$ is found as before, and is $-3·420u_1''/u_1'^2$. If r_0 is a given function of x, the equation (149) may now be integrated numerically or graphically for any special case.†

62. Approximate methods of calculating steady two-dimensional boundary layer flow. Outer and inner approximate solutions.

For flow in a region where the pressure gradient is adverse an application of the momentum equation gives unreliable results,

† Tomotika, *A.R.C. Reports and Memoranda*, No. 1678 (1936). A parabolic velocity distribution was assumed by C. B. Millikan, *Trans. Amer. Soc. Mechanical Engineers*, Applied Mechanics Section, **54** (1932), 29–34.

especially as the position of separation is approached; for a stream-line body the pressure distribution is such that the method of expansion in series is unusable; whilst step-by-step methods have, up to the present time, been found too laborious. Two other methods have been suggested for use especially in a region of re-tarded flow.

When the pressure gradient is adverse the graph of u against y has a point of inflexion, and in a method suggested by Kármán and Millikan† two different approximate solutions are found, one of which—the 'outer' solution—is applied in the region from the point of inflexion to the outside of the boundary layer, and the other—the 'inner' solution—in the region between the wall and the point of inflexion. At the pressure minimum the point of inflexion is at the wall (cf. eq. (16)), and it moves out from the wall farther down-stream. The inner solution therefore applies only in the region of retarded flow; in the region of accelerated flow the outer solution must be applied all the way to the wall.

The outer solution is obtained by approximating to the equation of steady motion in the form (19), namely,

$$\frac{\partial z}{\partial x} = \nu u \frac{\partial^2 z}{\partial \psi^2}, \tag{151}$$

where‡
$$z = u_1^2 - u^2. \tag{152}$$

Since
$$\frac{\partial^2 u}{\partial y^2} = -\tfrac{1}{2} u \frac{\partial^2 z}{\partial \psi^2}, \tag{153}$$

the point of inflexion is given by $\partial^2 z/\partial \psi^2 = 0$. In place of x the variable ϕ, defined by

$$\phi = \int_0^x u_1 \, dx, \tag{154}$$

is introduced, and from the given pressure or velocity distribution outside the boundary layer u_1^2 must be found as a function of ϕ. Equation (151) takes the form

$$\frac{\partial z}{\partial \phi} = \nu \frac{u}{u_1} \frac{\partial^2 z}{\partial \psi^2} = \nu \left(1 - \frac{z}{u_1^2}\right)^{\tfrac{1}{2}} \frac{\partial^2 z}{\partial \psi^2}. \tag{155}$$

The boundary conditions for z are $z = u_1^2$ at $\psi = 0$, $z \to 0$ when

† *N.A.C.A. Report* No. 504 (1934).

‡ Kármán and Millikan use z to denote $\tfrac{1}{2}(u_1^2 - u^2)$. In consequence the functions g defined below have twice their values as defined by these authors.

$\psi \to \infty$, and z given at $\phi = 0$. In view of the condition at infinity we take the equation in the approximate form

$$\frac{\partial z}{\partial \phi} = \nu \frac{\partial^2 z}{\partial \psi^2} \qquad (156)$$

for the outer solution.† This equation is exact both at $\psi = \infty$ and at the point of inflexion ($\partial^2 z/\partial \psi^2 = 0$); it is for this reason that the outer solution is applied from the point of inflexion outwards. The equation (156) has the same form as the equation for the temperature in the theory of the conduction of heat, and all the known solutions and methods of solution may be applied. In particular, if u_1^2 can be expressed as a polynomial:

$$u_1^2 = \sum_{m=1}^{n} b_m \phi^m, \qquad (157)$$

the solution is given by

$$z = b_0 g_0(\eta) + \sum_{m=1}^{n} b_m \phi^m \left[\sum_{r=0}^{m} \frac{m!}{r!\,(m-r)!} g_r(\eta) \right], \qquad (158)$$

where‡

$$\eta = \frac{\psi}{2(\nu\phi)^{\frac{1}{2}}}, \qquad (159)$$

and, with

$$\operatorname{erf} \eta = \frac{2}{\sqrt{\pi}} \int_0^{\eta} e^{-\alpha^2}\, d\alpha, \qquad (160)$$

the functions g are given by

$$g_0 = 1 - \operatorname{erf} \eta,$$

$$g_1 = -\frac{2}{\sqrt{\pi}}\, \eta e^{-\eta^2} + 2\eta^2 (1 - \operatorname{erf} \eta),$$

$$g_2 = \frac{2\eta}{3\sqrt{\pi}}(1 - 2\eta^2)e^{-\eta^2} + \tfrac{4}{3}\eta^4(1 - \operatorname{erf} \eta),$$

$$g_3 = -\frac{2\eta}{15\sqrt{\pi}}(3 - 2\eta^2 + 4\eta^5)e^{-\eta^2} + \tfrac{8}{15}\eta^6(1 - \operatorname{erf} \eta),$$

and, in general, for $r \geqslant 2$,

$$g_r = \frac{(r-1)!}{(2r-1)!}\left\{ \frac{(-1)^r}{\sqrt{\pi}}\, \eta e^{-\eta^2} \sum_{i=0}^{r-2} (-1)^i 2^{2i+2} \frac{(2r-2i-3)!}{(r-i-2)!}\eta^{2i} \right.$$

$$\left. -\frac{2^{2r-1}}{\sqrt{\pi}}\eta^{2r-1}e^{-\eta^2} + 2^{2r-1}\eta^{2r}(1 - \operatorname{erf} \eta) \right\}.$$

$$(161)$$

† With x and y as the independent variables this equation corresponds to

$$u\frac{\partial u}{\partial x} + v\frac{\partial u}{\partial y} = u_1 \frac{du_1}{dx} + \nu\frac{u_1}{u}\frac{\partial^2 u}{\partial y^2}.$$

‡ The definition of η in this section should be noted, since η has been used differently in previous sections.

(The error function, erf x, is tabulated.†) The solution (158), which may be found by known methods, makes $z = u_1^2$ at $\psi = 0$ and $z \to 0$ when $\eta \to \infty$. Since $\eta \to \infty$ when $\phi \to 0$, it holds if u is constant and equal to the value of u_1 at $\phi = 0$. In the most important case, $\phi = 0$ is at the forward stagnation point on the surface of a solid body, and $u = u_1 = 0$ at $\phi = 0$.

The representation (157) is too restricted for many purposes. A much wider application is obtained by approximating to u_1^2 by two polynomials, one in each of two different ranges of values of ϕ:

$$\left.\begin{array}{l} u_1^2 = \sum_{m=1}^{n} b_m \phi^m \quad (\phi \leqslant \phi_1), \\[2mm] = \sum_{m=1}^{N} B_m \phi^m \quad (\phi \geqslant \phi_1). \end{array}\right\} \tag{162}$$

For $\phi \leqslant \phi_1$ the solution is given by (158); for $\phi \geqslant \phi_1$ the solution is

$$z = z_1 - z_2 + z_3, \tag{163}$$

where z_1 is the value of z given in (158),

$$z_2 = b_0 g_0(\eta') + \sum_{m=1}^{n} b_m \left[\sum_{r=0}^{m} \frac{m!}{r!\,(m-r)!} g_r(\eta')\phi^{m-r}(\phi-\phi_1)^r \right], \tag{164}$$

z_3 is given by the same expression as z_2 with b_m and n replaced by B_m and N, the g's are the same functions as before, and

$$\eta' = \frac{\psi}{2[\nu(\phi-\phi_1)]^{\frac{1}{2}}}. \tag{165}$$

(The method of approximation, when applied to the flow with no pressure gradient along a plate at zero incidence (u_1 constant: see §53), leads to a value 0·282 for $(\tau_0/\rho u_1^2) \cdot (u_1 x/\nu)^{\frac{1}{2}}$, the accurate value being 0·332.‡)

When u_1 decreases as ϕ increases, the solution of (156) is used only for values of u equal to and greater than the value at the point of inflexion. The values of η, z, and $\partial z/\partial \eta$ at the point of inflexion ($\partial^2 z/\partial \eta^2 = 0$) are required, and since the value of η is usually fairly

---

† See, for example, Dale's *Mathematical Tables*, p. 84.

‡ A second approximation may be obtained by writing (155) in the form

$$\frac{\partial z}{\partial \phi} - \nu \frac{\partial^2 z}{\partial \psi^2} = \nu \frac{\partial^2 z}{\partial \psi^2} \left\{ \left(1 - \frac{z}{u_1^2}\right)^{\frac{1}{2}} - 1 \right\},$$

and substituting on the right-hand side the value found for the first approximation. The results are complicated, but the second approximation has been found by Kármán and Millikan for the simple problem of the flat plate at zero incidence, and they show a graph of the velocity for this second approximation which agrees rather well with the accurate solution.

small,† it may be found by expanding the functions g in (161) in powers of η. The outer and inner solutions are joined at the points of inflexion, and values there are denoted by a subscript j.

The inner solution is found by approximating to the equation for u^2 in terms of ϕ and ψ. Since $z = u_1^2 - u^2$,

$$\nu \frac{\partial^2}{\partial \psi^2}(u^2) = -\frac{2u_1^2 u_1'}{u}\left[1 - \frac{1}{2u_1 u_1'}\frac{\partial}{\partial \phi}(u^2)\right], \qquad (166)$$

where it is to be specially noted that the dash denotes differentiation with respect to ϕ. If the term $(2u_1 u_1')^{-1}\partial(u^2)/\partial\phi$ is replaced by a function of ϕ or u^2 alone, the equation (166) may be treated, for each value of ϕ, as an ordinary differential equation for u^2 in terms of ψ. At the wall $\partial(u^2)/\partial\phi = 0$; but if we simply neglect it in (166), the resulting solution gives values of $\partial^2(u^2)/\partial\psi^2$ which are of one sign for all values of ψ, and hence, since

$$\frac{\partial^2 u}{\partial y^2} = \tfrac{1}{2}u\frac{\partial^2}{\partial \psi^2}(u^2), \qquad (167)$$

there are no points of inflexion. Since the inner solution is to be joined to the outer solution at a point of inflexion, it is essential that $\partial^2(u^2)/\partial\psi^2$ should vanish when $u = u_j$, where u_j is the value of u at the point of inflexion as determined from the outer solution. Moreover, the function by which we replace $(2u_1 u_1')^{-1}\partial(u^2)/\partial\phi$ in (166) should vanish at the wall. Now u/u_j satisfies both these requirements, and leads to a solution in elementary functions.‡ Hence (166) is replaced by

$$\nu \frac{\partial^2}{\partial \psi^2}(u^2) = -\frac{2u_1^2 u_1'}{u}\left(1 - \frac{u}{u_j}\right), \qquad (168)$$

or, with η as defined in (159),

$$\frac{d^2}{d\eta^2}\left(\frac{u^2}{u_1^2}\right) = -\frac{8\phi u_1'}{u}\left(1 - \frac{u}{u_j}\right). \qquad (169)$$

† Since
$$y = \int_0^\psi \frac{d\psi}{u} = 2(\nu\phi)^{\frac{1}{2}}\int_0^\eta \frac{d\eta}{u}$$

(see equation (20)), and $u = 0$ at $\eta = 0$, a small value of η corresponds to a comparatively large value of $y/\nu^{\frac{1}{2}}$.

‡ $(u/u_j)^2$ also satisfies the above requirements, and has a double zero at the wall, but leads to the appearance of elliptic integrals in the solution. The results in the cases where both procedures—i.e. the substitution of u/u_j and of $(u/u_j)^2$—have been tested were found to be very similar, and so the procedure which leads to the simpler integral is adopted.

This equation integrates to

$$\frac{d}{d\eta}\left(\frac{u^2}{u_1^2}\right) = \frac{4}{u_1}(-u_1'\,u_j\,\phi)^{\frac{1}{2}}\left[C^2+2\frac{u}{u_j}-\left(\frac{u}{u_j}\right)^2\right]^{\frac{1}{2}}, \qquad (170)$$

where C^2 is a constant of integration whose value is

$$C^2 = \left[\frac{d}{d\eta}(u^2)\right]_{\eta=0}^{2}\Big/(-16u_1^2\,u_1'\,u_j\,\phi)$$

$$= \nu\left[\frac{\partial}{\partial\psi}(u^2)\right]_{\psi=0}^{2}\Big/(-4u_1^2\,u_1'\,u_j)$$

$$- \nu\left(\frac{\partial u}{\partial y}\right)_{y=0}^{2}\Big/(-u_1^2\,u_1'\,u_j). \qquad (171)$$

The equation (170) may be integrated again, with the condition $u = 0$ when $\eta = 0$, to give

$$\eta = \frac{u_j^{\frac{3}{2}}}{2u_1(-u_1'\,\phi)^{\frac{1}{2}}}\left\{C-\left[C^2+2\frac{u}{u_j}-\left(\frac{u}{u_j}\right)^2\right]^{\frac{1}{2}}\right.$$

$$\left. +\sin^{-1}\frac{1}{(1+C^2)^{\frac{1}{2}}}-\sin^{-1}\frac{1-u/u_j}{(1+C^2)^{\frac{1}{2}}}\right\}, \qquad (172)$$

but, as we shall see presently, this formula is not used in the final solution.

By putting $u = u_j$ in (170) we find

$$\left[\frac{d}{d\eta}(u^2)\right]_j = 4u_1(-u_1'\,u_j\,\phi)^{\frac{1}{2}}(C^2+1)^{\frac{1}{2}}. \qquad (173)$$

By putting $u = u_j$ in (172) we could also find the value of η_j from this solution. Now $d(u^2)/d\eta = -\partial z/\partial\eta$, and hence the values of $d(u^2)/d\eta$ and η at the point of inflexion ($u = u_j$) are known from the outer solution. We have already arranged that $d^2(u^2)/d\eta^2$ for the inner solution shall vanish at $u = u_j$; we now determine C so that $[d(u^2)/d\eta]_j$ for the inner solution, as given by (173), has the value determined from the outer solution. But then we cannot ensure that the value of η_j for the inner solution is equal to its value as determined from the outer solution. In fact (169) is a second-order differential equation: the conditions $u = 0$ at $\eta = 0$ and

$$d(u^2)/d\eta = [d(u^2)/d\eta]_j$$

at $u = u_j$ determine the solution completely. Thus of the four conditions we should like to impose at the join,

$$\eta = \eta_j, \qquad u = u_j, \qquad \frac{d}{d\eta}(u^2) = \left[\frac{d}{d\eta}(u^2)\right]_j, \qquad \frac{d^2}{d\eta^2}(u^2) = 0,$$

we can impose only the last three. Hence in the resulting graph of u^2 against η there is a discontinuity in η at $u = u_j$. When we come to find u in terms of y this difficulty is overcome, as we shall see, by a procedure which is effectively the same as displacing the outer solution parallel to the η-axis by an amount equal to the discontinuity.

To express u in terms of y for the inner solution $(u \leqslant u_j)$, we have, from equation (20),

$$y = \int_0^\psi \frac{d\psi}{u} = 2(\nu\phi)^{\frac{1}{2}} \int_0^\eta \frac{d\eta}{u} \tag{174}$$

$$= \frac{1}{u_1}\left(\frac{\nu}{-u_1'u_j}\right)^{\frac{1}{2}} \int_0^u \left[C^2 + 2\frac{u}{u_j} - \left(\frac{u}{u_j}\right)^2\right]^{-\frac{1}{2}} du, \tag{175}$$

the last expression being obtained from equation (170). Hence, for $u \leqslant u_j$, we find by performing the integration in (175) and inverting,

$$u/u_j = 1 - (1+C^2)^{\frac{1}{2}} \sin\{\sin^{-1}(1+C^2)^{-\frac{1}{2}} - u_1(-u_1'/\nu u_j)^{\frac{1}{2}}y\}, \tag{176}$$

u_j being determined from the outer solution and C by making $d(u^2)/d\eta$ continuous at the join as previously explained.

For the outer solution $(u \geqslant u_j)$ we have

$$u/u_1 = (1 - z/u_1^2)^{\frac{1}{2}}, \tag{177}$$

where z is given by (158) or (163), for example. This gives u in terms of η, and to connect u and y we express y in terms of η by the formula

$$y = \frac{1}{u_1}\left(\frac{\nu u_j}{-u_1'}\right)^{\frac{1}{2}} \sin^{-1}(1+C^2)^{-\frac{1}{2}} + 2(\nu\phi)^{\frac{1}{2}} \int_{\eta_j}^\eta \frac{d\eta}{(u_1^2 - z)^{\frac{1}{2}}}. \tag{178}$$

The first term is the value of y at the join as determined from (176). In the lower limit of the integral in the second term the value of η_j is to be taken from the outer solution. This is effectively the same as taking the value from the inner solution and supposing the curve of z against η displaced parallel to the η-axis through a distance equal to the difference of the two values.

From the final formulae it is apparent that the value of η for the inner solution is not required, except to check that the discontinuity in η is small. In the cases in which it has been calculated it is found that the discontinuity is a very small fraction of the value of η

which corresponds to the boundary layer thickness δ, as determined by taking $y = \delta$ where $u/u_1 = 0.995$.

The solution is now complete. Although the procedure adopted is complicated, the results are comparatively easy to apply since most of the formulae are given explicitly.

It remains to determine the position of the point of separation. From (171) we see that $C = 0$ at separation: hence from (173)

$$\left[\frac{d}{d\eta}(u^2)\right]_j = 4u_1(-u_1' u_j \phi)^{\frac{1}{2}} \qquad (179)$$

at separation, and this is equal to $-(\partial z/\partial \eta)_j$, which, together with u_j, is determined from the outer solution. Hence (179) is an equation to determine the value, ϕ_s, of ϕ at separation.

The method was applied by Kármán and Millikan (*loc. cit.*) to solve the problem in which

$$u_1 = \beta_0 - \beta_1 x, \qquad u_1^2 = \beta_0^2 - 2\beta_1 \phi. \qquad (180)$$

This corresponds to flow along a flat plate against a linearly decreasing adverse pressure gradient, with a constant value of u for all values of y at the leading edge. Separation was found to occur at $\beta_1 x/\beta_0 = 0.102$, whereas the value given by the use of the momentum equation with a quartic expression for the velocity (equation (145)) is 0.156. At separation, the boundary layer thickness, δ, defined as the value of y for which $u/u_1 = 0.995$, is given by $\delta(\beta_1/\nu)^{\frac{1}{2}} = 2.43$, and the Reynolds number $R_\delta (= u_1 \delta/\nu)$ by $(\beta_1 \nu)^{\frac{1}{2}} R_\delta/\beta_0 = 2.18$. The corresponding numbers for the solution from the momentum equation are 3.46 and 2.92 respectively.

A solution of the same problem by a method of expansion in series, which we shall consider more fully in the following section, gave $\beta_1 x/\beta_0 = 0.120$ at separation, compared with the value 0.102 from the method of outer and inner solutions, and 0.156 from the momentum equation. Of these three methods, that of expansion in series (in spite of the slowness of the convergence) is almost certainly the most accurate. If the result given by it be taken as correct, then the method of outer and inner solutions gives an answer 15 per cent. in error, and the use of the momentum equation an answer 30 per cent. in error. Whether the percentage errors in other problems (reckoned as percentages of the distance between the pressure minimum and the point of separation, for example) will be of the same order of magnitude, remains to be decided.

Millikan† and von Doenhoff‡ have applied the method of outer and inner solutions to the pressure distribution measured by Schubauer at an elliptic cylinder (p. 162). Millikan approximates to u_1^2 by two different cubics in ϕ for two ranges of values of ϕ, while von Doenhoff uses two quadratics. With the distance from the forward stagnation point expressed as a multiple x of the minor axis, Millikan finds

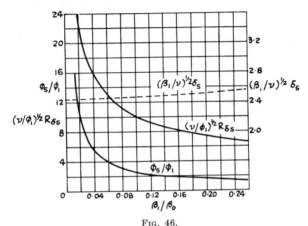

FIG. 46.

separation at $x = 1\cdot88$ and von Doenhoff at $x = 1\cdot92$, compared with an observed value $1\cdot99$ and no separation at all by Pohlhausen's method. The pressure minimum is at $x = 1\cdot30$.

Kármán and Millikan (*loc. cit.*) have also considered by their method the problem in which the graph of u_1 against x or u_1^2 against ϕ is composed of two straight lines:

$$
\begin{aligned}
u_1 &= \beta_0 x & (0 \leqslant x \leqslant x_1) \\
&= (\beta_0+\beta_1)x_1-\beta_1 x & (x \geqslant x_1), \\
\phi &= \tfrac{1}{2}\beta_0 x^2 & (0 \leqslant x \leqslant x_1) \\
&= -\tfrac{1}{2}(\beta_0+\beta_1)x_1^2+(\beta_0+\beta_1)xx_1-\tfrac{1}{2}\beta_1 x^2 & (x \geqslant x_1), \\
u_1^2 &= 2\beta_0\phi & (0 \leqslant \phi \leqslant \phi_1) \\
&= 2(\beta_0+\beta_1)\phi_1-2\beta_1\phi & (\phi \geqslant \phi_1), \\
\phi_1 &= \tfrac{1}{2}\beta_0 x_1^2.
\end{aligned}
\quad\Bigg\} \quad (181)
$$

This represents in certain circumstances a first, very rough, approximation to the velocity distribution outside the boundary layer at

† *Journ. Aero. Sciences*, **3** (1936), 91–94.
‡ *N.A.C.A. Technical Note* No. 544 (1935).

an aerofoil section. If the suffix s denotes values at separation, then ϕ_s/ϕ_1, $(\beta_1/\nu)^{\frac{1}{2}}\delta_s$ and $(\nu/\phi_1)^{\frac{1}{2}}R_{\delta_s}$ are functions of β_1/β_0 only, where δ is the boundary layer thickness (defined as the value of y for which $u/u_1 = 0.995$) and $R_\delta = u_1\,\delta/\nu$. The results obtained are reproduced in Fig. 46.

63. Approximate methods of calculating steady two-dimensional boundary layer flow. Application of the solution with a linear pressure gradient.

If
$$u_1 = \beta_0 - \beta_1 x, \tag{182}$$
with $u = u_1 = \beta_0$ at $x = 0$, then

$$-\frac{1}{\rho}\frac{\partial p}{\partial x} = -\beta_1(\beta_0 - \beta_1 x), \tag{183}$$

and the equation of motion is

$$u\frac{\partial u}{\partial x} + v\frac{\partial u}{\partial y} = -\beta_1(\beta_0 - \beta_1 x) + \nu\frac{\partial^2 u}{\partial y^2}. \tag{184}$$

This equation may be solved in series. Write

$$\left.\begin{array}{l} \xi = \beta_1 x/\beta_0, \qquad \eta = \tfrac{1}{2}(\beta_0/\nu x)^{\frac{1}{2}}y = \tfrac{1}{2}(\beta_1/\nu\xi)^{\frac{1}{2}}y, \\ \psi = (\nu\beta_0 x)^{\frac{1}{2}}f(\xi, \eta) = (\nu\beta_0 x)^{\frac{1}{2}}\{f_0(\eta) - 8\xi f_1(\eta) + (8\xi)^2 f_2(\eta) - ...\}, \end{array}\right\} \tag{185}$$

where ψ is the stream-function, so that

$$u = \frac{\partial\psi}{\partial y} = \tfrac{1}{2}\beta_0 f'_\eta(\xi, \eta) = \tfrac{1}{2}\beta_0\{f'_0(\eta) - 8\xi f'_1(\eta) + ...\}. \tag{186}$$

If we substitute in (184) and equate the coefficients of the various powers of ξ on the two sides of the equation, we obtain a series of ordinary differential equations for the f's. The boundary conditions are (since $u = v = 0$ at $y = 0$) $f_r(0) = f'_r(0) = 0$ and (since $u \to u_1$ as $\eta \to \infty$) $f'_0(\eta) \to 2$, $f'_1(\eta) \to \tfrac{1}{4}$, $f'_r(\eta) \to 0$ for $r \geqslant 2$ as $\eta \to \infty$. The function f_0 is the same as the function f which satisfies equation (45) in § 53. The equations are third-order equations, and all except the first are non-homogeneous linear equations. The first seven functions $(f_0, f_1, ..., f_6)$ have been tabulated by Howarth,† who also obtained rough values of f_7 and f_8. For values of ξ in the neighbourhood of 0·1 the first nine terms are no longer sufficient to give a sufficiently accurate representation; the value of ξ at separation is greater than 0·1 and cannot be determined from the series correct to three decimal places. Several approximate methods (specially devised for the particular problem) were applied to extend the solution to the position of separation, and checks were applied. The results

† *Proc. Roy. Soc.* A, **164** (1938), 547–564.

all agreed in giving separation at $\xi = 0\cdot120$. Now

$$
\left.
\begin{aligned}
\frac{\nu^{\frac{1}{2}}(\partial u/\partial y)_{y=0}}{\beta_0\beta_1^{\frac{3}{4}}} &= \frac{1}{4\xi^{\frac{1}{2}}}f''_\eta(\xi, 0), \\[2mm]
\frac{\beta_1^{\frac{1}{4}}\delta_1}{\nu^{\frac{1}{2}}} &= \xi^{\frac{1}{2}}\int_0^\infty \left\{2 - \frac{f'_\eta(\eta, \xi)}{1-\xi}\right\} d\eta, \\[2mm]
\frac{\beta_1^{\frac{1}{4}}\vartheta}{\nu^{\frac{1}{2}}} &= \xi^{\frac{1}{2}}\int_0^\infty \left\{\frac{f'_\eta(\eta, \xi)}{1-\xi} - \frac{1}{2}\left[\frac{f'_\eta(\eta, \xi)}{1-\xi}\right]^2\right\} d\eta,
\end{aligned}
\right\}
\tag{187}
$$

where δ_1 and ϑ are the displacement and momentum thicknesses as defined in equations (36) and (37), while

$$
u_1 = \beta_0(1-\xi), \qquad -u'_1 = \beta_1.
\tag{188}
$$

Hence the quantities

$$
\left.
\begin{aligned}
\frac{\nu^{\frac{1}{2}}(\partial u/\partial y)_{y=0}}{u_1(-u'_1)^{\frac{1}{2}}} &= \frac{\nu^{\frac{1}{2}}(\partial u/\partial y)_{y=0}}{\beta_0\beta_1^{\frac{1}{4}}(1-\xi)}, \\[2mm]
\frac{(-u'_1)^{\frac{1}{2}}\delta_1}{\nu^{\frac{1}{2}}} &= \frac{\beta_1^{\frac{1}{4}}\delta_1}{\nu^{\frac{1}{2}}}, \\[2mm]
\chi = \frac{(-u'_1)^{\frac{1}{2}}\vartheta}{\nu^{\frac{1}{2}}} &= \frac{\beta_1^{\frac{1}{4}}\vartheta}{\nu^{\frac{1}{2}}},
\end{aligned}
\right\}
\tag{189}
$$

are functions of ξ only. They are tabulated against ξ in Table 8, which also contains tables of $d\chi/d\xi$ and $\chi\left/\dfrac{d\chi}{d\xi}\right.$.

For small values of ξ, the first term in the expansion of χ is

$$
\chi = \xi^{\frac{1}{2}}\int_0^\infty f'_0(\eta)[1 - \tfrac{1}{2}f'_0(\eta)]\, d\eta = 0\cdot664\xi^{\frac{1}{2}}.
\tag{190}
$$

TABLE 8

ξ	$\dfrac{\nu^{\frac{1}{2}}(\partial u/\partial y)_{y=0}}{u_1(-u'_1)^{\frac{1}{2}}}$	$\dfrac{(-u'_1)^{\frac{1}{2}}\delta_1}{\nu_1}$	χ	$\dfrac{d\chi}{d\xi}$	$\chi\left/\dfrac{d\chi}{d\xi}\right.$
0·0000	∞	0·000	0·000	∞	0·000
0·0125	2·773	0·199	0·076	3·17	0·024
0·0250	1·817	0·292	0·110	2·39	0·046
0·0375	1·360	0·371	0·137	2·08	0·066
0·0500	1·064	0·447	0·162	1·93	0·084
0·0625	0·843	0·523	0·186	1·85	0·100
0·0750	0·663	0·603	0·209	1·82	0·115
0·0875	0·503	0·691	0·231	1·81	0·128
0·1000	0·345	0·794	0·254	1·84	0·138
0·1125	0·184	0·931	0·276	1·88	0·147
0·120	0·000	1·110	0·290	1·92	0·151

Table 9 contains values of u/u_1 for several values of ξ and η.

TABLE 9

Values of u/u_1

η \ ξ	0·0125	0·025	0·0375	0·050	0·0625	0·075	0·0875	0·100	0·1125	0·120
0·0	0·000	0·000	0·000	0·000	0·000	0·000	0·000	0·000	0·000	0·000
0·2	0·125	0·117	0·108	0·099	0·089	0·078	0·066	0·052	0·034	0·010
0·4	0·251	0·237	0·222	0·205	0·188	0·168	0·146	0·120	0·085	0·038
0·6	0·377	0·358	0·338	0·317	0·293	0·267	0·237	0·202	0·152	0·085
0·8	0·498	0·477	0·455	0·430	0·403	0·372	0·337	0·294	0·234	0·149
1·0	0·611	0·590	0·567	0·541	0·513	0·480	0·442	0·394	0·325	0·227
1·2	0·711	0·692	0·670	0·645	0·617	0·585	0·546	0·498	0·426	0·318
1·4	0·796	0·779	0·760	0·738	0·712	0·682	0·646	0·598	0·527	0·416
1·6	0·864	0·850	0·834	0·815	0·794	0·769	0·736	0·692	0·625	0·517
1·8	0·914	0·904	0·891	0·877	0·860	0·839	0·812	0·776	0·716	0·616
2·0	0·949	0·942	0·934	0·923	0·910	0·894	0·872	0·844	0·794	0·708
2·2	0·972	0·967	0·962	0·954	0·946	0·934	0·918	0·897	0·858	0·787
2·4	0·985	0·983	0·979	0·975	0·969	0·961	0·951	0·936	0·908	0·853
2·6	0·993	0·991	0·990	0·987	0·984	0·979	0·972	0·962	0·943	0·903
2·8	0·997	0·996	0·995	0·994	0·992	0·989	0·985	0·978	0·967	0·940
3·0	0·998	0·998	0·998	0·997	0·996	0·995	0·992	0·989	0·982	0·965
3·2	0·999	0·999	0·999	0·999	0·999	0·998	0·997	0·994	0·991	0·981
3·4	1·000	1·000	1·000	1·000	1·000	0·999	0·999	0·998	0·995	0·990
3·6	..	..	..	..	..	1·000	1·000	0·999	0·998	0·995
3·8	..	..	..	..	..	..	..	1·000	0·999	0·998
4·0	..	..	..	..	..	..	..	..	1·000	0·999
4·2	..	..	..	..	..	..	..	..	..	1·000

The above solution has been made the basis of a general method for any distribution of u_1 in a retarded region (u_1' negative).† In the first place, the graph of u_1 against x may be replaced approximately by a polygon. The value of ϑ being known at the first vertex (which may be taken at the pressure minimum, the solution up to the pressure minimum being supposed found by expansion in series from the stagnation point, or from the momentum equation, or by any other suitable method), and u_1' being the slope of the first side of the polygon, χ is known at the first vertex. The value, ξ_0, of ξ corresponding to the first vertex is found from a graph or table of χ against ξ. The value of $-\beta_1$ for the first side of the polygon is the slope of the side, and β_0 is obtained by equating $\beta_0(1-\xi_0)$ to the value of u_1 at the first vertex. The above solution is then applied along the first side of the polygon, with

$$\xi = \xi_0 + \beta_1 x/\beta_0, \qquad (191)$$

where x is measured from the first vertex of the polygon. At the second vertex we make ϑ continuous, and since there is a discon-

† Howarth, *op. cit.*, 565–578.

tinuity in u_1' there is a discontinuity in χ and therefore also in ξ. This discontinuity is found, and we proceed along the second side in the same way as along the first, and so on.

The discontinuity in ξ at each vertex of the polygon implies a discontinuity in the skin-friction; and since the skin-friction is one of the most important results of the calculation this is a grave objection. Conversely, if we made the skin-friction continuous at the vertices, we should introduce discontinuities in ϑ. There would be a violation of the momentum equation (38) (since $d\vartheta/dx$ would become infinite), corresponding to a series of impulses applied at the vertices of the polygon.

The discontinuities can be avoided by keeping ϑ continuous but taking the limit when the sides of the polygon tend to zero. In place of the relation (191) between ξ and x, together with a series of discontinuities in ξ, we then obtain a differential equation for ξ in terms of x. If two vertices are taken at a distance δx apart, then from (191) the variation in ξ corresponding to the side of the polygon joining them is $\beta_1 \delta x/\beta_0$, which, since $\beta_1 = -u_1'$ and $\beta_0(1-\xi) = u_1$, is equal to $-u_1'(1-\xi)\delta x/u_1$. To obtain the total variation in ξ corresponding to a variation δx in x we must add on the discontinuity at the second vertex. This is obtained by making ϑ or $\nu^{\frac{1}{2}}\chi/(-u_1')^{\frac{1}{2}}$ continuous, i.e.

$$\delta\left[\frac{\chi}{(-u_1')^{\frac{1}{2}}}\right] = 0 \quad \text{or} \quad \frac{\delta\chi}{\chi} = \tfrac{1}{2}\frac{u_1''}{u_1'}\delta x.$$

Since $\delta\chi = (d\chi/d\xi)\,\delta\xi$, this gives a variation

$$\delta\xi = \tfrac{1}{2}\frac{\chi}{d\chi/d\xi}\frac{u_1''}{u_1'}\delta x$$

in ξ. The total variation in ξ for a variation δx in x is therefore

$$\delta\xi = \left[\tfrac{1}{2}\frac{\chi}{d\chi/d\xi}\frac{u_1''}{u_1'} - \frac{u_1'(1-\xi)}{u_1}\right]\delta x, \qquad (192)$$

and the differential equation required is

$$\frac{d\xi}{dx} = \tfrac{1}{2}\frac{\chi}{d\chi/d\xi}\frac{u_1''}{u_1'} - \frac{u_1'}{u_1}(1-\xi). \qquad (193)$$

Since $\chi \div d\chi/d\xi$ is a known function of ξ, while u_1''/u_1', u_1'/u_1 are known functions of x, (193) gives ξ in terms of x if the initial value of ξ is known. This initial value of ξ is found as above from the initial value of χ. If, however, we start from the pressure minimum, where $u_1' = 0$, $\chi = 0$ and $\xi = 0$. Moreover, since $\chi = 0{\cdot}664\xi^{\frac{1}{2}}$ for small ξ, the equation (193) has then a singular point at the origin, through which an infinite number of integral curves pass, so that it is necessary to determine also the initial value of $d\xi/dx$. This determination is effected by considering the first side of the polygon, with vertices δx apart, as having zero slope, while the slope of the second side is the value of u_1' at δx, i.e. $u_1'' \, \delta x$. The value of χ at a distance δx from the pressure minimum is therefore $(-u_1'' \, \delta x)^{\frac{1}{2}}\vartheta_0/\nu$, where ϑ_0 is the value of ϑ at the pressure minimum, the variation of ϑ along the first side of the polygon being ignored since it is $O(\delta x)$. Equating the value of χ thus found to $0{\cdot}664(\delta\xi)^{\frac{1}{2}}$, where $\delta\xi$ is the value of ξ at δx, we find for the initial value of $d\xi/dx$,

$$\left(\frac{d\xi}{dx}\right)_0 = -\frac{2{\cdot}269 u_1'' \vartheta_0^2}{\nu}. \tag{194}$$

The values of ξ corresponding to values of x may now be found from (193); the corresponding values of the skin-friction and the displacement thickness are found by graphical interpolation from Table 8, and the velocity distributions from Table 9.

In this method of procedure we must again suppose that the graphs of velocity against distance from the wall at various sections are members of a singly-infinite family of curves—namely, the velocity curves obtained from (186). At the separation point ξ will be $0{\cdot}120$, and for values of ξ between 0 and $0{\cdot}120$ the skin-friction for this singly-infinite system of curves takes all positive values.

We have seen in § 54 that if $u_1 = cx^m$ there is a solution for which $(\partial u/\partial y)_{y=0} = 0$ for all x if $m = -0{\cdot}0904$. The method described above was tested by using (193) to find the value of m for which the skin-friction vanishes everywhere—i.e. for which $\xi = 0{\cdot}120$ and $d\xi/dx = 0$. (193) then reduces to

$$\frac{0{\cdot}151}{2}(m-1)-0{\cdot}880m = 0,$$

whence $m = -0{\cdot}0938$. It may be noted that when the momentum equation with a quartic expression for the velocity is used to determine the corresponding value of m we require $\Lambda = -12$ in (145) and (146), whence it is found that $m = -0{\cdot}100$.

With values of u_1', u_1'' determined graphically from the experimental values of u_1 obtained by Schubauer at the surface of an elliptic cylinder (pp. 162, 172), and with the solution up to the pressure minimum found from the momentum equation with a quartic expression for the velocity, Howarth found that, according to (193) and (194), separation occurs (i.e. $\xi = 0\cdot120$) at a distance from the forward stagnation point equal to $1\cdot925$ times the minor axis.

64. Approximate methods of calculating steady two-dimensional boundary layer flow. Expansion in powers of y; generalization of the solution with $u_1 = cx^m$; approximate solution in closed form for a nearly linear velocity distribution in an accelerated region; an iterative process.

Green† has attempted to find a solution by expanding the stream-function in a series of powers of y with coefficients which are functions of x. When the expressions

$$
\left.
\begin{aligned}
\psi &= f_1\frac{y^2}{2!} + f_2\frac{y^3}{3!} + f_3\frac{y^4}{4!} + \cdots, \\
u &= \frac{\partial\psi}{\partial y} = f_1 y + f_2\frac{y^2}{2!} + f_3\frac{y^3}{3!} + \cdots, \\
v &= -\frac{\partial\psi}{\partial x} = -\left\{f_1'\frac{y^2}{2!} + f_2'\frac{y^3}{3!} + \cdots\right\}
\end{aligned}
\right\}
\tag{195}
$$

(where the f's are functions of x and dashes denote differentiation with respect to x) are substituted into the equation of steady motion, and the coefficients of the various powers of y on the two sides of the equation are equated, it is found that

$$
\nu f_2 = -u_1 u_1', \qquad f_3 = 0, \qquad \nu f_4 = f_1 f_1', \qquad \nu f_5 = 2f_1 f_2',\ldots. \tag{196}
$$

The function f_1, which is $(\partial u/\partial y)_{y=0}$, must be determined so as to make $u \to u_1$ at the outside of the boundary layer. Apart from inaccuracies which may arise in numerical work from the repeated differentiations required by (196), the main difficulty lies in the determination of f_1. Green applied this method to an experimental pressure distribution for flow past a circular cylinder, and developed a trial and error step-by-step method of determining f_1. (Basically, the method depends on making $u = u_1$ and $\partial u/\partial y = 0$ at $y = \delta$, and eliminating δ between the resulting equations.) The pressure distribution and the calculated skin-friction are shown in Chap. IX, Fig. 164.

Several of the methods described in previous sections give values of the skin-friction which are more reliable than the values of the velocity in the middle of the boundary layer. Expansion in powers of y may then be used to obtain improved values of the velocity.

A method has been suggested by Falkner and Skan‡ of generalizing the solution described in § 54 for the case $u_1 = cx^m$ (c and m constants) so as to derive approximate solutions for any distribution of u_1. If in the equation of steady motion we write

$$
\eta = (u_1/\nu x)^{\frac12}y, \qquad \psi = (u_1\nu x)^{\frac12}f(x,\eta), \tag{197}
$$

† *Phil. Mag.* (7), **12** (1931), 2–30; *A.R.C. Reports and Memoranda*, No. 1313 (1930).

‡ *A.R.C. Reports and Memoranda*, No. 1314 (1930).

the equation becomes

$$M\left[\left(\frac{\partial f}{\partial \eta}\right)^2 - 1\right] - \tfrac{1}{2}(M+1)f\frac{\partial^2 f}{\partial \eta^2} - \frac{\partial^3 f}{\partial \eta^3} + x\left[\frac{\partial f}{\partial \eta}\frac{\partial^2 f}{\partial \eta \partial x} - \frac{\partial^2 f}{\partial \eta^2}\frac{\partial f}{\partial x}\right] = 0, \quad (198)$$

where

$$M = u_1' x / u_1. \quad (199)$$

In the special case $u = cx^m$, $M = m$, f is a function of η only; the term in square brackets goes out and (198) reduces to an ordinary differential equation.

In the general case Falkner and Skan replace (198) by an ordinary differential equation whose coefficients are functions of x:

$$G_1(x)\left[\left(\frac{\partial f}{\partial \eta}\right)^2 - 1\right] - G_2(x)f\frac{\partial^2 f}{\partial \eta^2} - \frac{\partial^3 f}{\partial \eta^3} = 0, \quad (200)$$

and determine G_1 and G_2 so that (200) shall agree with (198) as closely as possible. The method employed by Falkner and Skan is to make (200) agree with (198) for small values of η. Now from (197)

$$u = \frac{\partial \psi}{\partial y} = u_1\frac{\partial f}{\partial \eta}, \qquad v = -\frac{\partial \psi}{\partial x} = -\tfrac{1}{2}(u_1 v/x)^{\frac{1}{2}}\left[(M+1)f + \eta(M-1)\frac{\partial f}{\partial \eta} + 2x\frac{\partial f}{\partial x}\right],$$
$$(201)$$

and since u and v must vanish at $\eta = 0$ for all values of x, $\partial f/\partial \eta$ and f must vanish at $\eta = 0$ for all values of x. If we put $\eta = 0$ in (198), we obtain simply

$$\left(\frac{\partial^3 f}{\partial \eta^3}\right)_{\eta=0} = -M$$

(cf. equation (16)), whilst with $\eta = 0$ equation (200) becomes

$$\left(\frac{\partial^3 f}{\partial \eta^3}\right)_{\eta=0} = -G_1(x).$$

In order that these should be identical, we must have

$$G_1(x) = M. \quad (202)$$

If we differentiate (198) and (200) with respect to η, and put $\eta = 0$, we obtain in both cases $\partial^4 f/\partial \eta^4 = 0$. If we differentiate twice and put $\eta = 0$, we obtain from (198)

$$\left(\frac{\partial^2 f}{\partial \eta^2}\right)_{\eta=0}^2 [2M - \tfrac{1}{2}(M+1)] - \left(\frac{\partial^5 f}{\partial \eta^5}\right)_{\eta=0} + x\left(\frac{\partial^2 f}{\partial \eta^2}\frac{\partial^3 f}{\partial \eta^2 \partial x}\right)_{\eta=0} = 0,$$

and from (200)

$$\left(\frac{\partial^2 f}{\partial \eta^2}\right)_{\eta=0}^2 [2G_1(x) - G_2(x)] - \left(\frac{\partial^5 f}{\partial \eta^5}\right)_{\eta=0} = 0.$$

In order that these may be identical we require that

$$G_2(x) = \frac{M+1}{2} - \frac{x}{\alpha}\frac{d\alpha}{dx}, \quad (203)$$

where

$$\alpha = \left(\frac{\partial^2 f}{\partial \eta^2}\right)_{\eta=0} = \frac{1}{u_1}\left(\frac{vx}{u_1}\right)^{\frac{1}{2}}\left(\frac{\partial u}{\partial y}\right)_{y=0}. \quad (204)$$

Now (200) reduces to equation (69) with

$$[G_2(x)]^{\frac{1}{2}}\eta = Y, \qquad [G_2(x)]^{\frac{1}{2}}f = F, \qquad \beta = G_1/G_2, \quad (205)$$

so that, in particular, if α is taken from the solution of the approximate equation (200),

$$\frac{\alpha}{M^{\frac{1}{2}}} = \left(\frac{G_2}{M}\right)^{\frac{1}{2}}\left(\frac{d^2 F}{dY^2}\right)_{Y=0} = \frac{1}{\beta^{\frac{1}{2}}}\left(\frac{d^2 F}{dY^2}\right)_{Y=0}, \quad (206)$$

G_1 being equal to M. Since corresponding values of $(d^2F/dY^2)_{Y=0}$ and β are known, corresponding values of β and $\alpha/M^{\frac{1}{2}}$ are known. Hence G_2 ($= M/\beta$) is equal to M divided by a known function of $\alpha/M^{\frac{1}{2}}$. Since M is a known function of x, (203) is an ordinary differential equation for α. When this is solved the solution is complete. Some corresponding values of β and $(d^2F/dY^2)_{Y=0}$ are shown for reference below:

$$\beta = -0\cdot1988 \quad -0\cdot19 \quad -0\cdot18 \quad -0\cdot16 \quad -0\cdot14 \quad -0\cdot10 \quad 0 \quad 0\cdot1 \quad 0\cdot2$$

$$\left(\frac{d^2F}{dY^2}\right)_{Y=0} = \quad 0 \quad\quad 0\cdot086 \quad 0\cdot128_5 \quad 0\cdot190_5 \quad 0\cdot239_5 \quad 0\cdot319 \quad 0\cdot4696 \quad 0\cdot5870 \quad 0\cdot686_9$$

$$\beta = \quad 0\cdot3 \quad\quad 0\cdot4 \quad\quad 0\cdot5 \quad\quad 0\cdot6 \quad\quad 0\cdot8 \quad\quad 1\cdot0 \quad\quad 1\cdot2 \quad\quad 1\cdot6 \quad\quad 2\cdot0 \quad\quad 2\cdot4$$

$$\left(\frac{d^2F}{dY^2}\right)_{Y=0} = 0\cdot774_8 \quad 0\cdot854_2 \quad 0\cdot927_7 \quad 0\cdot996 \quad 1\cdot120 \quad 1\cdot2326 \quad 1\cdot336 \quad 1\cdot521 \quad 1\cdot687 \quad 1\cdot837$$

The somewhat different application of (203), involving further approximations, which was made by Falkner and Skan, has been criticized by Howarth,[†] who also points out that (203) will fail in the neighbourhood of the separation point. For since $\beta = -0\cdot1988$ at the separation point, G_2 remains finite there. Since α vanishes, (203) would make $d\alpha/dx$ vanish also at the separation point, and this is not correct.

Fairly satisfactory results are obtained in a region of accelerated flow, and the method may be used as an alternative to Dryden's modification[‡] to bridge over a region in which $\Lambda > 12$ when such a region occurs in an application of the momentum equation with a quartic velocity distribution (§ 60, p. 161).

The results obtained by Falkner and Skan for the skin-friction over the forward part of a circular cylinder with the use of a measured pressure distribution are shown together with those of Green in Chap. IX, Fig. 164.

Thom,[||] remarking that round the front of a circular cylinder u/u_1 is almost independent of x, writes $u/u_1 = f$, and seeks a first approximation with f a function of y by neglecting the term $v\,\partial u/\partial y$ in the equation of motion. Actually f is thus found as a function of $(u_1'/\nu)^{\frac{1}{2}}y$, and so is a function of y alone only when u_1' is constant. The first approximation is then used to evaluate the neglected term $v\,\partial u/\partial y$ and the neglected part $u_1\,\partial f/\partial x$ of $\partial u/\partial x$, and a second approximation is found, which results in the equation

$$y = \left(\frac{3\nu}{2u_1'}\right)^{\frac{1}{2}} \int_0^f \left\{ f^3 - 3f + 2 - \frac{3}{2}\frac{u_1 u_1''}{u_1'^2} \int_f^1 \frac{fF(f)}{F'(f)}\,df + 3\int_f^1 \phi(f)\,df \right\}^{-\frac{1}{2}} df,$$

where

$$F(f) = \log_e \frac{(\sqrt{3}-\sqrt{2})\sqrt{(1-f)}}{\sqrt{3}-\sqrt{(2+f)}},$$

$$\phi(f) = \frac{1}{F'(f)}\int_0^f fF'(f)\,df. \qquad\qquad (207)$$

The values obtained by Thom in this way for the skin-friction round the front of a circular cylinder are shown in Chap. IX, Fig. 164, together with those

† *A.R.C. Reports and Memoranda*, No. 1632 (1935), pp. 37–44.
‡ See footnote ‡, p. 161.
|| *A.R.C. Reports and Memoranda*, No. 1176 (1928).

of Green and of Falkner and Skan. Up to 45° from the forward stagnation point the solution is satisfactory; beyond that it departs widely from the values obtained by other writers and from the observed values. Up to 45° the velocity distribution outside the boundary layer is approximately linear, and we have seen in § 54 that for a linear velocity distribution u/u_1 is a function of $(u_1'/\nu)^{\frac{1}{2}}y$ only. It is, in fact, only in an accelerated region with the velocity distribution approximately linear that we should expect Thom's approximation to give satisfactory results, and then its only advantage over the solution in series is that the formulae can be expressed in terms of simple quadratures.

A very laborious iterative process has also been suggested by Thom (*loc. cit.*). He shows that, if A, B, C, D are the vertices of a small rectangle with AD and BC of length $2x$ and parallel to the wall, and AB and CD of length $2y$ and perpendicular to the wall, and if P is the centre of this rectangle, then, approximately,

$$
\left.
\begin{aligned}
u_P = {\textstyle\frac{1}{4}}(u_A + u_B + u_C + u_D) - Y_1 u_P(u_A + u_B - u_C - u_D) \\
- Y_2 v_P(u_A + u_D - u_B - u_C) + Y_3,
\end{aligned}
\right\}
\quad (208)
$$

where
$$
Y_1 = \frac{y^2}{8\nu x}, \qquad Y_2 = \frac{y}{8\nu}, \qquad Y_3 = -\frac{y^2}{2\nu\rho}\frac{\partial p}{\partial x}.
$$

The boundary layer having been divided into a rectangular net and plausible values of u assumed at the corners, the values of u at the centres are calculated from (208), the values of v being calculated from the equation of continuity. The centres of the new rectangular net at the corners of which the values of u are now known are the corners of the original net, and new values at these points are calculated from (208). This iterative process has to be repeated many times before the values are repeated sufficiently accurately.

65. Boundary layer growth. Motion started impulsively from rest.

When relative motion of a viscous incompressible fluid of constant density and of an immersed solid body is started impulsively from rest, the initial motion of the fluid is irrotational, without circulation. This is shown by observation, and may be proved theoretically in the same way as for inviscid fluids,† since it may be assumed that the viscous stresses remain finite. The fluid in contact with the solid body is, however, at rest relative to the boundary, whilst the adjacent layer of fluid is slipping past the boundary with a velocity determined from ideal fluid theory. There is thus initially a surface of slip, or vortex-sheet, in the fluid, coincident with the surface of the solid body. In other words there is a boundary layer of zero thickness. The vorticity in the sheet diffuses from the boundary into the fluid and is convected by the stream. The boundary layer

† Lamb's *Hydrodynamics* (1932), p. 11. It is assumed that any extraneous impulsive body forces acting on the fluid are conservative.

grows in thickness. (The same results follow from a consideration of the equations for the vorticity components in a viscous incompressible fluid, or of the equation for the circulation in a circuit moving with the fluid.†)

In any region along the boundary where the fluid is flowing against a pressure gradient, the forward stream will, after a time, leave the boundary if the pressure gradient extends far enough. Up to the time when separation begins, the velocity and pressure just outside the boundary layer may be taken to be the same as those at the surface in the irrotational motion without circulation, since this assumption provides a very close approximation to the facts. The pressure may also, as in boundary layer theory generally, be taken as constant across any section of the boundary layer.

Separation begins when the velocity gradient normal to the boundary vanishes at the boundary. For two-dimensional motion, the time, T, that elapses before separation begins, and the distribution of velocity in the boundary layer, may be approximately calculated. For an impulsive start, the second approximation to the velocity distribution, sufficient to give a first approximation to T, was calculated by Blasius.‡ The third approximation to the velocity distribution, and the second approximation to T, have been calculated by Goldstein and Rosenhead.‖

After separation has once begun, the position of separation moves upstream. The movement could be followed theoretically on the assumption that the velocity and pressure outside the boundary layer continue to be the same as in the irrotational motion without circulation; but this assumption is no longer valid, and the results would have at best only a qualitative value,—and then only for flow past a symmetrical cylinder, since for an asymmetrical cylinder a circulation begins to grow as soon as separation starts. Even for a symmetrical cylinder, the thickening of the boundary layer beyond the position of separation—or, rather, its projection into the main body of the fluid—and the consequent formation of a wake deprive results obtained on the above assumption of any quantitative value.

We assume that at time $t = 0$ a cylinder starts to move in a straight line with velocity u_0, and that this velocity remains constant

† Chap. III, § 36. See also Jeffreys, *Proc. Camb. Phil. Soc.* **24** (1928), 477–479.

‡ *Zeitschr. f. Math. u. Phys.* **56** (1908), 20–37.

‖ *Proc. Camb. Phil. Soc.* **32** (1936), 392–401.

thereafter. We take a frame of reference fixed relative to the cylinder. If x is distance along a section of the cylinder from the forward stagnation point and y distance normal to the surface of the cylinder, the approximate equation of motion in the boundary layer is

$$\frac{\partial u}{\partial t} + u\frac{\partial u}{\partial x} + v\frac{\partial u}{\partial y} = u_1\frac{du_1}{dx} + v\frac{\partial^2 u}{\partial y^2}, \tag{209}$$

where u_1 is the velocity just outside the boundary layer, as before. Initially the boundary layer has zero thickness, and at the beginning of the motion the diffusion far outweighs the convection and the influence of the pressure gradient,—i.e. the convection terms in the acceleration on the right can be neglected compared with $\partial u/\partial t$, and the term $u_1\,du_1/dx$ neglected compared with $v\partial^2 u/\partial y^2$. The equation for the first approximation to u is

$$\frac{\partial u}{\partial t} = v\frac{\partial^2 u}{\partial y^2}, \tag{210}$$

and the solution required is

$$\left.\begin{aligned} u &= u_1\,\mathrm{erf}\,\eta, \\ \eta &= \frac{y}{2(vt)^{\frac{1}{2}}}, \end{aligned}\right\} \tag{211}$$

where

and $\mathrm{erf}\,\eta$ is defined in equation (160). This solution makes $u = 0$ when $\eta = 0$, u practically equal to u_1 when η is large and theoretically equal to u_1 when $\eta = \infty$, and makes the thickness of the boundary layer zero when $t = 0$.

The first approximation to v must satisfy the equation of continuity and must vanish when $\eta = 0$. It is therefore given by

$$v = -2\sqrt{(vt)}u_1'[\eta\,\mathrm{erf}\,\eta - \pi^{-\frac{1}{2}}(1 - e^{-\eta^2})], \tag{212}$$

where the dash denotes differentiation with respect to x.† When $\eta \to \infty$,

$$v \sim -2(vt)^{\frac{1}{2}}\eta u_1' = -yu_1',$$

and becomes infinite. The solution therefore fails theoretically for infinite values of η. But for moderate values of η, at which u is practically equal to u_1, v is of order $(vt)^{\frac{1}{2}}u_1'$.

To find a second approximation, denote by u', v' the terms that must be added to the first approximations given by (211) and (212). u'/u and v'/v are of order tu_1', and to find u' it is sufficient to solve the equation

$$v\frac{\partial^2 u'}{\partial y^2} - \frac{\partial u'}{\partial t} = -u_1 u_1' + u\frac{\partial u}{\partial x} + v\frac{\partial u}{\partial y},$$

† In this section the dash is used to denote differentiation on u_1 only.

where on the right u and v have their values as given by (211) and (212) for the first approximation. Write

$$u' = tu_1 u_1' f(\eta). \tag{213}$$

Then

$$\frac{d^2f}{d\eta^2} + 2\eta\frac{df}{d\eta} - 4f = 4[\operatorname{erf}^2\eta - 2\pi^{-\frac{1}{2}}\eta e^{-\eta^2}\operatorname{erf}\eta - 1 + 2\pi^{-1}(e^{-\eta^2} - e^{-2\eta^2})]. \tag{214}$$

The solution of this equation is

$$\left.\begin{aligned}
f = {}& \tfrac{1}{2}(2\eta^2 - 1)\operatorname{erf}^2\eta + 3\pi^{-\frac{1}{2}}\eta e^{-\eta^2}\operatorname{erf}\eta + 1 \\
& - \tfrac{4}{3}\pi^{-1}e^{-\eta^2} + 2\pi^{-1}e^{-2\eta^2} + \alpha(2\eta^2 + 1) \\
& + \beta[\tfrac{1}{2}\pi^{-\frac{1}{2}}(2\eta^2 + 1)\operatorname{erf}\eta + \eta e^{-\eta^2}],
\end{aligned}\right\} \tag{215}$$

where α and β are constants to be chosen so that $u' = 0$ at $\eta = 0$ and at $\eta = \infty$. These conditions require

$$\left.\begin{aligned}
\alpha &= -\left(1 + \frac{2}{3\pi}\right) = -1{\cdot}21221, \\
\beta &= \frac{1}{\sqrt{\pi}}\left(1 + \frac{4}{3\pi}\right) = 0{\cdot}80364.
\end{aligned}\right\} \tag{216}$$

Then u is the sum of the expressions given by (211) and (213), i.e.

$$u = u_1\operatorname{erf}\eta + tu_1 u_1' f(\eta). \tag{217}$$

The position of separation of forward flow from the wall is given by $\partial u/\partial y = 0$, i.e. $\partial u/\partial\eta = 0$, at $\eta = 0$. The time at which separation occurs at any particular place is hence found to be given by

$$1 + \left(1 + \frac{4}{3\pi}\right)u_1' t = 0. \tag{218}$$

Separation will occur first where u_1' has its greatest negative value. The interval to separation is given by

$$T = 0{\cdot}70205/(-u_1')_{\max}. \tag{219}$$

The rather complicated calculation of the third approximation to the velocity has been carried out. It is found that the next approximation to the time at which separation occurs at any particular place is given by

$$t^{-1} = -0{\cdot}7122u_1' + \sqrt{\{0{\cdot}7271u_1'^2 + 0{\cdot}05975u_1 u_1''\}}. \tag{220}$$

t has its least value where $-u_1'$ is greatest if and only if u_1 is zero there.

For a circular cylinder $-u_1'$ is greatest at the rear stagnation point, and separation begins there both on the first and second approximations. If a is the radius of the cylinder, $u_1 = 2u_0 \sin x/a$, and the time that elapses from the commencement of the motion until separation first begins is given by $u_0 T_1 = 0.35a$ for the first approximation and by $u_0 T_2 = 0.32a$ for the second approximation. These expressions give the distance travelled by the cylinder from the commencement of the motion, and the second approximation is about 9 per cent. less than the first.

For a symmetrical cylinder of any section, it is to be remarked that whether $-u_1'$ attains its greatest value at the rear stagnation point or not depends on the shape of the section; and consequently separation may not begin at the rear stagnation point even according to the first approximation to T (equation (219)). This is especially the case for a bluff cylinder. Thus Tollmien[†] has pointed out that for an elliptic cylinder with its major axis across the stream separation begins at the rear stagnation point only if the ratio of the squares of the axes does not exceed $\frac{4}{9}$. As this ratio is further increased the positions of initial separation move symmetrically round towards the ends of the major axis, and the time interval to separation continually decreases.

As an example of a cylinder of asymmetrical section, the case of an ellipse with axes in the ratio $1 : 6$, and with its major axis at an angle of $7°$ to the stream, has been considered. For the irrotational motion without circulation the rear stagnation point is at a distance of $0.0221a$ from the end of the major axis, towards the upper side of the ellipse, where $2a$ is the length of the major axis. For the first approximation separation begins at a distance of $0.0173a$ from the rear stagnation point towards the lower side of the ellipse, after a time given by $u_0 T_1 = 0.0158a$. For the second approximation separation begins at $0.0170a$ from the rear stagnation point after a time given by $u_0 T_2 = 0.0144a$. The position of initial separation is not much altered. The interval is again reduced by about 9 per cent.[‡] Since the position of initial separation is not much altered, the term in $u_1 u_1''$ in (220) makes very little difference, and the same percentage reduction would always be found.

The second approximation to the velocity (corresponding to (217))

[†] *Handbuch der Experimentalphysik*, **4**, part 1 (Leipzig, 1931), **274**, 275.
[‡] Goldstein and Rosenhead, *loc. cit.* The first approximation had been calculated by Howarth.

has been found by Tollmien[†] for flow past a rotating cylinder, the whole system being started impulsively from rest.

The growth of the boundary layer at the surface of a body of revolution has been studied by Boltze[‡] and the results have been applied to a sphere. By numerical computation the value of $(\partial u/\partial y)_{y=0}$ was found up to the term involving t^3, and separation was found to begin at the rear stagnation point after the sphere has travelled (relatively to the undisturbed fluid) a distance equal to 0·39 times its radius.

66. Boundary layer growth.   Uniformly accelerated motion.

For uniformly accelerated motion starting from rest, u_0 is proportional to t, and the velocity u_1 outside the boundary layer, which before separation is again to be found from ideal fluid theory, will be of the form $tw_1(x)$. Since

$$-\frac{1}{\rho}\frac{\partial p}{\partial x} = \frac{\partial}{\partial t}(u_1 - u_0) + u_1\frac{\partial u_1}{\partial x},$$

the equation of motion is

$$\frac{\partial u}{\partial t} + u\frac{\partial u}{\partial x} + v\frac{\partial u}{\partial y} = w_1 + t^2 w_1\frac{dw_1}{dx} + \nu\frac{\partial^2 u}{\partial y^2}. \tag{221}$$

As before the equation may be solved by successive approximation (or by a series in t), the equation for the first approximation being

$$\frac{\partial u}{\partial t} = \nu\frac{\partial^2 u}{\partial y^2} + w_1.$$

The solution for which $u = 0$ at $y = 0$, $u/tw_1 \to 1$ when $y \to \infty$ or $t \to 0$ is

$$u = tw_1(x)\{-2\eta^2 + 2\pi^{-\frac{1}{2}}\eta e^{-\eta^2} + (2\eta^2 + 1)\mathrm{erf}\,\eta\}, \tag{222}$$

where $\eta = \frac{1}{2}y/(\nu t)^{\frac{1}{2}}$, as before. The second approximation, for which $t^3 w_1 w_1'$ multiplied by a certain function of η must be added to the value of u in (222), was found explicitly by Blasius,[||] who also obtained by numerical computation the next term (involving t^5) in $(\partial u/\partial y)_{y=0}$ and gave as the equation for the time at which separation begins at any particular place

$$1 + 0\cdot427w_1' t^2 - \{0\cdot026w_1'^2 + 0\cdot010w_1 w_1''\}t^4 = 0. \tag{223}$$

---

† *Göttingen Dissertation*, 1924; *Handbuch der Experimentalphysik*, **4**, part 1 (Leipzig, 1931), 276, 277.

‡ *Göttingen Dissertation*, 1908.

|| *Loc. cit.* in the footnote on p. 182. Fig. 23 on p. 60 was drawn from the second approximation.

For a circular cylinder of radius a separation begins again at the rear stagnation point according to either the first or second approximation, the calculated time intervals before separation begins being such that the distance travelled before separation is $0.585a$ for the first approximation, and $0.52a$ for the second. The second approximation is about 11 per cent. less than the first.

For the elliptic cylinder previously considered (incidence $7°$, ratio of axes $6:1$, length of major axis $= 2a$), separation begins at $0.0173a$ from the rear stagnation point when the distance travelled is $0.0264a$ for the first approximation, and at $0.0169a$ from the rear stagnation point when the distance travelled is $0.0234a$ for the second approximation. The position of initial separation is not much altered, and the term in $w_1 w_1''$ in (223) makes very little difference. The second approximation to the distance travelled is again 11 per cent. less than the first.

67. Boundary layers for periodic motion.

The existence of a boundary layer at an oscillating solid surface arises from the fact that the vorticity which is produced at the surface and diffuses into the body of the fluid changes sign periodically. (In previous cases boundary layers are produced because the vorticity produced at a solid surface, in addition to diffusing into the body of the fluid, is convected with the main stream.) The thickness of the boundary layer at an oscillating surface is proportional to the square root of the product of the kinematic viscosity and the period of the motion. The same results apply for a fixed surface and an oscillating stream.

The simplest example is an infinite lamina oscillating in its own plane in a viscous fluid in the absence of external pressure gradients: a solution of this problem was given by Stokes.† Due to a prescribed motion $u = \alpha \cos(\sigma t + \epsilon)$ at the boundary, a velocity distribution is produced in the fluid such that

$$u = \alpha e^{-\beta y} \cos(\sigma t - \beta y + \epsilon), \qquad (224)$$

where $\qquad \beta = (\sigma/2\nu)^{\frac{1}{2}}, \qquad (225)$

and the plane of the lamina is taken as the (z, x) plane, the fluid being

---

† *Trans. Camb. Phil. Soc.* **9** (1851), [20], [21] or *Math. and Phys. Papers*, **3**, 19, 20. See also Lamb, *Hydrodynamics* (Cambridge, 1932), pp. 619, 620, where a number of similar examples are also considered.

on the side of the plane for which y is positive. The amplitude of the resulting oscillation is diminished in the ratio e^{-C} when $y = C(2\nu/\sigma)^{\frac{1}{2}}$.

The influence of a rigid boundary on standing wave motion has been investigated by Rayleigh[†] without, and by Schlichting[‡] with, the approximations of boundary layer theory. The amplitude being supposed small, the 'first-order' motion, in which squares of the amplitude are neglected, is easily investigated. The investigation of the 'second-order' motion, in which squares of the amplitude are retained, yields results of more interest. The second-order motion contains a non-periodic part, and, corresponding to a 'first-order' velocity $\alpha \cos kx \cos \sigma t$ near the boundary just outside the 'thin frictional layer' (i.e. the boundary layer), Rayleigh finds that the components of this non-periodic velocity are, at distances from the boundary sufficient for $e^{-\beta y}$ to have become insensible,[||]

$$(3k/8\sigma)\alpha^2 \sin 2kx \, e^{-2ky}(1-2ky) \left.\right\}$$

and

$$-(2k^2/\beta\sigma)\alpha^2 \cos 2kx \, e^{-2ky}(-\tfrac{13}{16}+\tfrac{3}{8}\beta y), \left.\right\} \qquad (226)$$

parallel and perpendicular to the wall, respectively. The steady motion thus represented consists of a series of vortices periodic with respect to x in half a wave-length of the original standing wave. The fluid moves from the boundary at the nodes ($kx = \tfrac{1}{2}\pi, \tfrac{3}{2}\pi,...$) and towards the boundary at the loops ($kx = 0, \pi, 2\pi,...$). The horizontal motion is directed from the loops to the nodes near the boundary, and changes sign when $y = (2k)^{-1}$.

To ascertain the character of the motion in the frictional layer, the terms in $e^{-\beta y}$ which were omitted in (226) must be retained. When this is done it appears that the velocity parallel to the surface changes sign, as we go out from the wall, for a value of βy somewhat greater than $\tfrac{1}{4}\pi$, after which it stays of one sign until $2ky = 1$. The greatest magnitude of the velocity inside the layer for $\beta y < \tfrac{1}{4}\pi$ is found to be about $\tfrac{1}{7}$ of the velocity just outside the layer.

Rayleigh also investigated the circumstances when the motion has its origin in the assumed motion of a flexible plate, situated when in equilibrium at $y = 0$, which is such that to the second order the boundary conditions are $u = 0$, $v = \alpha \sin kx \cos \sigma t$, say, at

$$y = (\alpha/\sigma)\sin kx \sin \sigma t.$$

† *Phil. Trans.* A, **175** (1883), 1–21; *Scientific Papers*, **2**, 239–257. Rayleigh notes the existence of a 'thin frictional layer'.

‡ *Physik. Zeitschr.* **33** (1932), 327–335. || $\beta = (\sigma/2\nu)^{\frac{1}{2}}$ as in (225).

The results are rather similar to those above; but the fluid moves from the boundary at the loops and towards it at the nodes, with the horizontal motion directed from the nodes to the loops near the plate.†

It will be noted that according to (226) the velocity parallel to the boundary for small values of y (i.e. just outside the boundary layer) is equal to $(3k/8\sigma)\alpha^2 \sin 2kx$. Hence the effect of the condition of zero slip at the boundary is such that the assumed potential wave motion, $u = \alpha \cos kx \cos \sigma t$, produces, even outside the boundary layer, a steady second-order flow, with a magnitude independent of the viscosity. The same result was found by Schlichting (loc. cit.), who applied the approximations of boundary layer theory, and, for a velocity $w_1(x)\cos \sigma t$ outside the boundary layer, found for this steady second-order velocity component a limiting value $-(3/4\sigma)w_1 w_1'$ at the edge of the boundary layer. Since $w_1 = \alpha \cos kx$ in Rayleigh's investigation, the results are in agreement.

Flow in a long straight tube of radius a under the influence of a periodic pressure gradient has been investigated theoretically and experimentally by Richardson and Tyler‡ and theoretically by Sexl.‖ If the tube is long enough, the velocity (u) along the tube is independent of the distance (x) along the tube, and the velocity at right angles to the axis is zero. If r is radial distance from the axis of the tube, the exact equation of motion is

$$\frac{\partial u}{\partial t} = -\frac{1}{\rho}\frac{\partial p}{\partial x} + \nu\left(\frac{\partial^2 u}{\partial r^2} + \frac{1}{r}\frac{\partial u}{\partial r}\right), \tag{227}$$

where

$$-\frac{1}{\rho}\frac{\partial p}{\partial x} = \alpha \cos \sigma t. \tag{228}$$

The solution can be obtained exactly in terms of Bessel functions of order zero. When $a(\sigma/\nu)^{\frac{1}{2}}$ is small it assumes the parabolic form

$$u = (\alpha/4\nu)(a^2 - r^2)\cos \sigma t. \tag{229}$$

When $a(\sigma/\nu)^{\frac{1}{2}}$ is large the solution is

$$u = \frac{\alpha}{\sigma}\sin \sigma t - \frac{\alpha}{\sigma}\left(\frac{a}{r}\right)^{\frac{1}{2}} e^{-\beta(a-r)}\sin\{\sigma t - \beta(a-r)\}, \tag{230}$$

where β is $(\sigma/2\nu)^{\frac{1}{2}}$ as before. In the central portion of the tube where $\beta(a-r)$ is large only the first term is important. The first term

† The systems of vortices described above find application in the explanation of certain observed phenomena in acoustics. For references to these and related phenomena Rayleigh's paper may be consulted.

‡ Proc. Phys. Soc. **42** (1929), 1–15.

‖ Zeitschr. f. Phys. **61** (1930), 349–362.

represents an oscillation of the same period as the pressure gradient but with a phase difference of a quarter of a period.

When the approximations of the boundary layer theory are applied to this problem the term $vr^{-1} \, \partial u/\partial r$ in equation (227) is dropped and the solution (230) emerges quite simply.

In the experiments $\overline{u^2}$, the temporal mean value of the square of the velocity, was measured. $\overline{u^2}$ has its maximum value in the boundary layer near the wall and not in the central portion of the tube, for from (230)

$$\overline{u^2} = \frac{\alpha^2}{2\sigma^2}\{1-2(a/r)^{\frac{1}{2}}e^{-\beta(a-r)}\cos\beta(a-r)+(a/r)e^{-2\beta(a-r)}\}, \qquad (231)$$

and the maximum of this expression is at $\beta(a-r) = 2\cdot28$. This result is in good agreement with the experiments of Richardson and Tyler.

TURBULENCE

68. The mean flow.

In the mathematical treatment of turbulent flow it is assumed that the motion can be separated into a mean flow whose components are U, V, W, and a superposed turbulent flow whose components are u, v, w, the mean values of which are zero.[†] In most cases these means may be taken with regard to time at a fixed point, or with regard to one of the coordinates at a given instant of time. Some discussion of the methods of taking means was given by Reynolds,[‡] but there has been little subsequent discussion of this question.

In all cases of steady mean flow the means are taken over a long period of time at a fixed point. In other cases the appropriate method for taking means will depend on the particular problem which is being solved. If, for instance, the problem of the turbulent flow near an infinite plate moving with variable velocity were to be discussed, the mean values would be taken over planes parallel to the plate.

Difficulty occurs when the mean flow is variable. It is then necessary to assume that the fluctuations in u, v, w are so rapid that a significant mean velocity can be taken in an interval which is so short that the change in U, V and W during that interval can be neglected.

In taking averages the following principles will be adopted. If A and B are dependent variables which are being averaged and S is any one of x, y, z, t, then $\overline{\partial A/\partial S} = \partial \bar{A}/\partial S$,[||] and $\overline{AB} = \bar{A}\,\bar{B}$, where the bar denotes a mean value.

[†] In this chapter (except in equation (1)) U, V, W are the components of the mean velocity, u, v, w of the turbulent velocity, and $\boldsymbol{u}$, $\boldsymbol{v}$, $\boldsymbol{w}$ are the root-mean-square values of u, v, w. A bar over the top denotes a mean value.

[‡] 'On the Dynamical Theory of Incompressible Viscous Fluids and the Determination of the Criterion', *Phil. Trans.* A, **186** (1895), 123–164. See also Lamb's *Hydrodynamics* (1932), p. 674 *et seq.*

[||] For example, with time means

$$\frac{\overline{\partial A}}{\partial t} = \frac{1}{2\tau} \int\limits_{t-\tau}^{t+\tau} \frac{\partial A}{\partial t}\, dt = \frac{1}{2\tau}\{A(t+\tau) - A(t-\tau)\}$$

$$= \frac{1}{2\tau} \frac{\partial}{\partial t} \int\limits_{t-\tau}^{t+\tau} A\, dt = \frac{\partial}{\partial t}\left\{\frac{1}{2\tau} \int\limits_{t-\tau}^{t+\tau} A\, dt\right\} = \frac{\partial \bar{A}}{\partial t}.$$

If the method of averaging does not involve the variable of differentiation, no difficulty arises.

For a proof with a different method of averaging, see Taylor, *Proc. London Math. Soc.* (2), **20** (1922), 202, 203.

69. The Reynolds stresses.

The equation of motion of an incompressible fluid may be written[†]

$$\rho \frac{\partial u}{\partial t} = \frac{\partial}{\partial x}(p_{xx}-\rho uu) + \frac{\partial}{\partial y}(p_{xy}-\rho uv) + \frac{\partial}{\partial z}(p_{xz}-\rho uw) \tag{1}$$

and two similar equations. If $U+u$ be substituted for u, $V+v$ for v, and $W+w$ for w, and the mean value taken, (1) becomes

$$\rho \frac{\partial U}{\partial t} = \frac{\partial}{\partial x}(\overline{p_{xx}}-\rho UU - \rho\overline{uu}) + \frac{\partial}{\partial y}(\overline{p_{xy}}-\rho UV - \rho\overline{uv})$$
$$+ \frac{\partial}{\partial z}(\overline{p_{xz}}-\rho UW - \rho\overline{uw}). \tag{2}$$

This equation has the same form as (1) if the stress

$$p_{xx} \text{ is replaced by } \overline{p_{xx}}-\rho\overline{uu},$$
$$p_{xy} \quad ,, \quad ,, \quad \overline{p_{xy}}-\rho\overline{uv},$$
$$p_{xz} \quad ,, \quad ,, \quad \overline{p_{xz}}-\rho\overline{uw}.$$

Thus the equations of the mean flow are the same as the ordinary equations of motion provided that stress components $-\rho\overline{u^2}$, $-\rho\overline{v^2}$, $-\rho\overline{w^2}$, $-\rho\overline{vw}$, $-\rho\overline{wu}$, $-\rho\overline{uv}$ are added to the mean values of the stresses p_{xx}, p_{yy}, p_{zz}, p_{yz}, p_{zx}, p_{xy} which are due to viscous forces. These virtual stresses are called the Reynolds stresses, and are the mathematical representations of the transport of momentum across a surface due to the velocity fluctuations.[‡]

The equation of continuity, when averaged, becomes

$$\frac{\partial U}{\partial x} + \frac{\partial V}{\partial y} + \frac{\partial W}{\partial z} = 0.$$

70. Example. The Reynolds shearing stress for pressure flow between parallel planes.

A simple example in which the Reynolds stresses are known is that of pressure flow between parallel planes.

Let the axis of x be parallel to the direction of mean motion, and denote by v the component perpendicular to the parallel planes. The average state of affairs may be supposed independent both of z and of x, so that $\partial(\rho\overline{u^2})/\partial x = 0$, $\partial(\rho\overline{uw})/\partial z = 0$, etc. Hence (2) becomes

$$\frac{\partial}{\partial x}\overline{p_{xx}} + \frac{\partial}{\partial y}(\overline{p_{xy}}-\rho\overline{uv}) = 0, \tag{3}$$

[†] These are equivalent to equations (19) and (20) of Chap. III in virtue of the equation of continuity. In equation (1), u, v, w are taken temporarily as the components of total velocity.

[‡] Reynolds, *loc. cit.*; Lamb's *Hydrodynamics, loc. cit.*

and since
$$p_{xy} = \mu\left(\frac{\partial U}{\partial y} + \frac{\partial u}{\partial y} + \frac{\partial v}{\partial x}\right),$$

$$\overline{p_{xy}} = \mu\frac{\partial U}{\partial y}. \tag{4}$$

The second equation of motion is

$$\frac{\partial}{\partial x}(\overline{p_{xy}} - \rho\overline{uv}) + \frac{\partial}{\partial y}(\overline{p_{yy}} - \rho\overline{v^2}) + \frac{\partial}{\partial z}(\overline{p_{yz}} - \rho\overline{vw}) = 0,$$

and since in this case the first and last terms vanish, $(\overline{p_{yy}} - \rho\overline{v^2})$ is independent of y. Now

$$\overline{p_{yy}} = -\bar{p} - 2\mu\,\partial\bar{v}/\partial y,$$

and $\bar{v} = 0$, so that
$$(\bar{p} + \rho\overline{v^2}) \tag{5}$$

is independent of y. Since $\partial(\rho\overline{v^2})/\partial x = 0$, (5) shows that $\partial\bar{p}/\partial x$ is independent of y.

It has been shown above that $\overline{p_{yy}} = -\bar{p}$. Similarly, $\overline{p_{zz}} = -\bar{p}$. Hence since
$$3\bar{p} = -\overline{p_{xx}} - \overline{p_{yy}} - \overline{p_{zz}},$$

$\overline{p_{xx}} = -\bar{p}$. The integral of (3) is therefore

$$\rho\overline{uv} = -y\frac{\partial\bar{p}}{\partial x} + \mu\frac{\partial U}{\partial y} + \text{constant.} \tag{6}$$

71. Reynolds's equations of motion in cylindrical polar coordinates.

Reynolds's equations, expressed in cylindrical polar coordinates r, ϕ, z, are, with the viscous terms neglected,[†]

$$\frac{\partial V_r}{\partial t} + V_r\frac{\partial V_r}{\partial r} + \frac{V_\phi}{r}\frac{\partial V_r}{\partial \phi} + V_z\frac{\partial V_r}{\partial z} - \frac{V_\phi^2}{r}$$
$$= -\frac{1}{\rho}\frac{\partial\bar{p}}{\partial r} - \frac{\partial}{\partial r}\overline{v_r^2} - \frac{1}{r}\frac{\partial}{\partial\phi}(\overline{v_r\,v_\phi}) - \frac{\partial}{\partial z}(\overline{v_r\,v_z}) - \frac{\overline{v_r^2}}{r} + \frac{\overline{v_\phi^2}}{r},$$

$$\frac{\partial V_\phi}{\partial t} + V_r\frac{\partial V_\phi}{\partial r} + \frac{V_\phi}{r}\frac{\partial V_\phi}{\partial \phi} + V_z\frac{\partial V_\phi}{\partial z} + \frac{V_r V_\phi}{r}$$
$$= -\frac{1}{\rho}\frac{1}{r}\frac{\partial\bar{p}}{\partial\phi} - \frac{\partial}{\partial r}(\overline{v_r\,v_\phi}) - \frac{1}{r}\frac{\partial}{\partial\phi}(\overline{v_\phi^2}) - \frac{\partial}{\partial z}(\overline{v_\phi\,v_z}) - \frac{2\overline{v_r\,v_\phi}}{r},$$

$$\frac{\partial V_z}{\partial t} + V_r\frac{\partial V_z}{\partial r} + \frac{V_\phi}{r}\frac{\partial V_z}{\partial \phi} + V_z\frac{\partial V_z}{\partial z}$$
$$= -\frac{1}{\rho}\frac{\partial\bar{p}}{\partial z} - \frac{\partial}{\partial r}(\overline{v_r\,v_z}) - \frac{1}{r}\frac{\partial}{\partial\phi}(\overline{v_\phi\,v_z}) - \frac{\partial}{\partial z}(\overline{v_z^2}) - \frac{\overline{v_r\,v_z}}{r}.$$

[†] The components of mean velocity in cylindrical polar coordinates are here denoted by V_r, V_ϕ, V_z, and the turbulent velocity components by v_r, v_ϕ, v_z.

72. Coefficients of correlation.

Three of the Reynolds stresses depend only on the magnitude of one component of velocity, but the three components of shear stress depend on the magnitudes of two component velocities and on the correlation between them. The coefficient of correlation between u and v is defined as

$$R_{uv} = \frac{\overline{uv}}{\sqrt{\overline{u^2}}\sqrt{\overline{v^2}}} = \frac{\overline{uv}}{uv}. \tag{7}$$

u, v, w will be used to denote $\sqrt{\overline{u^2}}$, $\sqrt{\overline{v^2}}$, $\sqrt{\overline{w^2}}$ from now on.

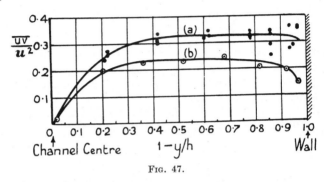

Fig. 47.

In the case of pressure flow between parallel plates $\rho\overline{uv}$ can be found from (6) by measuring the mean pressure gradient. To find R_{uv} it is necessary to measure u and v. Only provisional measurements of v in this case have been made,[†] but u has been measured by means of the hot wire technique.[‡] Since in general u is nearly equal to v,[||] $\overline{uv}/u^2$ is likely to be nearly equal to R_{uv}. Values of $\overline{uv}/u^2$ have been given by Kármán,[††] who based his calculations (a) on the measurements of Wattendorf, (b) on those of Reichardt. These are shown in Fig. 47.

73. Reynolds's energy criterion.

Reynolds's experiments with flow in pipes showed that if the Reynolds number of the flow $U_m a/\nu$[‡‡] is less than 1,000, the flow will become steady however large the disturbances at the entry may be.

[†] F. L. Wattendorf, *Journ. Aero. Sciences*, **3** (1936), 200–202.
[‡] Chap. VI, §§ 117, 119.   [||] See § 77, p. 200.
[††] *Proc. Fourth Internat. Congress for Applied Mechanics, Cambridge*, 1934 (Cambridge, 1935), pp. 63, 64.
[‡‡] U_m is the average velocity over a cross-section, and a the radius of the pipe.

Experiments with very carefully controlled conditions of entry have since shown that when the disturbances are very small the flow may remain steady when $U_m a/\nu$ is as high as 16,000.[†]

To account for the existence of a critical Reynolds number separating steady from turbulent conditions, Reynolds found the condition that the energy of the disturbed motion may increase. With any given form of small disturbance the criterion which distinguishes between an initial increase or an initial decrease in energy of the disturbed motion is a definite value for the Reynolds number of the motion. Thus for pressure flow with mean velocity U_m between parallel planes distant b apart Reynolds found that if $U_m b/\nu > 517$ the energy of the disturbed motion increases initially. This result was obtained by assuming a definite type of disturbance which satisfies the boundary conditions. Reynolds found that the calculated critical value of $U_m b/\nu$ depended on the form assumed for the disturbances. Orr[‡] pursued the matter farther and found the form of disturbance which gives the value 117 for $U_m b/\nu$ below which all small disturbances initially decrease. It is certain therefore that for Reynolds numbers below this all possible small disturbances will continually decrease. Orr also calculated the criterion ($U_0 b/\nu < 177$) for initial decrease of disturbance when one plane moves with velocity U_0 relative to the other.

These minimum criteria are well below the observed lower criteria. It appears therefore that, when the Reynolds number of the motion is between Orr's number and the observed lower criterion, disturbances can be imposed which increase initially but subsequently die away.

Disturbances of pure laminar flow of uniform vorticity which increase very greatly initially and subsequently die away have been discussed by Orr.[||] They are of the type

$$u = -(A/a_0) \cos a_0 x \sin b_0 y, \quad v = (A/b_0) \sin a_0 x \cos b_0 y,$$

where b_0 is large compared with a_0. If such a disturbance is superposed on the flow $U = d_0 y$, the vorticity of the disturbance, which is originally arranged as shown in Fig. 48 (a), is convected by the mean motion, and after time $t = b_0/a_0 d_0$ the areas of positive and negative vorticity are situated as in Fig. 48 (b). In the first position

[†] See Chap. VII, § 148.
[‡] *Proc. Roy. Irish Acad.* **27** (1907), 69–138 (especially pp. 128, 134).
[||] *Ibid.*, pp. 90–94.

(Fig. 48 (a)) the centres of positive and negative vorticity are close together in vertical lines, so that the velocities they produce are small. In the second position (Fig. 48 (b)) the centres of positive vorticity are close together on one set of vertical lines, while the centres of negative vorticity are on intermediate lines. This arrangement produces much greater velocities than that shown in Fig. 48 (a).

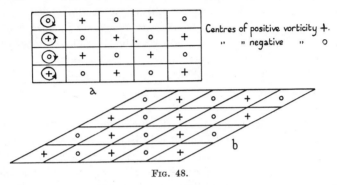

Centres of positive vorticity +.
  „   „   negative   „   o

FIG. 48.

74. Stability for infinitesimal disturbances.

The importance of stability in connexion with turbulence arises because a motion which is definitely unstable for small disturbances cannot remain steady for speeds higher than that at which instability sets in. On the other hand, a motion which is definitely stable for small disturbances may become turbulent when finite disturbances are imposed on it. Perhaps the simplest case of steady motion is that of flow parallel to the axis of x between parallel planes. It seems now to be generally admitted that when there is no pressure gradient, the steady flow being due to relative motion of the two planes, the motion is stable; but there seems little doubt that in fact the flow would be turbulent when some definite Reynolds number is exceeded, provided a sufficiently large finite disturbance were applied.

75. The stability of flow between rotating cylinders.

The only case in which instability has been proved by calcula- tion and verified experimentally is that of flow between rotating cylinders.† For given ratios of radii and of rotational speeds of the two cylinders a definite mode of disturbance appears when a calcu- lable Reynolds number of the flow is just exceeded. This instability

† Taylor, *Phil. Trans.* A, **223** (1923), 289–343.

PLATE 22

consists of alternate ring-shaped vortices symmetrical about the axis of the cylinders and spaced a definite distance apart. By arranging that the inner cylinder is covered with a thin coat of coloured fluid, the annular space between the cylinders being filled with water, the vortices can be observed, the planes between them appearing as

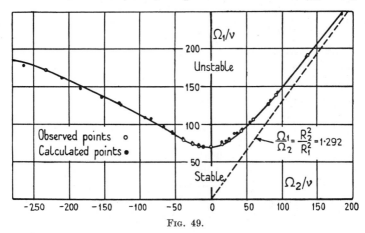

Fig. 49.

dark lines when viewed at right angles to the axis. A photograph of these lines is shown in Pl. 22, where regularity of the spacing may be seen. It appears that when the mean flow is such that only one mode of disturbance is just unstable, all others being stable, this mode immediately makes its appearance. The comparison between observed and calculated speeds at which instability sets in is shown in Fig. 49 for a particular pair of radii (3·55 and 4·035. cm.). The ordinates and abscissae are Ω_1/ν and Ω_2/ν, where Ω_1 and Ω_2 are the angular velocities of the inner and outer cylinders respectively.†

76. The stability of two-dimensional laminar flow.

The two-dimensional periodic disturbances of a field of flow in which U is a function of y only may be represented by a stream-function‡ $\psi = \phi(y)e^{i\alpha(x-ct)}$, and the differential equation for ϕ is

$$(U-c)(\phi''-\alpha^2\phi)-U''\phi = -\frac{i\nu}{\alpha}(\phi''''-2\alpha^2\phi''+\alpha^4\phi). \qquad (8)$$

† This work has been extended by Dean to the case of pressure flow in the annular space between two cylinders, the pressure acting round the cylinder and therefore, strictly, many-valued. See *Proc. Roy. Soc.* A, **121** (1928), 402–420. See also Chap. VII, §149.

‡ It is assumed that any initial disturbance may be analysed into periodic dis-

If all velocities are expressed as fractions of U_{max}, the maximum velocity, and all lengths as fractions of some length b (e.g. the distance between two planes between which the flow is confined), (8) can be written

$$(U-c)(\phi''-\alpha^2\phi)-U''\phi = -\frac{i}{\alpha R}(\phi''''-2\alpha^2\phi''+\alpha^4\phi), \tag{9}$$

where $R = U_{max}b/\nu$ and is defined as the Reynolds number of the flow, and the dashes refer to differentiation with respect to the new non-dimensional variable.

To explore the stability of flow between two planes it is necessary to write down the conditions that

$$\phi = \phi' = 0 \text{ at } y = 0 \text{ and } y = b.$$

Since (9) has four independent solutions these four boundary conditions will lead to a period equation for determining a relationship between c and α. If the imaginary part of αc is positive, the disturbance is unstable.

The case when $U'' = 0$ (i.e. the flow is a uniform shearing) has been extensively explored over a large range of values of R. All oscillations appear to be stable. For low values[†] of R the problem has been attacked by expansion in power series and for high values[‡] by the use of asymptotic series.

A method for obtaining solutions of (9) for high values of αR has been developed by Heisenberg,[||] Tietjens,[††] and Tollmien.[‡‡] These authors divide the four independent solutions into two classes,

turbances of this type, although this has never been rigorously proved except in the case of a simple shearing motion (Haupt, *Sitzungsber. d. k. bayr. Akad. d. Wiss., Math. Phys. Kl.* (1912), pp. 289–301). The reasons why the usual proof of the possibility of such an expansion fails have been set out by Southwell and Chitty, *Phil. Trans.* A, **229** (1930), 232–242.

On the assumption that any disturbance (possibly three-dimensional) may be analysed into constituents which are periodic in t, x, and z, it has been proved by Squire (*Proc. Roy. Soc.* A, **142** (1933), 621–628) that if instability arises for any Reynolds number, then it arises for the smallest Reynolds number when the motion is two-dimensional.

[†] Southwell and Chitty, *Phil. Trans.* A, **229** (1930), 205–253. (See also for the parabolic distribution *Proc. Camb. Phil. Soc.* **32** (1936), Goldstein, pp. 40–54, Pekeris, pp. 55–66.)

[‡] Hopf, *Ann. d. Phys.* (4), **44** (1914), 1–60.

[||] *Ann. d. Phys.* (4), **74** (1924), 577–627.

[††] *Zeitschr. f. angew. Math. u. Mech.* **5** (1925), 200–217.

[‡‡] *Göttinger Nachrichten, Math.-Phys. Klasse* (1929), pp. 21–44.

(a) solutions which are similar to those of an inviscid fluid, namely, solutions of

$$(U-c)(\phi''-\alpha^2\phi)-U''\phi = 0, \qquad (10)$$

and (b) those which involve very rapid variations of ϕ and are similar to the solutions of

$$(U-c)\phi''+\frac{i\phi''''}{\alpha R} = 0. \qquad (11)$$

At the point where $U = c$ the inviscid solution involves an infinite velocity and an infinite rate of shear, so that a solution which neglects viscosity (no matter how small) in the neighbourhood of this point is invalid. A finite viscosity prevents these infinite velocities from being attained. By superposing solutions of equations (10) and (11) it is possible to satisfy all the boundary conditions; but the full mathematical discussion is very complicated; the complications arising largely from the fact that any solution of (10) or (11) which is an asymptotic approximation to a solution of (9) for large values of αR, is not, in general, an approximation to the same solution of (9) on both sides of the point where $U = c$. Moreover, in the immediate neighbourhood of this point the method of approximation (approximating to solutions of (9) by solutions of (10) and (11)) breaks down.

Tollmien discussed the stability of an approximation to the Blasius distribution of velocity near a flat plate. He found that unstable waves can exist when $U_1\delta_1/\nu$ is greater than 420, where δ_1 is the displacement thickness of the boundary layer (defined by $\delta_1 = \int (1-U/U_1)\,dy$) and U_1 is the velocity outside the layer. At this calculated initial speed waves of length $17 \cdot 1\delta_1$ should become unstable, so that definite waves of this length might be expected to appear at the appropriate distance down the plate. In the original printing of these volumes it was stated that no such definite waves had been observed.[†] All the available experimental work seemed to show that the boundary layer of a flat plate became turbulent at a value of $U_1\delta_1/\nu$ which depended on the amount of turbulence in the main stream of air outside the layer.[‡] It was pointed out that the theory assumed that the velocity in the undisturbed motion is a function of y only, and that except when the velocity distribution

† Tollmien (*Handbuch der Experimentalphysik*, **4**, part 1 (Leipzig, 1931), 306) cites a photograph by Prandtl (*Zeitschr. f. angew. Math. u. Mech.* **1** (1921), 435) as evidence that such waves are produced, but the disturbances in the figure can hardly be said to look like definite waves.

‡ Cf. Dryden, *Proc. Fourth Internat. Congress for Applied Mechanics, Cambridge*, 1934 (Cambridge, 1935), p. 175; *N.A.C.A. Report* No. 562 (1936). See Chap. VII, § 151.

is parabolic (as it is for motion under the action of a uniform pressure gradient) or when the motion is a uniform shearing, it would be necessary to apply body forces to the fluid to maintain the undisturbed motion.† These doubts of the validity of the application of the theory for parallel flows were later removed by the experimental work of G. B. Schubauer and H. K. Skramstad, whose results confirmed the general characteristics predicted by the theory. See *Journ. Res. Nat. Bur. Standards*, **38** (1947), 251–292; *J. Aero. Sci.*, **14** (1947), 69–78; *N.A.C.A. Tech. Rep.* No. 909 (1948. Originally issued as an *N.A.C.A. A.R.C.* in 1943).

When the method is applied to shearing flow between parallel plates the difficulty just mentioned does not arise. The investigation of Hopf‡ seems to show that shearing flow is stable, and though Rayleigh|| cast some doubt on the validity of Hopf's work, Southwell and Chitty†† believe that 'it reveals with sufficient accuracy all the main features of the problem'.

77. Isotropic turbulence.

In all cases of turbulent motion there seems to be a strong tendency for the mean-square values of the three components of turbulent motion to become equal to one another. Observations made in a natural wind near the ground show that the transverse and vertical components are unequal near the ground but tend to equality at greater heights.‡‡ Ultramicroscopic and other observations of the turbulent components in a pipe show that they tend to become equal to one another near the centre of the pipe.||||

In a wind tunnel where turbulence is formed or controlled by a honeycomb, turbulence rapidly settles down to a condition for which the average-square values of the three components are nearly equal to

---

† Tollmien has also discussed the stability of velocity distributions in which the curve of U against y has a point of inflexion, and has shown that in such cases the motion is unstable for infinitely large Reynolds numbers (*Göttinger Nachrichten, Math.-Phys. Klasse*, New Series, **1** (1935), 79–114). A critical Reynolds number has, however, not yet been calculated.

‡ *Ann. d. Phys.* (4), **44** (1914), 1–60.

|| *Phil. Mag.* (6), **28** (1914), 619; *Scientific Papers*, **6**, 275.

†† *Phil. Trans.* A, **229** (1930), 208.

‡‡ Taylor, *Quarterly Journ. of the Roy. Meteorological Soc.* **53** (1927), 201–211.

|||| Fage and Townend, *Proc. Roy. Soc.* A, **135** (1932), 656–677; Townend, *ibid.* **145** (1934), 180–211; Fage, *Phil. Mag.* (7), **21** (1936), 80–105; Chap. VIII, § 172.

one another.† It seems that, apart from the effects of the large eddies, which have a long life and a long memory, the turbulence is then isotropic in the sense that the mean-square value of any component of turbulence is independent of the direction in which the component is taken.

A statistically isotropic condition of turbulence might be expected to arise when the time that has elapsed since the turbulence was formed is so great that there is no correlation between the motion of a particle and its initial motion. With this consideration in view, we might expect the turbulence behind a grid to become nearly isotropic in the sense that the average value of any function of the turbulent velocity components or their space derivatives is unaltered if the axes of reference are rotated.‡

78. The effect of contraction on turbulence in a wind tunnel.

In a wind tunnel the air comes to the working section through a contracting entrance in which the mean speed is greatly increased. The longitudinal component of turbulence decreases through the contraction. The effect of the contraction on turbulence may be regarded as due partly to the extension of the fluid parallel to the axis of the tunnel, with corresponding contraction in perpendicular directions, and partly to the readjustment of the components of turbulent velocity which takes place when the normal isotropic condition is upset. Though both these causes are operating simultaneously in the contracting entrance to a wind tunnel, some insight into the effect of contraction may be obtained by considering only the effect of the first. An instantaneous or impulsive change in the dimensions of a volume of fluid containing turbulent motions, the principal axes of the strain being parallel to the coordinate axes, causes the components of vorticity ξ_0, η_0, ζ_0 to change to ξ_1, η_1, ζ_1, where
$$\xi_1 = l\xi_0, \qquad \eta_1 = m\eta_0, \qquad \zeta_1 = n\zeta_0, \| \qquad (12)$$
l, m, n being the expansion or contraction ratios in the directions of the axes. The condition of continuity for an incompressible fluid is $lmn = 1$.

When ξ_0, η_0, ζ_0 are known, equations (12) give ξ_1, η_1, ζ_1, and the

† Taylor, 'Statistical Theory of Turbulence', Part 4, *Proc. Roy. Soc.* A, **151** (1935), 465–478. See also § 88 (p. 219) *infra*.

‡ For further discussion of this definition of isotropy, see § 91.

‖ This is a direct application of Cauchy's equations for the vorticity. Lamb's *Hydrodynamics* (1932), pp. 204, 205.

corresponding velocities can be found.† An example in which the complete solution of the problem has been obtained is that of the motion represented by

$$\left.\begin{array}{l} u_0 = A_0 \cos ax_0 \sin by_0 \sin cz_0, \\ v_0 = B_0 \sin ax_0 \cos by_0 \sin cz_0, \\ w_0 = C_0 \sin ax_0 \sin by_0 \cos cz_0, \end{array}\right\} \tag{13}$$

with $A_0 a + B_0 b + C_0 c = 0$ to satisfy the equation of continuity. This motion becomes

$$\left.\begin{array}{l} u_1 = A_1 \cos l^{-1}ax_1 \sin m^{-1}by_1 \sin n^{-1}cz_1, \\ v_1 = B_1 \sin l^{-1}ax_1 \cos m^{-1}by_1 \sin n^{-1}cz_1, \\ w_1 = C_1 \sin l^{-1}ax_1 \sin m^{-1}by_1 \cos n^{-1}cz_1, \end{array}\right\} \tag{14}$$

where $A_1 = l\left(\dfrac{cm^2(A_0 c - C_0 a) - bn^2(B_0 a - A_0 b)}{a^2 l^{-2} + b^2 m^{-2} + c^2 n^{-2}}\right)$, etc.

In (13) and (14) (x_0, y_0, z_0) are the coordinates of a fluid particle before, and (x_1, y_1, z_1) its coordinates after the change in dimensions; and (u_0, v_0, w_0), (u_1, v_1, w_1) the corresponding turbulent velocity components.

When the contraction is large and symmetrical, so that

$$m = n = l^{-\frac{1}{2}},$$

$$A_1 = A_0 l^{-1}\left(\frac{a^2 + b^2 + c^2}{b^2 + c^2}\right), \qquad B_1 = l^{\frac{1}{2}}\left(\frac{c(B_0 c - C_0 b)}{b^2 + c^2}\right),$$

$$C_1 = l^{\frac{1}{2}}\left(\frac{b(C_0 b - B_0 c)}{b^2 + c^2}\right). \tag{15}$$

Thus the longitudinal component of turbulent velocity is inversely proportional to l while the lateral components increase in proportion to $l^{\frac{1}{2}}$.‡

The turbulence represented by (13) is not isotropic. If we suppose $a = b = c$ the initial turbulence is more nearly like isotropic turbulence than with any other choice of $a:b:c$. In this case (15) becomes

$$\frac{A_1}{A_0} = \frac{3}{2}l^{-1},$$

so that it is useful to compare the effect of contraction on the ratio

---

† By the use of a method due to Helmholtz (see Lamb's *Hydrodynamics* (1932), pp. 208–210). The investigation given here is due to Taylor, 'Turbulence in a Contracting Stream', *Zeitschr. f. angew. Math. u. Mech.* **15** (1935), 91–96.

‡ This idea was first put forward by Prandtl, *The Physics of Solids and Fluids* (London, 1930), p. 358.

of the longitudinal components of turbulence after and before contraction with $1 \cdot 5l^{-1}$. The comparison of observed and calculated components is given in Table 10.† ($u_{0_{max}}$ and $u_{1_{max}}$ denote observed maximum values.)

TABLE 10

l	$1 \cdot 5l^{-1}$	$(\overline{u_1^2}/\overline{u_0^2})^{\frac{1}{2}}$	$u_{1_{max}}/u_{0_{max}}$	Authority	Method
3·26	0·46	0·50	..	Simmons	Hot wire
,,	,,	0·38 ⎫ 0·41 ⎭	..	Townend	Heated spot
,,	,,	..	0·38 ⎫ 0·52 ⎭	Fage	Ultramicroscope
13·2	0·114	..	0·12*	Simmons	Hot wire
,,	,,	..	0·15*	,,	,,
2·7	0·55	..	0·33	,,	,,
,,	,,	..	0·38	,,	,,

* Early measurements using uncompensated amplification.

79. Statistical theories of turbulence.

The object of a statistical theory of turbulence is to find methods of representing the turbulent field by considering the mean values and frequency distributions of quantities connected with the motion. Burgers‡ has attempted to apply to turbulence the statistical methods developed in connexion with the Kinetic Theory of Gases. For this purpose he considers a two-dimensional field of turbulence determined by a stream-function ψ. He then considers the values of ψ at a rectangular network of points with spacing ϵ. If ψ_A, ψ_B, ψ_C, ψ_D, ψ_O are the values at the corners A, B, C, D and the centre O of a square whose sides are 2ϵ, then, if ϵ is small,

$$u = \frac{\psi_B - \psi_A}{2\epsilon},$$

$$v = \frac{\psi_B - \psi_C}{2\epsilon},$$

$$\zeta' = \frac{1}{2\epsilon^2}(4\psi_O - \psi_A - \psi_B - \psi_C - \psi_D),$$

ζ' denoting the turbulent vorticity.

As in the Kinetic Theory of Gases any state of motion is represented by a point in N-dimensional space, where N is here the total

† Cf. Taylor, *loc. cit.* The comparison of observed and calculated lateral components is also given in the paper cited.

‡ *Proc. Roy. Acad. Sci. Amsterdam*, **32** (1929), 414–425, 643–657, 818–833; **36** (1933), 276–284, 390–399, 487–496.

number of points in the rectangular network. In order to apply this conception to the discussion of turbulence it is necessary to make some assumption in order to determine the frequency distribution of the representative point in the N-dimensional space, and it is here that the chief difficulty arises. Burgers attempts to use the dissipation function in this connexion in the same way that entropy is used in statistical mechanics. In so doing he leaves the equations of motion out of account. This theory seems promising, but it cannot be said that it has yet been developed far enough to be regarded as a definite theory of turbulence.

Another statistical representation of turbulent flow depends on the conception that the scale of turbulence can be described in terms of the correlation between the velocities u_A at a point A and u_B at another point B. If A and B are very close together, u_A and u_B are closely correlated: if they are far apart compared with the scale of the turbulence, this correlation may be expected to disappear. The coefficient of correlation R_y between u_A and u_B is

$$R_y = \frac{\overline{u_A u_B}}{u_A u_B}, \tag{16}$$

where y is the distance between the points A and B, and the axis of y is along AB.

If u represents the downstream component of turbulent velocity, $\overline{u_A u_B}$, u_A^2, u_B^2 can be measured by the hot wire technique. In such measurements it is convenient to fix one hot wire and to traverse the second wire perpendicular to the air-stream in the direction y. Correlations can be measured in other directions provided that one wire is not so nearly downstream of the other that the heat wake of the upstream wire falls on the downstream wire.

If the coordinates of B relative to A are x, y, z, the correlation coefficient between u_A and u_B may be represented by R_{xyz}; and the turbulence may be described statistically in terms of surfaces $R_{xyz} = $ const. The correlations between u_A and u_B at pairs of stations situated on the axes of reference will be denoted by R_x, R_y, R_z.

The relationship between R_y and y is shown by the points (and full-line curve) in Fig. 50 (p. 225) for turbulence produced in an airstream by passage over a grid of square meshes 3 in. × 3 in. At a wind speed of 15 ft./sec., R_y tends to zero at $y = 2 \cdot 3$ inches. Measurements behind a similar screen of $M = 0 \cdot 9$ in. mesh show that, except near $y = 0$, R_y seems to depend on y/M, i.e. the values of R_y at corresponding values of y/M in the two cases are the same. The scale of the turbulence produced by similar grids of different sizes may be expected to be proportional to the mesh of the grids.† This expectation is therefore satisfied if the scale of the R_y curve is taken as a measure of the scale of the turbulence. The scale of the R_y curve may conveniently be defined as

$$l_2 = \int\limits_0^Y R_y \, dy, \tag{17}$$

where Y is the value of y above which R_y is sensibly zero.‡

80. Mixture length theories.

Up to the present time the centre of interest in turbulent motion has been its relationship to the mean flow. The statistical effect of turbulence on the mean flow has been regarded as similar to that of viscosity. Lumps of fluid are supposed to transfer the transferable properties from one layer to another just as molecular agitation transfers properties like heat and momentum in a non-turbulent fluid. In such theories a mixture length, l, plays a part analogous to the mean free path in molecular diffusion. The transfer of transferable properties is supposed to be effected by the motion of lumps of fluid which leave a layer in which their properties are those of the mean flow in the neighbourhood, and move in a direction transverse to the mean flow through a distance l. At this point they are supposed to mix with the surrounding fluid, so that their properties become identical with the average properties of the fluid in that region. The simplest case that can be discussed by this method is that of the transfer of a property θ in the direction of the axis y when the mean value of θ is constant over planes perpendicular to this direction. Suppose that a particle starts from a layer $y = h_1$ and that it carries with it the value $\theta(h_1)$, the mean value of θ at $y = h_1$. After moving to $y = h_2$, where the mean value of θ is $\theta(h_2)$, θ differs from the mean by an amount $\theta(h_1) - \theta(h_2)$. The mean rate of transfer of θ across a unit area perpendicular to y is

$$Q = \overline{v[\theta(h_1) - \theta(h_2)]}, \tag{18}$$

where the bar indicates that the mean value over $y = h_2$ is taken.

† Cf. § 94 (p. 227 *infra*).

‡ Taylor, 'Statistical Theory of Turbulence', *Proc. Roy. Soc.* A, **151** (1935), 421–454.

Expanding $\theta(h_1) - \theta(h_2)$ in a Taylor series we find that Q is the average value of

$$v\left\{-(h_2-h_1)\frac{d\theta}{dy} + \frac{1}{2}(h_2-h_1)^2\frac{d^2\theta}{dy^2} + \ldots\right\},$$

so that $\qquad Q = -\overline{v(h_2-h_1)}\frac{d\theta}{dy} + \frac{1}{2}\overline{v(h_2-h_1)^2}\frac{d^2\theta}{dy^2} + \ldots.$

If the change in θ in the path $h_2 - h_1$ is small, only the first term need be considered, so that

$$Q = -\overline{v(h_2-h_1)}\frac{d\theta}{dy}. \tag{19}$$

The meaning of the expression $\overline{v(h_2-h_1)}$ will be considered later in connexion with diffusion, but by analogy with the Kinetic Theory of Gases we may suppose that there is some mean distance l' between the beginning of a path and its final end by the process of mixture such that

$$\overline{v(h_2-h_1)} = l'v. \tag{20}$$

The length l' so defined may be called the mixture length.

The effect of turbulence on the transfer of a property is therefore represented according to mixture length theories by

$$Q = -l'v\frac{d\theta}{dy}. \tag{21}$$

81. The momentum transfer theory.

To account for the distribution of mean velocity in turbulent fields of flow the hypothesis that momentum is a transferable property in the sense of equation (18) has been put forward. If the mean velocity U is parallel to the axis of x, and U is a function of y only, then the assumption that momentum is a transferable property enables us to write ρU instead of θ in (21). The Q in (21) then represents the rate of transfer of momentum in the y direction, and is identical with the Reynolds stress $\rho\overline{uv}$. This will be represented by $-\tau$, so that (21) becomes

$$\tau = -\rho\overline{uv} = \rho l'v\frac{dU}{dy}. \tag{22}$$

It will be seen from (22) that $\rho l'v$ is virtually a coefficient of viscosity.

The rate at which momentum is communicated to unit volume by turbulence is therefore

$$M = \frac{d}{dy}\left(\rho l' v \frac{dU}{dy}\right). \tag{23}$$

The values of the coefficient of virtual viscosity $\rho l' v$ can be found by analysing cases where the distribution of mean velocity has been measured; but before it is possible to put forward a theory by the aid of which distributions of mean velocity can be predicted, it is necessary to find out how the virtual viscosity depends on the mean velocity and the boundary conditions. For this purpose Prandtl[†] has put forward the hypothesis that

$$\overline{uv} = -l^2\left(\frac{dU}{dy}\right)\left|\frac{dU}{dy}\right|.$$

The idea underlying Prandtl's hypothesis is that it has been observed that the mean values of the squares of the three components of turbulent velocity tend to be equal to one another.[‡] If u and v were absolutely correlated and $u^2 = v^2$, then $u = v$ and $|\overline{uv}| = \overline{uv} = \overline{u^2}$. Since the momentum is assumed to be transferable

$$u = (h_1 - h_2)\frac{dU}{dy},$$

so that

$$u^2 = \overline{(h_1 - h_2)^2}\left(\frac{dU}{dy}\right)^2,$$

and hence when u and v are absolutely correlated

$$\overline{uv} = -\overline{(h_1 - h_2)^2}\left(\frac{dU}{dy}\right)\left|\frac{dU}{dy}\right|. \tag{24}$$

In fact u and v are not absolutely correlated, so that $|\overline{uv}|$ is less than u^2 or v^2; but the hypothesis that there is a length analogous to $\sqrt{\overline{(h_2 - h_1)^2}}$, for which

$$\overline{uv} = -l^2\left(\frac{dU}{dy}\right)\left|\frac{dU}{dy}\right|, \tag{25}$$

opens up the possibility of a partial explanation of the effect of turbulence on the mean flow of fluids.

With this hypothesis equations (22) and (23) become

$$\tau = \rho l^2\left(\frac{dU}{dy}\right)\left|\frac{dU}{dy}\right| \tag{26}$$

† *Zeitschr. f. angew. Math. u. Mech.* **5** (1925), 137, 138; *Verhandlungen des 2. internationalen Kongresses für technische Mechanik, Zürich,* 1926, pp. 62–74.

‡ See § 77 (p. 200).

and
$$M = \frac{d}{dy}\left\{\rho l^2 \left(\frac{dU}{dy}\right) \left|\frac{dU}{dy}\right|\right\}. \qquad (27)$$

It will be noted that the mixture length l defined in this way is not identical with the mixture length l'. The former can be evaluated in cases where τ is known (e.g. flow through a pipe), but l' can be evaluated only when both τ and ν are known.

Mixture length theories cannot be subjected to complete experimental verification. Their usefulness must be judged either by comparing the values of l obtained from (26), using experimental values of τ and U, with what might be expected from *a priori* considerations, or by making further assumptions about l and comparing the distributions of mean velocity calculated from (26) with those observed experimentally.

A generalized version of the momentum transfer theory applicable to cases where neither the mean nor the turbulent motions are confined to two dimensions has been given by Prandtl, who suggests, particularly when one component of the mean rate-of-deformation tensor is much greater than the others, the substitution

$$-\rho\overline{u^2} = 2\rho l^2 J \frac{\partial U}{\partial x}, \qquad -\rho\overline{uv} = \rho l^2 J\left(\frac{\partial V}{\partial x}+\frac{\partial U}{\partial y}\right), \quad \text{etc.,}$$

where
$$J^2 = 2\left(\frac{\partial U}{\partial x}\right)^2 + 2\left(\frac{\partial V}{\partial y}\right)^2 + 2\left(\frac{\partial W}{\partial z}\right)^2$$
$$+ \left(\frac{\partial W}{\partial y}+\frac{\partial V}{\partial z}\right)^2 + \left(\frac{\partial U}{\partial z}+\frac{\partial W}{\partial x}\right)^2 + \left(\frac{\partial V}{\partial x}+\frac{\partial U}{\partial y}\right)^2. \qquad (28)$$

82. Hypotheses for predicting l.

The simplest hypothesis for predicting l is that of Prandtl—that near a plane wall $l = By$, where y is the distance from the wall and B is a constant.[†] In a jet or wake Prandtl assumes that at any section l is proportional to the breadth of the section.[‡] Another hypothesis is that of Kármán—that l depends not directly on the distance from the wall but on the distribution of mean velocity. If l is to depend on the mean flow in the neighbourhood it must, in the case of two-dimensional mean flow parallel to the axis of x, depend on dU/dy, d^2U/dy^2, etc. The simplest length that can be derived from

† *Zeitschr. des Vereines deutscher Ingenieure*, **77** (1933), 105–113. See also Chap. VIII, § 153.
‡ *Verhandlungen des 2. internationalen Kongresses für technische Mechanik, Zürich*, 1926, pp. 62–74. See also Chap. XIII, § 252.

a measured distribution of U is $(dU/dy)/(d^2U/dy^2)$, and Kármán takes

$$l = K\frac{dU}{dy}\bigg/\frac{d^2U}{dy^2}, \qquad (29)$$

where K is a constant.† When there is no pressure gradient Prandtl's and Kármán's hypotheses come to the same thing close to a wall, for the value of τ is then independent of y. Prandtl's hypothesis gives

$$\tau = B^2\rho y^2\left(\frac{dU}{dy}\right)^2, \qquad (30)$$

while Kármán's gives

$$\tau = K^2\rho\frac{(dU/dy)^4}{(d^2U/dy^2)^2}. \qquad (31)$$

The solution of (30) is

$$U = \frac{\sqrt{(\tau/\rho)}}{B}\log y + \text{const.}$$

The solution of (31)‡ is

$$U = \frac{1}{K}\sqrt{\left(\frac{\tau}{\rho}\right)}\log y + \text{const.}$$

These are identical if $B = K$.

83. The vorticity transfer theory.‖

The assumption that momentum is a transferable property necessarily involves the assumption that the fluctuating variations in pressure, which certainly exist in a turbulent field of flow, are ineffective so far as the mean transport of momentum is concerned. The only case in which this can be proved to be true is when the momentum in the direction x is transferred in the plane yz by turbulent motion in which lines of particles parallel to the x-axis remain parallel to this axis throughout the motion. On the other hand, if the turbulent motion is two-dimensional in the plane xy, the ζ-component of vorticity is conserved, so that ζ is a transferable property.

Taking the case when the mean velocity U is in the x direction and

---

† *Göttinger Nachrichten, Math.-Phys. Klasse* (1930), pp. 58–76. See also Chap. VIII, § 158.

‡ For large speeds and small viscosity, dU/dy takes very large values at the wall. In solving (31) dU/dy has been taken as infinite at the wall. The solution of (30) automatically makes dU/dy infinite at the wall.

‖ Taylor, *Phil. Trans.* A, **215** (1915), 1–26; *Proc. Roy. Soc.* A, **135** (1932), 685 *et seq.*

is a function of y only, the full equation of motion, neglecting viscosity, may be written

$$-\frac{\partial}{\partial x}\left(\frac{p}{\rho}+\tfrac{1}{2}(U+u)^2+\tfrac{1}{2}v^2\right)=\frac{\partial}{\partial t}(U+u)-v\left(\zeta'-\frac{dU}{dy}\right),$$

where ζ' is the turbulent vorticity. Taking the mean value we get

$$\frac{1}{\rho}\frac{\partial\bar{p}}{\partial x}=\overline{v\zeta'}, \tag{32}$$

since the average value of u^2+v^2 will not alter with x. It appears, therefore, that in this case the effect of turbulence is to communicate momentum at rate $\rho\overline{v\zeta'}$ to unit volume per unit time. Hence in the notation of (23)

$$M=\rho\overline{v\zeta'}. \tag{33}$$

Since ζ is a transferable property,

$$\overline{v\zeta'}=-\overline{v(h_2-h_1)}\frac{d\bar{\zeta}}{dy}=-l'v\frac{d\bar{\zeta}}{dy}, \tag{34}$$

and since $\bar{\zeta}=-dU/dy$,

$$M=\rho l'v\frac{d^2U}{dy^2}. \tag{35}$$

Comparison of (35) with (23) shows that they are identical only when $l'v$ is independent of y.

Prandtl's hypothesis may be applied to the vorticity transfer theory by taking $l'v=l^2|dU/dy|$. The equation analogous to (27) is then

$$M=\rho l^2\left|\frac{dU}{dy}\right|\frac{d^2U}{dy^2}. \tag{36}$$

The expressions (27) and (36) may be used in comparing the results of the vorticity and momentum transfer theories in cases when M is known, as it is for instance in the turbulent flow through a pipe.†

84. The generalized vorticity transfer theory.‡

Averaging the equations of motion with the last expression in equation (20) of Chapter III for the acceleration, we see that, if viscosity is neglected, the equations of steady mean motion may be put in the form

$$U\frac{\partial U}{\partial x}+V\frac{\partial U}{\partial y}+W\frac{\partial U}{\partial z}=-\frac{1}{\rho}\frac{\partial\bar{p}}{\partial x}-\frac{\partial}{\partial x}(\overline{\tfrac{1}{2}q^2})+\overline{v\zeta'-w\eta'}, \tag{37}$$

† See Chap. VIII, §§ 156, 157.
‡ Taylor, *Proc. Roy. Soc.* A, **135** (1932), 697–700.

with two similar equations; or, in the vector notation of Chapter III,

$$\operatorname{grad} \tfrac{1}{2}V^2 - V \times \boldsymbol{\omega} = -\operatorname{grad}\!\left(\frac{\bar{p}}{\rho} + \tfrac{1}{2}\overline{q^2}\right) + \overline{\mathbf{v} \times \boldsymbol{\omega}'}. \tag{38}$$

In these equations (U, V, W) are the components of the mean velocity, denoted by $\mathbf{V}$; $\bar{p}$ is the mean pressure; (u, v, w) are the turbulent velocity components, with a resultant of magnitude q denoted, when considered as a vector, by $\mathbf{v}$; $\boldsymbol{\omega}$ is the vorticity of the mean motion, with components (ξ, η, ζ), and $\boldsymbol{\omega}'$ the vorticity of the superposed turbulent motion, with components (ξ', η', ζ').

(The equations in this form are exactly the same as Reynolds's equations, since the turbulent velocity satisfies the equation of continuity.)

When the motion is not confined to two dimensions the vorticity components are not conserved, and so the vorticity components are not transferable in the sense that heat is a transferable property. On the other hand, in a non-viscous fluid the components of vorticity at any point depend only on the vorticity of the same element of fluid at some initial time and on the nine components of strain and rotation which transform the element from its initial to its final state. This may be expressed in the Lagrangian system by Cauchy's equations†

$$\xi + \xi' = \xi_0 \frac{\partial x}{\partial a} + \eta_0 \frac{\partial x}{\partial b} + \zeta_0 \frac{\partial x}{\partial c} \tag{39}$$

and two similar equations, where (a, b, c) are the initial positions of the element whose coordinates are (x, y, z), (ξ_0, η_0, ζ_0) are its initial, and $(\xi + \xi', \eta + \eta', \zeta + \zeta')$ its final components of vorticity (in accordance with the notation above).

With the assumptions previously made, ξ_0, η_0, ζ_0 are also the components of the *mean* vorticity at (a, b, c). Thus if the mean motion is steady, and if only the first-order terms in a Taylor series are retained,

$$\xi_0 = \xi - (x-a)\frac{\partial \xi}{\partial x} - (y-b)\frac{\partial \xi}{\partial y} - (z-c)\frac{\partial \xi}{\partial z}, \tag{40}$$

with two similar expressions for η_0 and ζ_0. The substitution of these expressions in (39) provides formulae for (ξ', η', ζ'), and hence for $\overline{v\zeta' - w\eta'}$, etc. These formulae will be found in the paper by G. I. Taylor cited above.

If, with $(x-a)$, $(y-b)$, $(z-c)$ denoted by L_1, L_2, L_3, we are content

† Lamb, *Hydrodynamics* (1932), pp. 204, 205.

to neglect not only the squares of the L's, as in (40), but all terms quadratic in the L's and their derivatives with respect to x, y, or z, then the formulae for ξ', η', ζ' may be considerably simplified. It is convenient to start, not from the final form of Cauchy's equations for the vorticity, but from certain equations that occur in their derivation (equations (2) of § 146 of Lamb's *Hydrodynamics* or p. 42 of Cauchy's memoir, *Théorie de la propagation des ondes*). In the present notation these equations are

$$\xi_0 = (\xi+\xi')\frac{\partial(y,z)}{\partial(b,c)}+(\eta+\eta')\frac{\partial(z,x)}{\partial(b,c)}+(\zeta+\zeta')\frac{\partial(x,y)}{\partial(b,c)} \qquad (41)$$

and two similar equations. The equation of continuity in this, the Lagrangian, system is†

$$\frac{\partial(x,y,z)}{\partial(a,b,c)} = 1 \quad \left(\text{or} \quad \frac{\partial(a,b,c)}{\partial(x,y,z)} = 1\right),$$

and if, with the help of the equation of continuity, we express the derivatives of a, b, c with respect to x, y, z in terms of those of x, y, z with respect to a, b, c, we find

$$\frac{\partial a}{\partial x} = \frac{\partial(y,z)}{\partial(b,c)}, \qquad \frac{\partial a}{\partial y} = \frac{\partial(z,x)}{\partial(b,c)}, \qquad \frac{\partial a}{\partial z} = \frac{\partial(x,y)}{\partial(b,c)}, \quad \text{etc.}$$

But $\qquad \dfrac{\partial a}{\partial x} = 1-\dfrac{\partial L_1}{\partial x}, \qquad \dfrac{\partial a}{\partial y} = -\dfrac{\partial L_1}{\partial y}, \qquad \dfrac{\partial a}{\partial z} = -\dfrac{\partial L_1}{\partial z},$

and so, if second-order terms are neglected, the equation (41), together with (40), gives

$$\xi' = \xi\frac{\partial L_1}{\partial x}+\eta\frac{\partial L_1}{\partial y}+\zeta\frac{\partial L_1}{\partial z}-L_1\frac{\partial\xi}{\partial x}-L_2\frac{\partial\xi}{\partial y}-L_3\frac{\partial\xi}{\partial z}, \qquad (42)$$

with two similar expressions for η' and ζ'. Since

$$\frac{\partial\xi}{\partial x}+\frac{\partial\eta}{\partial y}+\frac{\partial\zeta}{\partial z} = 0,$$

and in terms of the L's the equation of continuity reduces to

$$\frac{\partial L_1}{\partial x}+\frac{\partial L_2}{\partial y}+\frac{\partial L_3}{\partial z} = 0$$

if second-order terms are neglected, (42) is equivalent to

$$\xi' = \frac{\partial}{\partial y}(L_1\eta-L_2\xi)-\frac{\partial}{\partial z}(L_3\xi-L_1\zeta) \qquad (43)$$

† Lamb, *op. cit.*, p. 14.

and two similar equations. In vector notation

$$\boldsymbol{\omega}' = \operatorname{curl}(\mathbf{L} \times \boldsymbol{\omega}), \tag{44}$$

where $\mathbf{L}$ has the components L_1, L_2, L_3.[†]

When the mean motion is confined to the direction of x, and U is a function of y only,

$$\zeta = -\frac{dU}{dy}, \qquad \xi = \eta = 0.$$

Then from (42)

$$\overline{v\zeta' - w\eta'} = \overline{L_2 v}\frac{d^2U}{dy^2} - \overline{\left(v\frac{\partial L_3}{\partial z} - w\frac{\partial L_2}{\partial z}\right)}\frac{dU}{dy}, \tag{45}$$

or from (43), on the assumption that $\overline{L_1 v'}$ does not vary with x or $\overline{L_2 w'}$ with z,

$$\overline{v\zeta' - w\eta'} = \frac{d}{dy}\left(\overline{L_2 v}\frac{dU}{dy}\right) - \overline{\left(L_1\frac{\partial v}{\partial x} - L_2\frac{\partial u}{\partial x}\right)}\frac{dU}{dy}. \tag{46}$$

If now the turbulent motion is two-dimensional in the (x, y) plane, the last term on the right in (45) goes out, and (37) becomes

$$0 = -\frac{1}{\rho}\frac{\partial \bar{p}}{\partial x} + \overline{L_2 v}\frac{d^2U}{dy^2}, \tag{47}$$

which is identical with (32) and (34), since $\overline{L_2 v}$ here has the same meaning as $\overline{v(h_2 - h_1)}$ in (34). On the other hand, if

$$\partial u/\partial x = \partial v/\partial x = \partial w/\partial x = 0,$$

so that lines of particles parallel to the axis of x move as a whole, the last term on the right in (46) goes out, so that (37) becomes

$$0 = -\frac{1}{\rho}\frac{\partial \bar{p}}{\partial x} + \frac{d}{dy}\left(\overline{L_2 v}\frac{dU}{dy}\right), \tag{48}$$

which is the equation of the momentum transfer theory. It is easy to show that when $\partial u/\partial x = \partial v/\partial x = \partial w/\partial x = 0$ (37) always reduces to the momentum transfer equation for mean motion in one direction, whether U is a function of y only or not.

85. The modified vorticity transfer theory.[‡]

The intractability of equations (42) makes it desirable to introduce some further assumptions with a view to simplification. One such assumption is that the components of vorticity are transferable in the sense that heat is transferable. With this assumption

$$\xi + \xi' = \xi_0, \qquad \eta + \eta' = \eta_0, \qquad \zeta + \zeta' = \zeta_0.$$

† Goldstein, *Proc. Camb. Phil. Soc.* **31** (1935), 351–359.
‡ Taylor, *Proc. Roy. Soc.* A, **151** (1935), 494–497; **159** (1937), 499–502.

These equations are satisfied if

$$\frac{\partial x}{\partial a} = \frac{\partial y}{\partial b} = \frac{\partial z}{\partial c} = 1$$

and
$$\frac{\partial x}{\partial b} = \frac{\partial x}{\partial c} = \frac{\partial y}{\partial c} = \frac{\partial y}{\partial a} = \frac{\partial z}{\partial a} = \frac{\partial z}{\partial b} = 0.$$

Under these conditions

$$\overline{v\zeta' - w\eta'} = \overline{(x-a)w\frac{\partial \eta}{\partial x}} + \overline{(y-b)w\frac{\partial \eta}{\partial y}} + \overline{(z-c)w\frac{\partial \eta}{\partial z}}$$
$$- \overline{(x-a)v\frac{\partial \zeta}{\partial x}} - \overline{(y-b)v\frac{\partial \zeta}{\partial y}} - \overline{(z-c)v\frac{\partial \zeta}{\partial z}}. \quad (49)$$

Equation (49), with the two equations formed by cyclic permutation of xyz, are the equations of the modified vorticity transfer theory.

If in addition we assume that the turbulent motion is statistically isotropic,

$$\overline{(x-a)w} = \overline{(y-b)w} = \overline{(x-a)v} = \overline{(z-c)v} = \overline{(y-b)u} = \overline{(z-c)u} = 0$$

and
$$\overline{(x-a)u} = \overline{(y-b)v} = \overline{(z-c)w} = K \text{ (say)},$$

so that
$$\overline{v\zeta' - w\eta'} = K\left(\frac{\partial \eta}{\partial z} - \frac{\partial \zeta}{\partial y}\right) = K\nabla^2 U \text{ simply.}† \quad (50)$$

86. Diffusion in turbulent motion.

Diffusion by turbulent motion is related to the mixture length in somewhat the same way that molecular diffusion is related to the mean free path. The coefficient of diffusion in the direction y is $\overline{v(h_2 - h_1)}$ or $l'v$, where l' is the mixture length (equation (20), p. 206).

If a diffusable property starts from a concentrated plane source the concentration after time T is proportional to $T^{-\frac{1}{2}}e^{-Y^2/4KT}$, K being the coefficient of diffusion and Y the distance from the source. If it starts from a line source the concentration is proportional to $T^{-1}e^{-Y^2/4KT}$, and if it starts from a point source the concentration is proportional to $T^{-\frac{3}{2}}e^{-Y^2/4KT}$. According to the mixture length theory K may be taken as $l'v$.

Measurements of the diffusing power of turbulence can be made in a wind tunnel by exploring the distribution of temperature downstream from a line or point source of heat. Taking the case

† When the mean velocity U is in the x-direction and is a function of y only, Prandtl's hypothesis is $K = l^2|dU/dy|$.

of a line source (e.g. an electrically heated wire) placed along the axis of z in a wind tunnel the centre line of which is the axis of x, the heat will diffuse, according to the mixture length theory, in the same way that it would under the influence of molecular conductivity in a non-turbulent stream, but the coefficient of conductivity will be much greater than in the molecular case. Except at points very close to the source the diffusion of heat in the wake behind a heated wire placed in a stream of velocity U_0 is nearly identical with the diffusion of heat from a concentrated plane source. Thus if the decay of turbulence down the wind tunnel is neglected, so that $l'\nu$ may be taken as constant, the temperature in the wake due to turbulent diffusion is

$$\theta = \frac{A}{\sqrt{x}}\exp\left(-\frac{Y^2}{4l'\nu T}\right);$$

and T, the time of diffusion, is x/U_0, so that

$$\theta = \frac{A}{\sqrt{x}}\exp\left(-\frac{Y^2 U_0}{4xl'\nu}\right) = \frac{A}{\sqrt{x}}\exp\left(-\frac{Y^2}{2\overline{Y^2}}\right), \tag{51}$$

where
$$\overline{Y^2} = 2l'\nu T = 2xl'\nu/U_0. \tag{52}$$

$\overline{Y^2}$ is the mean square of the distances of heated particles from the middle of the heat wake.

87. Discontinuous diffusion from a source in one dimension.

To simplify the calculation of diffusion we may suppose that a large number of particles start at time $T = 0$ from the origin $Y = 0$. We may suppose that they move with velocity ν through a distance d and that another path also of length d then starts, the direction of motion being independent of the initial direction, so that, at the end of a path of length d, there is no correlation of the velocity with its value at the beginning of the path. After n flights, i.e. after time $T = nd/\nu$, a fraction $(\frac{1}{2})^n$ of the total number of particles will be at distances $\pm nd$ from the origin. The proportions at distances $(n-2)d$, $(n-4)d$, etc., are the successive terms of the binomial expansion of $(\frac{1}{2}+\frac{1}{2})^n$. Thus if $n = 4$, $\frac{1}{16}$th will be at a distance $\pm 4d$, $\frac{1}{4}$ at $\pm 2d$, and $\frac{3}{8}$ at the origin. In general, the proportion at distance $(n-2s)d$ is $\dfrac{1}{2^n}\dfrac{n!}{(n-s)!\,s!}$.

In the limit when n is large the distribution tends to become Gaussian. To prove this Stirling's formula for large n,

$$n! \sim e^{-(n+1)}(n+1)^{n+\frac{1}{2}}(2\pi)^{\frac{1}{2}},$$

may be used, so that

$$\frac{1}{2^n}\frac{n!}{(n-s)!\,s!} \sim \frac{1}{2^n}\frac{(n+1)^{n+\frac{1}{2}}(2\pi)^{-\frac{1}{2}}}{(n-s+1)^{n-s+\frac{1}{2}}(s+1)^{s+\frac{1}{2}}}. \tag{53}$$

The maximum value of the right-hand side of (53) occurs when $s = \frac{1}{2}n$, i.e. near the origin. If we put $m = s - \frac{1}{2}n$ and take logarithms, we find

$$\log\!\left(\frac{1}{2^n}\frac{n!}{(n-s)!\,s!}\right) \sim f(n) - (\tfrac{1}{2}n - m + \tfrac{1}{2})\log(\tfrac{1}{2}n - m + 1)$$
$$- (\tfrac{1}{2}n + m + \tfrac{1}{2})\log(\tfrac{1}{2}n + m + 1). \tag{54}$$

If m is small compared with n,

$$\log(\tfrac{1}{2}n - m + 1) = \log\tfrac{1}{2}n - \frac{2(m-1)}{n} - \tfrac{1}{2}\!\left(\frac{m-1}{\frac{1}{2}n}\right)^{2} - \dots \tag{55}$$

The largest terms containing m in the right-hand side of (54) are

$$-m\!\left(\frac{m-1}{\frac{1}{2}n}\right) - m\!\left(\frac{m+1}{\frac{1}{2}n}\right) + \tfrac{1}{4}n\!\left(\frac{m-1}{\frac{1}{2}n}\right)^{2} + \tfrac{1}{4}n\!\left(\frac{m+1}{\frac{1}{2}n}\right)^{2}.$$

If m is large compared with unity, these reduce to $-2m^2/n$, so that

$$\log\!\left(\frac{1}{2^n}\frac{n!}{(n-s)!\,s!}\right) \sim f(n) - 2\frac{m^2}{n}.$$

The frequency of particles at distance $Y = (n-2s)d = -2md$ from the origin is therefore proportional to $e^{-2m^2/n}$, or

$$\exp\!\left(-\frac{Y^2}{2dTv}\right) = \exp\!\left(-\frac{Y^2}{2\overline{Y^2}}\right), \tag{56}$$

where $T\ (= nd/v)$ is the total time of diffusion, and

$$\overline{Y^2} = dvT. \tag{57}$$

Comparison of (56) and (57) with the expressions (51) and (52) previously obtained in terms of the mixture length l' shows that they are identical if $d = 2l'$. Since $l'v$ is the *average value* of $v \times$ (the distance moved by the particle since the beginning of its flight), it will be seen that l' might be expected *a priori* to be equal to $\frac{1}{2}d$.

The formula (57) could have been proved directly, since

$$\overline{Y^2} = \overline{(y_1 + y_2 + y_3 + \dots + y_n)^2}, \tag{58}$$

where $y_1, y_2, \dots, y_n$ are each numerically equal to d but may be either positive or negative. There is no correlation between the directions of successive jumps, so that

$$\overline{y_1 y_2} = \overline{y_2 y_3} = \overline{y_1 y_3} = \dots = 0.$$

Hence $$\overline{Y^2} = nd^2 = dvT. \tag{59}$$

88. Diffusion by continuous movements.[†]

The diffusion theory outlined above depends on a physical conception very like that of the mixture length theory. The process is carried out in definite jumps of length d, and at the end of each jump the previous history of any particle is, as it were, completely wiped out. In the discontinuous diffusion theory this idea is introduced by assuming that there is no correlation between the direction of any flight and the directions of previous flights. In the mixture length theory the particle is supposed to mix with its surroundings and to lose its identity at the end of each flight.

It is difficult to form a concept of any definite physical process equivalent to mixture in this sense. The processes involved are not in fact discontinuous as is assumed in these theories. The velocities in turbulent motion are continuous and the motions of particles are continuous.

To discuss diffusion of particles in continuous movement it is necessary to find some method for defining statistically the velocity of a particle and its variation with time. For simplicity we may consider a field of turbulent flow which is statistically uniform,[‡] so that the value of v^2 and the mean squares of all the derivatives of v with respect to time are the same at all points. We shall consider diffusion from a plane xz where all the diffusing particles are concentrated at time $t = 0$. If Y is the coordinate of a particle at time T, $Y = \int_0^T v \, dt$, and

$$\frac{1}{2}\frac{d}{dT}\overline{Y^2} = \overline{Y\frac{dY}{dT}} = \overline{Yv_T} = \overline{v_T \int_0^T v \, dt}. \tag{60}$$

Now in finding the average value of $v_T \int_0^T v \, dt$ we may imagine the whole time from 0 to T divided into n intervals. In each of these intervals the summation over all particles is made. Thus in the sth interval the contribution to the average value of $v_T \int_0^T v \, dt$ is $(\overline{v_T v_{Ts/n}})(T/n)$. Since the value of v^2 at time T is equal to that at Ts/n, $\overline{v_T v_{Ts/n}} = v^2 R$, where R is the coefficient of correlation

† Taylor, *Proc. London Math. Soc.* (2), **20** (1922), 196–212.

‡ For a theoretical discussion of the case where the turbulence is decreasing, as it is down a wind tunnel, see Taylor, 'Statistical Theory of Turbulence', *Proc. Roy. Soc.* A, **151** (1935), 429.

between v at time T and v at time Ts/n. It is clear that in continuous motion R becomes equal to 1 as Ts/n approaches T. If ξ is the time interval between T and Ts/n, we may use the symbol R_ξ to represent the coefficient of correlation between v at time T and v at time $T-\xi$. Then if $d\xi$ is the interval T/n, $(\overline{v_T\, v_{Ts/n}})(T/n) = v^2 R_\xi\, d\xi$. Hence (60) becomes

$$\frac{1}{2}\frac{d}{dT}\overline{Y^2} = \overline{Yv_T} = v^2 \int_0^T R_\xi\, d\xi \tag{61}$$

and

$$\tfrac{1}{2}\overline{Y^2} = v^2 \int_0^T\int_0^t R_\xi\, d\xi dt. \tag{62}$$

In general we may expect R_ξ to decrease with increasing ξ. Suppose that for all times greater than $\xi = T_1$, $R_\xi = 0$. Then $\int_0^T R_\xi\, d\xi = \int_0^{T_1} R_\xi\, d\xi$, so that when $T > T_1$,

$$\frac{1}{2}\frac{d}{dT}\overline{Y^2} = \text{constant} = v^2 \int_0^{T_1} R_\xi\, d\xi \tag{63}$$

and

$$\tfrac{1}{2}\overline{Y^2} = v^2 T \int_0^{T_1} R_\xi\, d\xi + \text{constant.} \tag{64}$$

Equations (64) and (52) may be identified except for the constant if

$$l' = v \int_0^{T_1} R_\xi\, d\xi. \tag{65}$$

The length $v \int_0^{T_1} R_\xi\, d\xi$ is therefore analogous, so far as diffusion is concerned, to a mixture length, but no assumption has been made about mixture in deriving it; indeed this theory of diffusion by continuous movements is equally valid if mixture never takes place.

When T is small $R_\xi = 1$, and in these circumstances the diffusion formula (62) gives

$$\overline{Y^2} = v^2 T^2, \quad \text{or} \quad \sqrt{\overline{Y^2}} = vT. \tag{66}$$

It appears therefore that, when T is small, $\sqrt{\overline{Y^2}}$ is proportional to T. This is clearly so, because over the time interval in which R_ξ is nearly equal to 1 the velocities of particles are nearly constant, so that for each particle $Y = vT$. In this case therefore not only is $\sqrt{\overline{Y^2}} = vT$, but the frequency distribution of Y is the same as the frequency distribution of v, which has been shown experimentally

to be the error distribution.[†] Measurements by Schubauer[‡] and Simmons[||] confirm this distribution at points near the source. Farther from the source the distribution seems to depend on the turbulence upstream of the grid.

The above-mentioned experiments were carried out by examining the distribution of temperature at various sections downstream from a heated wire placed across a wind tunnel down which a turbulent stream of mean velocity U_0 was blowing. If all particles leaving the heated source are supposed to have acquired the temperature of the source, the difference in temperature between any point in the heated region and that of the main stream is a measure of the frequency at which heated particles pass the point in question. The distribution of temperature near the source was found to be representable by the formula $\theta = Ax^{-1}\exp(-Y^2/2\overline{Y^2})$, where $\sqrt{\overline{Y^2}}$ was proportional to the distance downstream from the source and A is a constant.

It is a little confusing that the distribution of temperature close to the source is the error curve, just as it is when the distribution is due either to molecular diffusion or to the fact that a large number of uncorrelated paths have been traversed since the heated particles left the source. The distribution close to the source is the same as the frequency distribution of turbulent velocity, which happens to be the error distribution. If the frequency distribution of velocities had obeyed some other law, the distribution of temperature near the source would not have fitted an error curve. On the other hand, the temperature distribution very far from the source must necessarily fit an error curve whatever be the frequency distribution of velocities.

Since in the experiments the turbulent velocities were small compared with U_0, the time of diffusion T was x/U_0. Hence from (66)

$$\sqrt{\overline{Y^2}}/x = \nu/U_0. \qquad (67)$$

The value of ν found in this way from Schubauer's experimental results was very nearly the same as the value of u found at the same point in the air stream by means of a hot wire. These measurements therefore confirm the idea that turbulence produced, as in this case, by grids with regular spacing is isotropic.

The analysis of the diffusion of heat at greater distances down-

† Simmons and Salter, *Proc. Roy. Soc.* A, **145** (1934), 212–234. See also Townend, *ibid.*, pp. 180–211.

‡ *N.A.C.A. Report* No. 524 (1935).

|| Taylor, 'Statistical Theory of Turbulence', *op. cit.*, pp. 468–470.

stream, where R_ξ differs appreciably from 1, has been carried out, but is complicated by the fact that the turbulence dies away downstream, so that $\overline{v^2}$ is not constant down a wind tunnel.[†]

89. Atmospheric turbulence.

Most of the earlier discussions of the effect of turbulence on the temperature and velocity of the atmosphere were based on mixture length theories in which, for lack of information and for simplicity, a virtual coefficient of viscosity and of conductivity was assumed which was constant at all heights. These approximate theories yielded some useful results when applied to large-scale phenomena, such as the distribution of mean velocity in the lower layers of the atmosphere. They are not applicable to small-scale phenomena such as the diffusion of concentrated puffs of smoke. To discuss this the theory of diffusion by continuous movements has been adopted.[‡]

Taking
$$R_\xi = (a/v\xi)^n,$$

when $v\xi$ is large, (62) leads to

$$\overline{Y^2} = \tfrac{1}{2}c^2(vT)^{2-n}, \tag{68}$$

where $c^2 = \dfrac{4a^n}{(1-n)(2-n)}.$

For diffusion in the lower atmosphere it has been found that (68) fits the observations made with smoke clouds provided $2-n = 1\cdot75$, i.e. $n = 0\cdot25$.

The frequency distribution of velocities in the atmosphere is approximately Gaussian,[||] as it is in the turbulent air of a wind tunnel.

90. The dissipation of energy in turbulent motion.

When air flows through a pipe in turbulent motion at high Reynolds numbers it is known[††] that if the surface stress is expressed in the form $\tau_0 = \rho U_\tau^2$, then there is a universal velocity distribution of the form

$$\frac{U_c-U}{U_\tau} = f\!\left(\frac{r}{a}\right),$$

[†] Taylor, 'Statistical Theory of Turbulence', *op. cit.*, pp. 429, 468 *et seq.*

[‡] O. G. Sutton, 'Eddy Diffusion in the Atmosphere', *Proc. Roy. Soc.* A, **135** (1932), 143–165.

[||] Hesselberg and Björkdal, *Beiträge zur Physik der freien Atmos.* **15** (1929), 121–133; Graham, *A.R.C. Reports and Memoranda*, No. 1704 (1936).

[††] See Chap. VIII, §§ 154, 156, 157, 159.

where U_c is the maximum velocity along the axis of the pipe, U is the velocity at a distance r from the axis, and a is the radius of the pipe. Now τ, the Reynolds stress at radius r, is equal to $r\tau_0/a$, so that at any point $\tau/\rho U_\tau^2$, and therefore also $\tau/\rho(U_c-U)^2$, are constant if the speed varies. On the assumption that the root-mean-square value of each turbulent component of velocity is proportional to the observed maximum value, Fage[†] has shown that in a pipe u/U_τ, v/U_τ, w/U_τ stay constant as the speed changes at high Reynolds numbers, so that at any point τ/ρ (or $\overline{uv}$), $\overline{u^2}$, $\overline{v^2}$, $\overline{w^2}$ are all proportional to $(U_c-U)^2$. These conditions would be satisfied if, when U_c-U is increased in any ratio, the field of turbulent flow is increased at every point in the same ratio.

This hypothetical relationship between the turbulence patterns at different speeds would, however, be inconsistent with the condition that the dissipation of energy by viscosity must be equal to the work done. The rate of dissipation of energy per unit volume in geometrically similar fields is proportional to $\mu u_1^2 l^{-2}$, where u_1 is some typical velocity in the field, which may be either a mean velocity (e.g. U_c-U) or a turbulent component, and l is some typical length. Since the Reynolds stresses are proportional to ρu_1^2, the rate at which work is done per unit volume is proportional to $\rho u_1^3 l^{-1}$.

It is impossible therefore to account for the dissipation of energy in turbulent motion by imagining that a series of fields of flow which are possible at one speed can be repeated at a higher speed—though this hypothesis would account for other observed phenomena.

On the other hand, the fact that, when $U_c a/\nu$ is sufficiently high (a being the radius of the pipe), τ is proportional to $\rho(U_c-U)^2$ while u, v, w are proportional to $U-U_c$, shows that the rate of dissipation of energy per unit volume is proportional to $\rho u^3 a^{-1}$, even when there is no geometrical similarity between the flow patterns at different speeds.

91. Dissipation in isotropic turbulence.[‡] The length λ.

The simplest case in which the decay of energy can be discussed by statistical methods is that of isotropic turbulence, i.e. turbulence in which the average value of any function of the velocity components or their space derivatives is unaltered if the axes of reference are

[†] *Proc. Roy. Soc.* A, **155** (1936), 576–596.
[‡] Taylor, *Proc. Roy. Soc.* A, **151** (1935), 430–454.

rotated in any manner or are reflected.† Turbulent fields of this type can be produced in a stream of air by passing it through a regularly spaced grid of parallel bars.

The general expression for the mean rate of dissipation is

$$\overline{W} = \mu \left\{ 2\overline{\left(\frac{\partial u}{\partial x}\right)^2} + 2\overline{\left(\frac{\partial v}{\partial y}\right)^2} + 2\overline{\left(\frac{\partial w}{\partial z}\right)^2} \right.$$
$$\left. + \overline{\left(\frac{\partial v}{\partial x} + \frac{\partial u}{\partial y}\right)^2} + \overline{\left(\frac{\partial w}{\partial y} + \frac{\partial v}{\partial z}\right)^2} + \overline{\left(\frac{\partial u}{\partial z} + \frac{\partial w}{\partial x}\right)^2} \right\}. \quad (69)$$

For isotropic turbulence

$$\overline{\left(\frac{\partial u}{\partial x}\right)^2} = \overline{\left(\frac{\partial v}{\partial y}\right)^2} = \overline{\left(\frac{\partial w}{\partial z}\right)^2} = a_1,$$

$$\overline{\left(\frac{\partial u}{\partial y}\right)^2} = \overline{\left(\frac{\partial u}{\partial z}\right)^2} = \overline{\left(\frac{\partial v}{\partial x}\right)^2} = \overline{\left(\frac{\partial v}{\partial z}\right)^2} = \overline{\left(\frac{\partial w}{\partial x}\right)^2} = \overline{\left(\frac{\partial w}{\partial y}\right)^2} = a_2,$$

and
$$\overline{\frac{\partial v}{\partial x}\frac{\partial u}{\partial y}} = \overline{\frac{\partial w}{\partial y}\frac{\partial v}{\partial z}} = \overline{\frac{\partial u}{\partial z}\frac{\partial w}{\partial x}} = a_3,$$

where a_1, a_2, a_3 are symbols introduced for brevity. Hence

$$\overline{W} = \mu(6a_1 + 6a_2 + 6a_3). \quad (70)$$

The quantities a_1, a_2, a_3 are not independent. Since the fluid is assumed incompressible

$$\overline{\left(\frac{\partial u}{\partial x} + \frac{\partial v}{\partial y} + \frac{\partial w}{\partial z}\right)^2} = 0,$$

so that in isotropic turbulence

$$a_1 + 2a_4 = 0, \quad (71)$$

where
$$a_4 = \overline{\frac{\partial u}{\partial x}\frac{\partial v}{\partial y}} = \overline{\frac{\partial v}{\partial y}\frac{\partial w}{\partial z}} = \overline{\frac{\partial w}{\partial z}\frac{\partial u}{\partial x}}.$$

Another relationship between a_1, a_2, a_3, a_4 can be obtained by turning the axes through 45° about the z-axis. The transformation is

$$\begin{array}{ll} \sqrt{2}x' = x + y \\ \sqrt{2}y' = -x + y \end{array} \Bigg\} \qquad \begin{array}{ll} \sqrt{2}u' = u + v \\ \sqrt{2}v' = -u + v \end{array} \Bigg\}.$$

The transformation for $\partial u/\partial x$ is

$$\frac{\partial u}{\partial x} = \frac{1}{2}\left(\frac{\partial u'}{\partial x'} - \frac{\partial v'}{\partial x'} - \frac{\partial u'}{\partial y'} + \frac{\partial v'}{\partial y'}\right).$$

† This definition of isotropy implies strictly that there is no mean motion relative to the frame of reference. The results will be unaltered if a constant mean motion is superposed. If applied to other cases the results can, at best, be only approximate.

Hence $\left(\dfrac{\partial u}{\partial x}\right)^2 = a_1 = \dfrac{1}{4}\left\{\overline{\left(\dfrac{\partial u'}{\partial x'}\right)^2} + \overline{\left(\dfrac{\partial v'}{\partial x'}\right)^2} + \dots - 2\,\overline{\dfrac{\partial u'}{\partial x'}\,\dfrac{\partial v'}{\partial x'}} + \dots\right\}.$ (72)

The conditions of isotropy necessitate that terms like

$$\overline{(\partial u'/\partial x').(\partial v'/\partial x')}$$

shall vanish, for they would change sign by a rotation of the axes through 180°.

Collecting together such terms as $\overline{(\partial u'/\partial x')^2}$ and $\overline{(\partial v'/\partial y')^2}$ which are equal to one another in isotropic turbulence, and remembering that isotropy also necessitates that $\overline{(\partial u'/\partial x')^2} = a_1$, etc., we find from (72) that

$$a_1 = \tfrac{1}{2}(a_1+a_2+a_3+a_4),$$

or $a_1-a_2-a_3-a_4 = 0.$ (73)

Yet another relation between a_1, a_2, a_3, a_4 can be obtained by considering the mean value of $\nabla^2 p$. The equations of motion of an incompressible viscous fluid are

$$-\frac{1}{\rho}\frac{\partial p}{\partial x} = \frac{\partial u}{\partial t}+u\frac{\partial u}{\partial x}+v\frac{\partial u}{\partial y}+w\frac{\partial u}{\partial z}-\nu\nabla^2 u$$

with two similar equations.† Differentiating these three equations by x, y, z respectively, and adding, we get

$$-\frac{1}{\rho}\nabla^2 p = \left(\frac{\partial u}{\partial x}\right)^2+\left(\frac{\partial v}{\partial y}\right)^2+\left(\frac{\partial w}{\partial z}\right)^2+2\left(\frac{\partial v}{\partial x}\frac{\partial u}{\partial y}+\frac{\partial w}{\partial y}\frac{\partial v}{\partial z}+\frac{\partial u}{\partial z}\frac{\partial w}{\partial x}\right),\ (74)$$

and when we take the mean value of both sides of (74) we arrive at the equation

$$-\frac{1}{\rho}\overline{\nabla^2 p} = 3a_1+6a_3.$$

In a uniform field of turbulence $\overline{\nabla^2 p} = 0$,‡ so that

$$a_1+2a_3 = 0.$$ (75)

Combining (71), (73), and (75) we find that

$$a_1 = \tfrac{1}{2}a_2 = -2a_3 = -2a_4.$$ (76)

† These are the equations if there is no mean flow. If there is a constant mean velocity, the average value of the right-hand side of (74) is unaltered.

‡ Take integrals over a large volume V_1. Then

$$V_1\,\overline{\nabla^2 p} = \iiint \nabla^2 p\ dxdydz = \iint\left(l\frac{\partial p}{\partial x}+m\frac{\partial p}{\partial y}+n\frac{\partial p}{\partial z}\right)dS,$$

where the surface integral is over the boundary of V_1, and l, m, n are the direction cosines of the outward normal. Since the integrand of the surface integral does not continually increase as the volume increases, the surface integral divided by the volume tends to zero. Hence $\overline{\nabla^2 p} = 0$.

Hence (70) may be written

$$\overline{W} = 15\mu a_1 \quad \text{or} \quad 7{\cdot}5\mu a_2 \quad \text{or} \quad 7{\cdot}5\mu \overline{(\partial u/\partial y)^2}. \tag{77}$$

The value of $\overline{(\partial u/\partial y)^2}$ is closely related to the manner in which R_y† falls off from its initial value, $1{\cdot}0$, as y increases from zero. It has been shown in fact‡ that

$$R_y = 1 - \frac{1}{2!}\frac{y^2}{\boldsymbol{u}^2}\overline{\left(\frac{\partial u}{\partial y}\right)^2} + \dots . \tag{78}$$

The curvature of the R_y curve at the origin is therefore a measure of $\overline{(\partial u/\partial y)^2}$, and

$$\overline{\left(\frac{\partial u}{\partial y}\right)^2} = 2\boldsymbol{u}^2 \lim_{y\to 0}\left(\frac{1-R_y}{y^2}\right). \tag{79}$$

The significance of (79) can be appreciated by defining a length λ such that

$$\frac{1}{\lambda^2} = \lim_{y\to 0}\left(\frac{1-R_y}{y^2}\right). \tag{80}$$

λ is then the intercept on the axis of y of the parabola drawn to touch the (R_y, y) curve at its vertex (see Fig. 50).

From (77), (79), and (80)

$$\overline{W} = 15\mu\boldsymbol{u}^2/\lambda^2. \tag{81}$$

Since $\boldsymbol{u}^2$ and R_y can be measured by the hot wire technique, the relationship (81) can be verified if $\overline{W}$ can be measured by other methods. In the case of turbulence in a wind stream behind a grid, $\overline{W}$ can be found by measuring the rate of decay of turbulence downstream from the grid. The mean rate of loss of kinetic energy per unit volume is

$$-\tfrac{1}{2}\rho U_0 \frac{d}{dx}(\boldsymbol{u}^2 + \boldsymbol{v}^2 + \boldsymbol{w}^2),$$

or $-\tfrac{3}{2}\rho U_0\, d\boldsymbol{u}^2/dx$ in the case of isotropic turbulence.

† For the definition of R_y see equation (16), p. 204.

‡ Cf. Taylor, *Proc. Lond. Math. Soc.* (2), **20** (1922), 205, equation (14). Taking $\boldsymbol{u}^2$ as independent of y, and expanding u_y in a Taylor series, we have

$$R_y = \frac{\overline{uu_y}}{\boldsymbol{u}^2} = \frac{1}{\boldsymbol{u}^2}\left\{\boldsymbol{u}^2 + \overline{yu\frac{\partial u}{\partial y}} + \frac{y^2}{2!}\overline{u\frac{\partial^2 u}{\partial y^2}} + \dots\right\}.$$

But since $\boldsymbol{u}^2$ is independent of y,

$$\overline{u\frac{\partial u}{\partial y}} = 0, \quad \text{and} \quad \overline{u\frac{\partial^2 u}{\partial y^2}} = -\overline{\left(\frac{\partial u}{\partial y}\right)^2}.$$

Hence

$$R_y = 1 - \frac{1}{2!}\frac{y^2}{\boldsymbol{u}^2}\overline{\left(\frac{\partial u}{\partial y}\right)^2} + \dots .$$

This must be equal to $\overline{W}$, so that

$$-\tfrac{3}{2}\rho U_0 \frac{d}{dx}\,\boldsymbol{u}^2 = 15\mu\frac{\boldsymbol{u}^2}{\lambda^2}, \tag{82}$$

and all the quantities in this equation can be measured. The value of λ calculated in this way for the stream in which R_y was measured

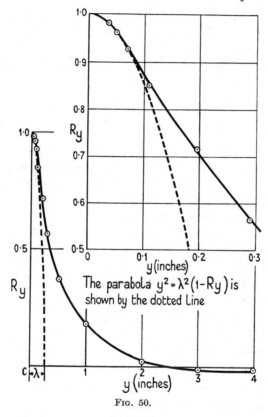

Fig. 50.

(see Fig. 50) was 0·26 in. The parabola $y^2/\lambda^2 = (1-R_y)$ is shown in Fig. 50. It will be seen that it lies close to the observed points near the apex of the R_y curve.

92. Relationship between λ and the scale of the turbulence.

We now consider how the length λ, which determines the dissipation, is related to the scale of the eddy-producing system. It has been pointed out that in a pipe the dissipation of energy is proportional to $\rho u^3 a^{-1}$, where a is the radius of the pipe. The scale of the turbulence produced is clearly limited by the diameter of the pipe. It seems therefore that, in comparing the dissipation in the turbulence produced by geometrically similar turbulence-producing mechanisms on different scales and at different speeds, we may suppose that the dissipation is proportional to $\rho u^3 l^{-1}$, where l is any linear dimension which defines the scale of the turbulence-producing mechanism.

It has been shown (equation (81)) that in isotropic turbulence the rate of dissipation is $15\mu u^2/\lambda^2$, so that, when geometrically similar systems are compared on different scales and at different speeds, then at any point $15\mu u^2/\lambda^2$ is proportional to $\rho u^3 l^{-1}$. Thus

$$\frac{\lambda}{l} \propto \sqrt{\left(\frac{\nu}{lu}\right)}. \tag{83}$$

When the turbulence is produced by a grid of regularly spaced bars distant M apart (i.e. of mesh M) placed across a stream of wind, each bar leaves a wake in the stream. This wake disappears some way downstream, leaving turbulence the scale of which must be determined in some way by the mesh (M) or by the diameter (D) of the bars. The distance downstream at which the wake disappears depends on the ratio D/M; when D/M is as great as $\frac{1}{5}$ the wake disappears within a length of about $20M$. Farther downstream we may suppose that the turbulence is statistically uniform across the stream, and we may take the mesh length M as the typical length l.†
Thus (83) becomes

$$\frac{\lambda}{M} = A \sqrt{\left(\frac{\nu}{Mu}\right)}, \tag{84}$$

where A is a constant to be determined by experiment.

A may be expected to be constant only when geometrically similar grids are used: it is found experimentally to be practically constant for all square-mesh grids, whatever the ratio D/M may be (p. 228).

93. The Reynolds number of turbulence.

It will be remembered that the considerations on which (84) is based are derived from observations on the proportionality of $\sqrt{(\tau/\rho)}$, u, v, w, and $U-U_c$ in a pipe, and that these hold only when $U_c a/\nu$, and hence ua/ν, are greater than certain numbers. It follows that (84) can be expected to hold only when uM/ν exceeds some definite number. This quantity, uM/ν, may be called the Reynolds

† In some cases the typical length must be taken as increasing with distance downstream from the grid. See the reference to *N.A.C.A. Report* No. 581 on p. 233.

number of turbulence. The lowest value for which (84) holds must be determined by experiment.

94. The law of decay of turbulence behind grids.

With the expression (84) for λ, (82) may be integrated: the integral is

$$\frac{U_0}{u} = \frac{5x}{A^2 M} + \text{constant}. \qquad (85)$$

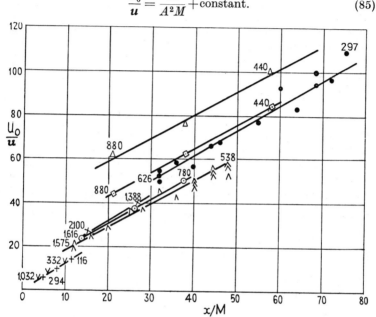

FIG. 51. Collected results of turbulence behind grids and honeycombs.

Dryden
$\begin{cases} \times & \text{5-inch grid, } M = 5 \text{ inches, } D = 1 \text{ inch.} \\ \odot & 3\frac{1}{4}\text{-inch grid, } M = 3 \cdot 25 \text{ inches, } D = 0 \cdot 65 \text{ inch.} \\ \boxdot & \text{Hexagonal honeycomb, } M = 3 \text{ inches.} \\ \triangle & \text{Honeycomb of 3-inch tubes, } M = 3 \text{ inches.} \end{cases}$

Simmons and Salter
$\begin{cases} \bullet & \text{3-inch square-mesh honeycomb, } M = 3 \text{ inches.} \\ \wedge & \text{3-inch grid of circular rods, } M = 3 \text{ inches, } D = \frac{7}{8} \text{ inch.} \\ + & \text{grid, } M = 0 \cdot 62 \text{ inch in 4-inch pipe.} \\ \vee & \text{grid, } M = 1 \cdot 5 \text{ inches in 1-foot tunnel.} \end{cases}$

Figures shown in the diagram give values of $u/M\nu$.

Thus if u is measured at different distances behind a grid, U_0/u should increase linearly. In Fig. 51 are shown measurements taken behind a square-mesh grid which verify this prediction.

If U_0/u is plotted as ordinate and x/M as abscissa, each set of observations taken at various distances down a wind tunnel behind a square-mesh grid should be on a straight line whose slope is $5/A^2$. In this way, with a range of grids from $M = 5''$ down to $M = 0.62''$, values of A were obtained varying only between the limits 1.95 and 2.20. Since the values of D/M were not the same in all the experiments, it seems that the scale of the turbulence depends on M, and not on D.

95. An experimental verification of isotropy in turbulence behind grids.

The comparison between the observed values of u^2 and the values of v^2 found by analysis of Schubauer's diffusion measurements (§ 88, p. 219) has shown that in a turbulent stream behind regularly spaced grids $u = v = w$. These conditions, however, do not form a complete verification of isotropy. A more complete verification can be obtained by measuring the correlation (R) between the values of u at pairs of points distant d apart along lines at various inclinations (θ) to the axis of a wind tunnel. If $\partial u/\partial x'$ is the gradient of u in a direction inclined at an angle θ to the tunnel axis (which is taken as the axis of x), then in the same way as (79) was found it may be shown that

$$\lim_{d \to 0} \frac{1 - R}{d^2} = \frac{1}{2u^2} \overline{\left(\frac{\partial u}{\partial x'}\right)^2}.$$

But

$$\frac{\partial u}{\partial x'} = \cos\theta \frac{\partial u}{\partial x} + \sin\theta \frac{\partial u}{\partial y}.$$

Also $\overline{(\partial u/\partial x).(\partial u/\partial y)}$ vanishes (since it would change sign with a reversal of the direction of the y-axis), so that

$$\overline{\left(\frac{\partial u}{\partial x'}\right)^2} = \cos^2\theta \overline{\left(\frac{\partial u}{\partial x}\right)^2} + \sin^2\theta \overline{\left(\frac{\partial u}{\partial y}\right)^2}.$$

From (79) and (80)

$$\frac{1}{2u^2} \overline{\left(\frac{\partial u}{\partial y}\right)^2} = \frac{1}{\lambda^2},$$

and from (76)

$$\overline{\left(\frac{\partial u}{\partial x}\right)^2} = \frac{1}{2} \overline{\left(\frac{\partial u}{\partial y}\right)^2},$$

so that

$$\lim_{d \to 0} \frac{1 - R}{d^2} = \frac{1}{\lambda^2} (\tfrac{1}{2}\cos^2\theta + \sin^2\theta). \qquad (86)$$

Hence, if $d/\sqrt{(1 - R)}$ is taken as the radius vector (r) in polar coordinates (r, θ), and plotted against θ, the resulting curve for sufficiently small values of d should be the ellipse

$$\frac{1}{r^2} = \frac{\cos^2\theta}{2\lambda^2} + \frac{\sin^2\theta}{\lambda^2},$$

with semi-axes $\sqrt{2}\lambda$ and λ.

Measurements of $(1-R)/d^2$ have been made by Simmons in a stream of wind rendered turbulent by a square-mesh grid of mesh 3 inches, and are shown in Fig. 52. The full-line curve in Fig. 52 is the theoretical ellipse, with axes in the ratio $\sqrt{2}:1$. It will be seen

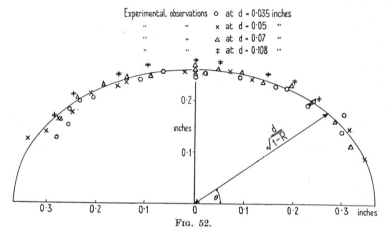

FIG. 52.

that the theory, which is based on the conception of isotropic turbulence, is very well confirmed.

96. The effect of a density gradient on stability.

The effect of gravity in suppressing turbulence in a fluid of variable density has been discussed from various points of view. Richardson and Prandtl† calculated the work done by turbulence against gravity in a fluid whose density decreases upwards. If Y is the height to which any particle in the fluid has risen above its original level, the work done per unit volume against gravity by the turbulence is

$$\tfrac{1}{2}\rho g\beta\overline{Y^2}, \quad \text{where} \quad \beta = \frac{1}{\rho}\left|\frac{d\rho}{dy}\right|. \tag{87}$$

† Richardson, *Proc. Roy. Soc.* A, **97** (1920), 354–373; *Phil. Mag.* (6), **49** (1925), 81–90. Prandtl, 'Einfluss stabilisierender Kräfte auf die Turbulenz', *Vorträge aus dem Gebiete der Aerodynamik und verwandter Gebiete, Aachen*, 1929 (Berlin, 1930), pp. 1–7.

The rate at which work is done is therefore

$$\tfrac{1}{2}\rho g\beta \frac{d}{dt}\overline{(Y^2)}.$$

When the turbulent energy is not decreasing this work must be supplied by the Reynolds stresses. If the mean motion is a uniform shearing parallel to the axis of x, so that $dU/dy = \alpha$, the rate at which the Reynolds stresses are doing work is $|\tau\alpha|$. Thus

$$|\tau\alpha| > \tfrac{1}{2}\rho g\beta \frac{d}{dt}\overline{(Y^2)}. \tag{88}$$

Now Y in (88) is identical with the Y used in the theory of diffusion by continuous movements, so that from (63) and (65)

$$\frac{1}{2}\frac{d}{dt}\overline{Y^2} = \mathbf{v}^2 \int_0^{T_1} R_\xi \, d\xi = l'\mathbf{v},$$

where l' is the mixture length. Hence

$$|\tau\alpha| > g\rho\beta l'\mathbf{v}. \tag{89}$$

If it is assumed that the momentum transfer theory of turbulent motion holds, then

$$\tau = \rho l'\mathbf{v}\alpha, \tag{90}$$

so that the momentum transfer theory necessarily gives the relationship[†]

$$\frac{\alpha^2}{g\beta} > 1. \tag{91}$$

This is Richardson's relationship. If therefore a motion is established such that $\alpha^2/g\beta < 1$, it cannot, according to the momentum transfer theory, be turbulent.

Taylor[‡] has calculated the stability equation for a non-viscous fluid of small uniform density gradient in uniform shearing motion. He finds that there is stability if $\alpha^2/g\beta < 4$.

Consideration of the stability of a system consisting of three superposed fluids moving with uniform shear led to the result that unstable oscillations can occur when

$$\alpha^2 > 2g\frac{\Delta\rho}{\rho h},$$

where $\Delta\rho$ is the small change in density at each interface, and h is the thickness of the central layer. Similar calculations for four fluids gave the lower limit for unstable waves as $\alpha^2 > 2\cdot 11g\beta$.

Similar results were obtained from calculations[||] for the case when

[†] Prandtl's version gives $\alpha^2/g\beta > \tfrac{1}{2}$, but the factor $\tfrac{1}{2}$ appears to be due to a mistake (see Taylor, *Rapports et Procès-Verbaux du Conseil Permanent International pour l'Exploration de la Mer*, **76** (1931), 35–43).　　　[‡] *Proc. Roy. Soc.* A, **132** (1931), 499–523.

[||] *Ibid.*, p. 509, and Goldstein, *ibid.*, pp. 524–548.

upper and lower fluids, each of infinite extent and moving with uniform velocity, are separated by a layer of uniform vorticity and intermediate density. The above stability results apply only to fluids of infinite extent. Schlichting[†] has extended the calculations of Tollmien on the stability of the boundary layer in a viscous fluid, and has found that the effect of gravity is to make all oscillations stable provided $\alpha^2 < 25g\beta$, where α now represents the rate of shear at the wall, and it is assumed that the density distribution is such that β is constant in the boundary layer and zero outside it. Measurements by Reichardt[‡] in a wind tunnel heated at the top seem to confirm Schlichting's theoretical result. It was to be expected that this result would differ from that which is valid in an infinite fluid.

97. Diffusion in a turbulent field with a density gradient.

It is not possible from the stability calculations to say anything about the possibility or otherwise of turbulent motion with any given density gradient. On the other hand, Richardson's criterion—that turbulence is possible only when $\alpha^2/g\beta > 1$—must be valid if the momentum transfer theory of turbulent motion is valid. Hydrographic measurements by Jacobsen of the current and density at all depths at various stations near Denmark have been analysed (partly by Jacobsen and partly by Taylor[||]) to find the transport of momentum and of salt in a vertical direction, together with values of $\alpha^2/g\beta$. The values of $\alpha^2/g\beta$ ranged from 0·008 to 0·38, yet the calculated rate of diffusion of salt and the calculated shear stress were thousands of times as great as could be accounted for by molecular diffusion and viscosity. It is clear therefore that turbulence can exist even when $\alpha^2/g\beta$ is as small as 0·008. For this reason it seems that the momentum transfer theory must be very far from the truth when there is a density gradient.

If we abandon the momentum transfer theory we can still get some information from the energy relation (88). If K_S is defined as the virtual coefficient of diffusion of salt, then $K_S = \frac{1}{2}d\overline{Y^2}/dt$, so that (88) becomes

$$|\tau\alpha| > g\rho\beta K_S. \qquad (92)$$

† *Zeitschr. f. angew. Math. u. Mech.* **15** (1935), 313–338.

‡ Prandtl and Reichardt, 'Einfluss von Wärmeschichtung auf die Eigenschaften einer turbulenten Strömung', *Deutsche Forschung*, Part **21** (1934), 110–121.

|| *Rapports et Procès-Verbaux du Conseil Permanent International pour l'Exploration de la Mer*, **76** (1931), 35–43.

Hence the energy relationship can be expressed in the form

$$\frac{\alpha^2}{g\beta} > \frac{K_S}{\tau/\rho\alpha}. \tag{93}$$

τ/α is a virtual coefficient of viscosity, so that $\tau/\rho\alpha$ may be regarded as a coefficient of diffusion of momentum. If we put† $\tau/\rho\alpha = K_u$, (93) becomes

$$\frac{\alpha^2}{g\beta} > \frac{K_S}{K_u}. \tag{94}$$

This equation can be verified, because both K_S and K_u can be calculated from the distributions of velocity and density in a stream where fresh water is flowing over salt water. The results of these calculations in two such cases (at Schultz's Grund and Randers Fjord) are given in Table 11.

TABLE 11

Schultz's Grund.   Randers Fjord.

Depth, metres	$\dfrac{K_S}{K_u}$	$\dfrac{\alpha^2}{g\beta}$	Depth, metres	$\dfrac{K_S}{K_u}$	$\dfrac{\alpha^2}{g\beta}$
2·5	0·09	0·14	1	0·17	0·17
5·0	0·13	0·26	2	0·20	0·38
7·5	0·067	0·17	3	0·15	0·26
10·0	0·023	0·098			
12·5	0·021	0·035			
15·0	0·05	0·008			

It will be seen that all the observations, except that at 15 metres at Schultz's Grund, satisfy (94). The exceptional observation is near a velocity maximum, so that α is nearly zero.

ADDITIONAL REFERENCES

Taylor and Green (*Proc. Roy. Soc.* A, **158** (1937), 499–521) show that when a special type of initial motion is given to a viscous fluid the rate of dissipation increases until it reaches a maximum, at which its value is in fair agreement with the formula (84) (p. 226) when A is given its experimentally determined value 2·0.

Kármán, *Proc. Nat. Acad. Sci.* **23** (1937), 98–105; *Journ. Aero. Sciences*, **4** (1937), 131–138. The correlation between the velocity components in fixed directions at two points is expressed as a tensor. If R_1 is the correlation between the velocity components in the direction AB at the two points A and B at a distance r apart, R_2 the correlation between the components at right angles to AB, it is shown that

$$r\frac{dR_1}{dr} + 2(R_1 - R_2) = 0. \tag{95}$$

(This is a generalization of (86) (p. 228).) On the assumption that the mean

† The momentum transfer theory assumes that $K_u = K_S$.

values of all triple products of components of velocities at A and B vanish, a theory is developed for the decay of turbulence behind a grid. With this assumption the (R_1, r) curve may be of constant shape; in such a case the decay of turbulence is expressed by the formula

$$\frac{U_0}{u} = \text{constant}\left(1 + \frac{x}{U_0 t_0}\right)^{5\alpha}, \tag{96}$$

which may be compared with (85) (p. 227): according to (96) it is only when $5\alpha = 1$ that U_0/u is a linear function of x.

Taylor (*Journ. Aero. Sciences*, **4** (1937), 311–315) shows that the special form of the (R_1, r) curve necessitated by Kármán's assumption (see above) is not in agreement with observation.

Taylor, *Proc. Roy. Soc.* A, **164** (1938), 15–23. In Kármán's expression for the rate of change of mean-square vorticity (*Journ. Aero. Sciences, op. cit.*) the terms neglected on the assumption that the mean values of triple products vanish (see above) can be evaluated from measured R_x curves. This is done in a particular case, and it is found that the value of the term which has been neglected is three times as great as the one which is not neglected.

Kármán and Howarth (*Proc. Roy. Soc.* A, **164** (1938), 192–215) show that a law of decay similar to (96) can arise when the triple correlations do not vanish, if further assumptions are made.

Dryden, Schubauer, Mock, and Skramstad, *N.A.C.A. Report* No. 581. In the Bureau of Standards tunnel the scale of turbulence increases with distance from the grid. The rate of decay is consistent with the formula

$$\frac{\lambda}{L} = B \sqrt{\left(\frac{\nu}{Lu}\right)}, \tag{97}$$

where L is the observed scale of turbulence defined by

$$L = \int_0^\infty R_y \, dy. \tag{98}$$

Some measurements are described in which band filters are inserted in hot wire anemometer circuits, thus eliminating all turbulence the frequency of which falls outside the band. (Cf. Chap. VI, § 121.)

Simmons and Salter (*Proc. Roy. Soc.* A, **165** (1938), 73–89) have constructed a set of high and low pass filters by means of which the turbulence behind a grid has been analysed into a spectrum. (Cf. Chap. VI, § 121.)

Taylor (*Proc. Roy. Soc.* A, **164** (1938), 476–490) shows that the spectrum of turbulence at a fixed point is connected with R_x by the pair of relations

$$R_x = \int_0^\infty F(n)\cos\frac{2\pi n x}{U_0} \, dn, \tag{99}$$

$$F(n) = \frac{4}{U_0}\int_0^\infty R_x \cos\frac{2\pi n x}{U_0} \, dx, \tag{100}$$

where $F(n) \, dn$ is the proportion of $\overline{u^2}$ which is due to components with frequencies between n and $n + dn$.

Dryden (*Journ. Applied Mechanics*, **4** (1937), 105–108) gives a bibliography of 31 papers and an account of developments between 1935 and 1937.

EXPERIMENTAL APPARATUS AND METHODS OF MEASUREMENT

98. Introduction.

THIS chapter is intended to give the reader a sufficiently detailed account of the apparatus and of the methods of measurement used in aerodynamic experiments to enable him to appreciate the general nature of the experimental investigations to which reference is made elsewhere in the volumes, and to have some idea of the accuracy and also of the limitations of present-day experimental technique.

SECTION I
WIND TUNNELS, WATER TANKS, AND WHIRLING ARMS

99. Wind tunnels.

A wind tunnel is an apparatus for producing a uniform air-stream in which the aerodynamic properties of bodies can be observed and measured. There are three main types of wind tunnel: (1) open circuit tunnels, (2) closed circuit (return flow) tunnels, and (3) compressed air (variable density) tunnels. In each of these types the stream at the working section may be either free (open jet type) or bounded by rigid walls (closed jet). A brief outline of the characteristics of each of these types follows: details can be found in reports published by aerodynamic institutions throughout the world.†

100. Open circuit tunnels.

The open circuit type (Fig. 53 (a) and (b), p. 236) consists essentially of a duct, usually of square or rectangular cross-section, through which air is sucked by a fan at the outlet end. The air is afterwards discharged into the room, and returns slowly to the bell-mouthed inlet. The fan is of the airscrew type, which gives a steadier flow than a centrifugal fan. Even so, the eddies created by the rotating blades

---

† See Eiffel, *Nouvelles Recherches sur la Résistance de l'Air et l'Aviation* (Paris, 1914); *Ergebnisse der Aerodynamischen Versuchsanstalt zu Göttingen*; *A.R.C. Reports and Memoranda*; *N.A.C.A. Reports*. For a summary see Hoerner, *Zeitschr. des Vereines deutscher Ingenieure*, **80** (1936), 949–957.

The area of the working section of a wind tunnel is usually of the order of 50 sq. ft., but one or two existing tunnels can house full-size aeroplanes. The biggest, at Langley Field, U.S.A., has an oval jet 60 ft. broad by 30 ft. high, in which a wind speed of about 120 m.p.h. can be reached with an expenditure of 8,000 horse-power. (See De France, *N.A.C.A. Report* No. 459 (1933).)

constitute a serious source of disturbance in the flow, and measures must be taken to minimize their effect. Behind the airscrew in the N.P.L.† type a 'distributor', consisting of a large rectangular compartment perforated on all sides with fairly small holes or slots, serves to return the air to the tunnel room at a fairly low speed and over a considerable area, and so to break up the violently disturbed flow behind the airscrew into reasonably small eddies which have time to die away during their slow passage through the room back to the intake. Alternatively, the distributor may be considerably reduced in size or even entirely dispensed with, a honeycomb wall being built across the tunnel room (Fig. 53 (b)) to break up the large disturbances discharged by the fan.

If the jet is open, as in the tunnels designed by Eiffel in France, it is necessary to surround it by an air-tight working chamber, since the pressure at the working section is necessarily below atmospheric. In either the Eiffel or N.P.L. type the room containing the tunnel should have a cross-sectional area many times that of the tunnel itself, in order that the return flow in the room may be very slow. Disturbances leaving the outlet are thus given time to die away, and the tunnel virtually takes its supply from still air at the intake end. In addition, there is fitted near the intake end, to prevent swirl about the tunnel axis, a honeycomb, i.e. a bank of thin-walled tubes of fairly small cross-section. Its chief function is to maintain the direction of flow parallel to the axis of the tunnel. It also serves to break up any occasional large eddies which may reach the intake.

101. Closed circuit tunnels.

The chief disadvantages of the open circuit type are the large room-space it needs and its low efficiency, consequent upon the waste of practically the whole of the kinetic energy of the air at the discharge end. By the continual circulation of the air in a closed circuit much of this loss is avoided, and a given wind speed is obtained for an expenditure of much less power than in the open circuit type. The arrangement has the disadvantages that the return flow is now not slow enough to allow disturbances from the airscrew to die away, and that the air current has to be turned smoothly through four right angles in its passage from outlet to inlet. The first difficulty is largely overcome by the gradual expansion of the return-flow ducts to about

† National Physical Laboratory, Teddington.

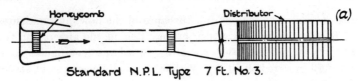

Standard N.P.L. Type 7 Ft. No. 3.

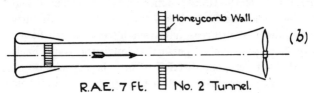

R.A.E. 7 Ft. No. 2 Tunnel.

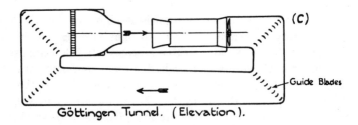

Göttingen Tunnel. (Elevation).

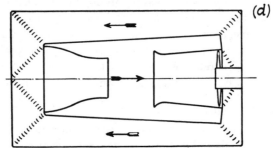

N.P.L. Return Flow Tunnel. (Elevation).

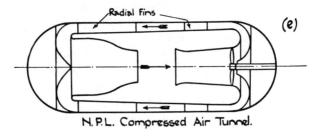

N.P.L. Compressed Air Tunnel.

Fig. 53.

four times the area of the working section, followed by a rapid contraction of the stream just before the working section is reached; the second is effectively surmounted by the provision of suitable guide vanes to turn the air smoothly round each right-angled bend.† Both the rapid contraction at the inlet and the guide vanes, which are the two essential features in the design of a successful closed circuit tunnel, were first used by Prandtl at Göttingen.

A honeycomb is usually placed just before the rapid contraction, but does not appear to be always essential; it has, for example, been omitted in the two new tunnels at the N.P.L. A definite improvement in both velocity distribution and power efficiency is obtained by placing radial aerofoils either behind or in front of the airscrew, set in such a way as to remove the rotation from the slipstream of the screw, and so to allow the air-current to reach the aerofoil cascade at the first bend behind the screw with only an axial velocity component.

The flow may be returned either by a single duct, or by two ducts symmetrically placed one on each side of the jet. Given a free choice, the single return duct is somewhat simpler to construct. The closed circuit open jet tunnels at Göttingen and the R.A.E.‡ are of this type; two at the N.P.L. have double return passages (Fig. 53 (c) and (d)).

The closed circuit type lends itself equally well to either a closed or open working section; as the return circuit is completely airtight the pressure at an open jet may be the atmospheric pressure, with free access to the jet from the tunnel room. The wind speed obtainable for a given power expenditure is appreciably lower with an open jet than with a closed one, but this is offset by greater accessibility and by smaller corrections for constraint of the tunnel flow in some experiments, e.g. airscrew tests.

102. Compressed air tunnels.

This type of wind tunnel, of which at present only two examples exist,‖ enables the Reynolds numbers of flight to be reached in a

---

† Klein, Tupper, and Green, *Canadian Journ. of Research*, **3** (1930), 272–285; Frey, *Forsch. Ingwes.* **5** (1934), 105–117; Collar, *A.R.C. Reports and Memoranda*, No. 1768 (1937); *Patterson, ibid.*, No. 1773 (1937); *Aircraft Engineering*, **9** (1937), 205–208.

‡ Royal Aircraft Establishment, Farnborough.

‖ A modified type of compressed air tunnel has recently been built at Göttingen. The pressure can be raised to 3 atmospheres, but it can also be reduced to 0·3 atmosphere. The latter condition enables high jet speeds to be reached without an excessive expenditure of power. This feature is of use mainly in connexion with tests

model test by the use of air at high pressure. It consists of a closed circuit wind tunnel, with jet open or closed, entirely enclosed in a steel shell capable of withstanding the requisite pressure. To economize space and to fit the tunnel neatly into the shell the return duct takes an annular form surrounding the working section (Fig. 53 (e)). Tests on a model at the N.P.L. showed that guide blades at the bends could be dispensed with, if a number of straight vanes was placed in the annular return duct to prevent a general swirl and a honeycomb employed immediately before the contracting jet. This is presumably because the return duct, completely surrounding the tunnel proper, has a comparatively small width perpendicular to the flow, so that its boundaries have a sufficient directive influence at the bends without intermediate guiding aerofoils.

The compressed air tunnel at the N.P.L.,† which has a jet 6 feet in diameter and a pressure range of 1 to 25 atmospheres, was first used for tests of wings and complete aeroplane models to provide data applicable to full-scale machines. It was later used to investigate certain fundamental problems at high Reynolds numbers, including the effects of surface roughness on the drag of aerofoils, the behaviour of flaps and other high-lift devices, and the drag of stream-line bodies. By the adoption of the momentum method of drag measurement (§ 115), the measurements of aerofoil drag in the tunnel have recently been extended to Reynolds numbers of the order of 24×10^6, the highest yet reached in wind tunnel tests.‡

103. Turbulence in wind tunnels and its effects.

Turbulence in the air-stream has an important influence on the nature of results obtained in wind tunnels, especially in certain kinds of measurement, of which the drag of stream-line bodies is a long-known example and the maximum lift of aerofoils a more recent one. In ordinary atmospheric tunnels the interpretation of results and their application to design is greatly complicated if

of airscrews or, with sufficient power and reduction of pressure, for the investigation of compressibility effects. See H. Winter, *Aircraft Engineering*, **8** (1936), 335, 336; *Luftwiss.* **3** (1936), 237–241.

† See Relf, *Engineering*, **131** (1931), 428–433.

‡ Relf, *Journ. Roy. Aero. Soc.* **39** (1935), 1–28; Relf, Jones, and Bell, *A.R.C. Reports and Memoranda*, No. 1706 (1936); Relf, Bell, and Smyth, *ibid.*, No. 1636 (1935); Jones and Williams, *ibid.*, No. 1708 (1936); No. 1710 (1936); No. 1804 (1937); Williams, Brown, and Smyth, *ibid.*, No. 1717 (1936); Williams and Brown, *ibid.*, No. 1772 (1937).

turbulence effects are present, since the results are then functions both of the Reynolds number and of the turbulence, and it is exceedingly difficult to separate the two effects.† In the compressed air tunnel, where full-scale Reynolds numbers are obtained, turbulence effects may prevent a direct application of results to full-scale prediction. Further, in order to study turbulence effects it is often desirable to be able to vary the degree of turbulence in a wind tunnel. It is thus of great importance in wind tunnel technique to be able to estimate the degree of turbulence present and to form some idea of the effects of such turbulence on the application of tunnel results to the problems confronting the designer.

Attempts to specify the degree of turbulence in a wind tunnel have been made in two different ways.† In one method a hot wire anemometer‡ is used to define the ratio of the root-mean-square longitudinal velocity fluctuation to the mean wind speed. In the second method the Reynolds number at which the drag coefficient $\left(\dfrac{D}{\frac{1}{2}\rho U_0^2 \pi d^2/4}\right)$ of a sphere is 0·30 is used as a measure of turbulence.‖ In certain tests in America the two methods were compared, and it was shown that a unique relation exists between the measured values of R_{crit} and $(\sqrt{u^2}/U_0)(d/M)^{\frac{1}{5}}$,†† where R_{crit} is the Reynolds number for the sphere defined above, and M is the cross-dimension of the mesh used to introduce the turbulence. These tests were made in a tunnel of N.P.L. type at different distances from the honeycomb, and the result was confirmed by similar tests at the N.P.L. This result is, however, not general: a unique relation is to be expected only if the turbulence is isotropic. As regards turbulence not produced by grids or honeycombs, it may be remarked that in tests of a sphere in flight made in America‡‡ it was found that even in the disturbed air near the ground in a wind the critical Reynolds number was practically the same as that on a calm day higher up, when conditions must have been almost non-turbulent. There is little doubt that the value of $\sqrt{u^2}/U_0$ was appreciable in the disturbed conditions

† See, for example, Dryden, *Journ. Aero. Sciences*, **1** (1934), 67–75.

‡ See §§ 117 and 119.

‖ For some results of measurements of this kind see Platt, *N.A.C.A. Report* No. 558 (1936).

†† Dryden, Schubauer, Mock, and Skramstad, *N.A.C.A. Report* No. 581 (1937). The existence of such a relation was first suggested by Taylor (see Chap. XI, § 219).

‡‡ Millikan and Klein, *Aircraft Engineering*, **5** (1933), 167–174.

close to the ground, and it must be concluded that the eddies present were so large that they affected the sphere as variations of total relative velocity and not as disturbances to the boundary layer. The effect of non-isotropic turbulence has not yet been investigated, but it has great practical interest, since most modern wind tunnels are of the return flow type with a large contraction ratio, and the transverse turbulent velocity components are in this case certainly not equal to the longitudinal one.

Very little can be said at present in regard to the correlation of turbulence measurements by methods suggested above with the effects of turbulence on the aerodynamic behaviour of various kinds of models tested in wind tunnels. The problem is under investigation, but so far the relevant results seem to indicate no general correlation. For example, the compressed air tunnel has given maximum lift results on certain aerofoils which agree well with full-scale observations, although the critical turbulence number for a sphere is 225,000 for the tunnel (6 in. sphere) and about 365,000 for the free air.† It would appear that in this instance the sphere drag is more sensitive to small degrees of turbulence than is the maximum lift of these aerofoils. On the other hand, tests in the compressed air tunnel at high Reynolds numbers, with the turbulence considerably augmented by means of screens, showed that different aerofoils react very differently as regards maximum lift variations. On the aerofoil section R.A.F. 28 a moderate increase of maximum lift with turbulence occurs at all Reynolds numbers, and appears to be roughly proportional to the degree of turbulence; but with the section Göttingen 387 the effect is small and indefinite at low Reynolds numbers, but very great at high Reynolds numbers (see Chap. X, § 198). These observations show the complexity of the subject, and suggest that much further research is required on the connexion between turbulence in the air-stream and the aerodynamic effects it produces by modifying the flow in the boundary layer.

104. The augmentation of turbulence in wind tunnels.

Screens or grids may be used to augment the turbulence in a wind tunnel. Such screens are often used when turbulence effects are being studied, since they are the only convenient way of producing varying degrees of turbulence in the same wind tunnel: varying

---

† Millikan and Klein, *loc. cit.* (15 cm. sphere).

turbulence on the model may be attained both by altering its distance from the screen and by altering the spacing of the cords or strips composing the screen. In practice the method is complicated by the difficulty in defining the mean speed behind the screen without very detailed velocity explorations,† and by the fact that the turbulence decreases with distance from the screen so that with a model of any length, such as a stream-line body, the turbulence is by no means constant along the body. Another method which has been used to render the boundary layer of a body turbulent is to attach excrescences to the body itself, e.g. to put one or more rings of fine wire around the nose of a stream-line body.‡ This method is open to the objection that, in addition to producing changes in the drag by making the boundary layer turbulent, it may alter the form drag; but this effect can be separated if the form drag is determined by pressure plotting. When this is done it is found that in the case of a stream-line body a sufficient number of rings near the nose will render the whole boundary layer turbulent behind them, and the addition of further rings does not then affect the skin-friction drag.

105. The degree of turbulence desirable in a wind tunnel.

Opinion is at present divided on the degree of turbulence desirable in a wind tunnel. It may logically be argued that an atmospheric wind tunnel ought to be fairly turbulent—not only because increased turbulence often simulates the effects of an increased Reynolds number, but because in a turbulent stream the boundary layer of a body is more easily rendered turbulent and the conditions are more definite than in a non-turbulent stream. Consider, for example, the measurement of the drag of a stream-line body. If the tunnel stream is very turbulent, the boundary layer of the body will become turbulent fairly near the nose at all reasonably high Reynolds numbers, and a consistent variation of drag with Reynolds number will be measured, similar to the variation obtained on a flat plate in turbulent flow. There is therefore a possibility of extrapolation to higher Reynolds numbers, where the boundary layer would be turbulent even in a non-turbulent flow, by using flat plate data as a guide. If, however, the body is tested in a tunnel of low turbulence, the drag results will in general lie on some transition curve, i.e.

† Ower and Warden, *A.R.C. Reports and Memoranda*, No. 1559 (1934).
‡ Ower and Hutton, *ibid.*, No. 1409 (1931).

the boundary layer will be partly laminar and partly turbulent, and any rational basis of extrapolation becomes impossible. On the other hand, it may be argued that since it is at present impossible to correlate the measurement of turbulence with the effects it produces on different aerodynamic phenomena, and since the free air is believed to be effectively non-turbulent, tunnels should have as low a degree of turbulence as possible. Moreover, in a non-turbulent tunnel any desired degree of turbulence can be introduced by a grid. Whichever of these views ultimately proves to be the best as regards the practical use of atmospheric wind tunnels, there is no doubt that the different turbulence characteristics of the various types of present-day tunnel are a great handicap in the comparison of results from such tunnels, and that a complete knowledge of the effects of turbulence would clear up many discrepancies at present existing between results from different sources. Only in the particular case of the compressed air tunnel is the position clear. Here the full-scale Reynolds number is reached, and it is obviously desirable that the degree of turbulence should be that appropriate to the free air, which, as far as boundary layer flow is concerned, is believed to be very small. Since it is difficult to make a non-turbulent tunnel of compact design, the only question which arises in practice is the definition of a minimum tunnel turbulence which is sufficiently low to satisfy the above requirement.

106. Force measurements.

The number of methods which have been used in this and other countries to support models in a wind tunnel and to measure the forces and moments acting upon them is very large, and it is impossible to deal with them all. In general, it may be said that the method adopted in any particular experiment depends very much upon the nature of the force to be measured and on the ultimate accuracy required. The chief concern in accurate work is to avoid undue interference between the supporting members and the model itself, and to devise the system so that any interference which may unavoidably be present is easy to determine accurately. For example, in measuring the lift and drag of a complete aeroplane model supported on wires from roof balances, both the wire drag and the interference effects of the wires are small compared with the forces on the model, and no difficulty is experienced. On the other hand, in measuring the drag of a body of very good form, such as a model airship hull, the wire drag may be greater than that of the model, and the interference of even very fine wires with the flow near the model may introduce serious errors, making an accurate determination of the drag of the model alone a very difficult matter. A few notes are given below on the more commonly employed methods of force measurement, with particular reference to those which bear most directly on experiments relating to the study of fluid flow.

107. Forces on a model aerofoil or complete aeroplane.

This class forms by far the largest group of wind tunnel measurements. Generally, such work is primarily undertaken to provide practical data for the designer, but the results obtained, particularly the maximum lift and minimum drag of aerofoils, are of great interest in connexion with the study of the flow near the model. In one method of making tests of this kind the model is supported in an inverted position in the tunnel by two wires from the wings, while the tail of the aeroplane model, or a short 'sting' at the trailing edge of an aerofoil, is attached by a pin joint to a vertical arm, shielded as far as possible from the wind (Fig. 54). The wing wires, generally vertical, are attached to a balance, enabling the tension in them to be measured, while the tail arm forms part of a composite balance which measures both the vertical and horizontal components of the force transmitted through the pin joint at the tail of the model. From a knowledge of the vertical reaction at the forward wires and at the tail, of the horizontal reaction at the latter point, and of the geometrical dimensions of the system, the lift, drag, and pitching moment about any chosen axis can be evaluated. The wire drag is found by repeating the measurements with two dummy wires added, and the drag of the exposed part of the tail support by detaching the model from that support and holding it rigidly by wires as close to the support as possible.

Other methods of measuring the forces and moments on complete model aeroplanes have been devised. At Göttingen† there is a six-wire suspension system in use which enables the three forces and three moments that completely define the force system on an asymmetrical body to be determined at one setting of the model. The total lift is given by the sum of the tensions in three vertical

† *Ergebnisse der Aerodynamischen Versuchsanstalt zu Göttingen*, **4** (1932), 8–12.

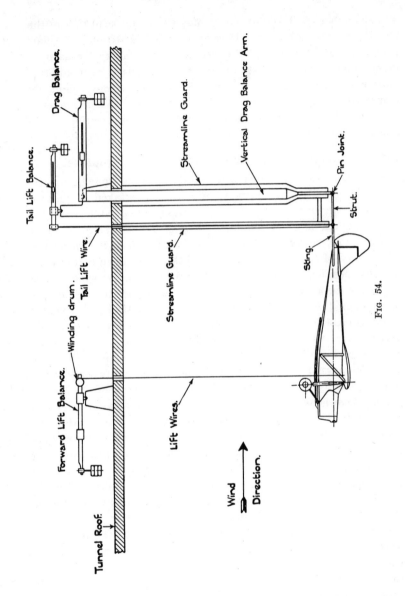

Fig. 54.

wires, the drag by the sum of the tensions in two horizontal wires, and the lateral force by the tension in a third horizontal wire perpendicular to the drag wires. The latter are led forwards in the horizontal plane and are attached to two rings, each of which is tied down by a wire inclined forwards. A third vertical wire passes from each ring to a roof balance, the tension in these vertical wires being defined by the unknown drag and the known or measurable inclination of the wires by which the rings are anchored. A similar arrangement is used for measuring the lateral force. Thus, the three moments and forces can be measured with the model supported entirely by means of a wire suspension. The absence of rigid supports reduces the interference with the natural flow near the model to a minimum.

For special experiments, special balances are often used. Thus an addition to an existing balance at the N.P.L. enabled yawing and rolling moments to be measured on a complete model aeroplane when yawed.† Another system of suspension has been used to measure separately the forces on the wings and bodies of a number of body-wing combinations. Automatically recording balances have been installed in some modern aeronautical laboratories.

108. Drag of stream-line bodies.

The method illustrated in Fig. 54 has been frequently used to determine the drag of stream-line bodies. Two wires, as fine as possible, are attached at the ends of a horizontal diameter of the body near its centre of gravity to form a V in a vertical plane perpendicular to the wind direction, with their upper ends attached to the tunnel roof. A short spike in the tail of the model is attached by a free joint to the end of the arm of a drag balance placed either above or below the tunnel. Wire drag is measured by attaching two extra wires to the body, at the same point as the main supporting wires, and taking them to the floor of the tunnel so as to form a V of the same dimensions as that formed by the supporting wires. It is arguable that the interference of two wires attached at the same point of the model but leaving it in different directions might not be twice that of one wire, and that there might be an error in the drag correction in consequence. This was examined at one time by

† Lavender, Fewster, and Henderson, *A.R.C. Reports and Memoranda*, No. 822 (1923).

supporting the model also by a single vertical wire and then adding successively one vertical wire underneath, and two forming a V. It was found that the values of the drag of the model alone, measured in several ways involving different wire arrangements, were in reasonably good agreement, and the conclusion was drawn that the standard method of test was reasonably accurate. In the light of later knowledge of boundary layer flow it would be expected that the wires would produce only a small effect due to interference if they were well behind the region of transition to turbulent flow in the boundary layer. This would usually be the fact with normal-sized models in a 7-foot tunnel at high speeds, but not at the lower speeds.

109. Force measurement in the compressed air tunnel.

It will be seen from the above that the general principle followed has been to support the model with as few wires or spindles as possible while allowing it the requisite freedom of movement in the direction of the force component to be measured. In the N.P.L. compressed-air tunnel the procedure is different, and the balance takes the form of a ring-frame surrounding the jet and shielded from stray air-currents. The model is attached to this ring by any convenient system of wiring or spindles, the sole requisite being that the attachment must be rigid so that the model cannot move relatively to the ring-frame. The aerodynamic reactions on the model are thus transferred to the ring-frame, and are determined by measuring successively the moments produced about three parallel horizontal axes perpendicular to the wind direction. The corrections for the drag of the supporting wires or spindles are determined as in other tunnels either by the method of duplication, or by separately supporting the model by wires from the balance guard, whichever is more convenient.

110. Water tanks and whirling arms.

Most of the aerodynamic data of experimental origin available at the present time have been obtained from work carried out in wind tunnels. There are, however, other possible methods of experiment, of which the two that are most widely used are the towing of models through still water or air. In the former method the water is generally contained in a long tank and the model is attached to a carriage which carries the necessary measuring apparatus, spans the width of the tank, and travels along its length. When models are to be moved through still air, they are usually attached to the end of a long arm capable of rotation about a fixed axis (whirling arm). Tank tests are used mainly in connexion with the design of ships and the hulls of flying boats or the floats of seaplanes. They have also provided some interesting information on surface friction.† Higher Reynolds numbers can generally be more easily reached in a large tank than in an ordinary wind tunnel, both because the kinematic viscosity of water is only about one-thirteenth of that of air and because larger models can be used.

Whirling arms are not much used to-day, except for special classes of experiments such as fundamental calibrations of anemometers or investigations of the effects of a steady rotation about an axis. The measurement of forces on models carried by a whirling arm is obviously much more difficult than the corresponding measurement in wind tunnel work.

It will be seen that the fundamental difference between the two methods of experiment described, viz. wind tunnel work and towing models through stationary air or water, is that in the one case the relative translational velocity between model and fluid is obtained by moving the fluid and in the other by moving the model. Theoretically, if we allow for effects due to the fact that on the whirling arm the motion of the model is not rectilinear, this difference in technique should make no difference to the fluid forces acting on the model. But in practice it is found impossible to generate a wind tunnel stream without imparting turbulence to the air (see above). Turbulence is absent, or at least widely different in character, in the fluid in the tank or the whirling shed. Hence differences in the results may be

---

† Froude, 'Experiments on the Surface Friction Experienced by a Plane moving through Water', *Report of the British Association, 42nd Meeting* (1872), pp. 118–124. See also *Report of the 44th Meeting* (1874), pp. 249–255.

Gebers, 'Das Ähnlichkeitsgesetz für den Flächenwiderstand im Wasser geradlinig fortbewegter polierter Platten', *Schiffbau*, **22** (1921), 687–690, 713–717, 738–741, 767–770, 791–795, 842–845, 899–902, 928–930.

Kempf ,'Über den Reibungswiderstand von Flächen verschiedener Form', *Proc. 1st Internat. Congress for Applied Mechanics, Delft*, 1924, pp. 439–448.

Perring, 'Some Experiments upon the Skin Friction of Smooth Surfaces', *Trans. Inst. Naval Arch.*, **68** (1926), 91–103.

Kempf, 'Neue Ergebnisse der Widerstandsforschung', *Werft, Reederei, Hafen*, **10** (1929), 234–239, 247–253.

Gebers, 'Einige Versuche über den Einfluss der Flächenform auf den Flächenwiderstand', *Schiffbau*, **34** (1933), 18–20.

anticipated in certain cases where the particular reaction to be measured is sensitive to changes of turbulence, even though the Reynolds numbers of two experiments are identical.

SECTION II
VELOCITY AND PRESSURE MEASUREMENTS

111. The pitot-static tube. Total-head and static-pressure tubes.

The pitot-static tube is the standard instrument for measuring air speed. It consists in effect of two tubes each of which includes a right-angled bend forming two branches, one usually shorter than the other. The head or shorter branch of one of the tubes is aligned with its axis along the wind direction and terminates in an open end. This tube—the total-head or pitot tube—measures the sum of the kinetic and static pressures acting in the air at its open end. The other tube, which in a suitably designed instrument measures the static pressure, is open to the stream through a number of small orifices in the walls of the head, with their axes normal to the axis of the tube, which is itself aligned with the stream. When the open ends of the stems are connected to opposite sides of a differential manometer the kinetic pressure is measured.

In the most convenient form of instrument the two tubes are arranged concentrically, with the static tube outermost, as shown in Fig. 55, which represents the N.P.L. standard pitot-static tube. Another form, shown in Fig. 56, differs from the first mainly in that the thin edge in which the tapered head of the standard terminates is replaced by a hemispherical nose. This facilitates manufacture and also makes the instrument more robust, for a thin edge is rather liable to damage. A round-nosed instrument (see Fig. 57) has also been designed by Prandtl, who has replaced the more usual static holes by an annular slit in the head of the static tube.

It is a matter for experiment whether the differential pressure measured by a pitot-static combination is in fact equal to the kinetic pressure. In general, the relation between the differential pressure and the velocity and density of the fluid can be expressed in the form

$$p = k \cdot \tfrac{1}{2}\rho q^2,$$

where k is a numerical factor which has to be determined by experiment. Apart from its dependence on the compressibility of the

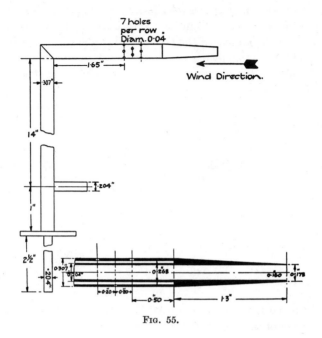

FIG. 55.

FIG. 56.

fluid, which for our purposes may usually be ignored, k will depend
on the form of the instrument, on the turbulence in the stream, and
on the Reynolds number of the flow past the tube. In those forms of
tube which are commonly used k is nearly constant and equal to unity.

A careful calibration of the N.P.L. standard instrument was made
at the N.P.L. in 1912.† For this purpose the instrument was attached
to the end of a whirling arm (see § 110) of about 30-foot radius and
moved through the initially still air in a large shed at speeds ranging

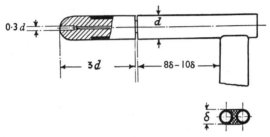

FIG. 57.

from 20 to 60 feet per second. After allowance was made for the
'swirl' speed of the air set up by the motion of the arm, the value of
k was found to be unity within $\pm 0 \cdot 1$ per cent. over this speed range.‡
Subsequent experiments in a water tank at equivalent water
speeds showed that this value of k could be taken to hold up to air
speeds of about 250 feet per second, while more recently a model
twenty-five times the linear dimensions of the original was also
found to have a factor of 1 between 20 and 90 feet per second. The
instrument shown in Fig. 56 has been calibrated in a wind tunnel
against the N.P.L. standard and found to have a mean factor of
$1 \cdot 000$ over the speed range 20 to 70 feet per second. Prandtl's tube
also has a factor very close to 1.‖

Calibrations of the two British instruments have been made at
air speeds below 20 feet per second.†† Although pitot-static tubes
are not often used at such low speeds in view of the difficulty of

† Bramwell, Relf, and Fage, *A.R.C. Reports and Memoranda*, No. 71 (1912).

‡ This close approach to unity must be regarded as fortuitous, for it was not until
some years later (see p. 252) that the distribution of pressure along the static tube
was investigated experimentally.

‖ Kumbruch, *Forschungsarbeiten des Ver. deutsch. Ing.*, No. 240 (1921), 29, 30.

†† Ower and Johansen, *A.R.C. Reports and Memoranda*, No. 1437 (1932); *Proc.
Roy. Soc.* A, **136** (1932), 153–175.

measuring accurately the very small kinetic pressures that are set up, yet very sensitive manometers (see footnote †, p. 276) have been designed for this purpose, so that the pitot-static combination can, if desired, be used at a speed of about 2 feet per second with 1 per cent. accuracy on speed. The following table gives the mean value of the factor k for the N.P.L. standard and for the round-nosed instrument over the range 2 to 20 feet per second.

Air speed 15° C. and 760 mm. (ft./sec.)	Mean k N.P.L. standard	Mean k Round-nosed instrument
2	1·020	1·055
4	0·989	1·006
6	0·995	1·001
8	0·992	0·996
10	0·991	0·992
12	0·992	0·991
14	0·995	0·992
16	0·998	0·996
18	0·999	0·999
20	1·000	1·001

It should be remarked that the accuracy of the results for the round-nosed instrument is probably inferior to that for the standard, but it is considered that the values given will enable an accuracy of 1 per cent. on air speed to be obtained even with this instrument at 2 feet per second. With the standard instrument the accuracy at 3 feet per second is believed to be within 0·5 per cent. on speed.

In use the head of the pitot-static combination has to be aligned with the wind direction. Fig. 58 shows for the N.P.L. standard instrument the variation in kinetic pressure reading with rotation about the axis of the stem,† and it will be seen that the correct position with the tube pointing into the wind ($\theta = 0°$) corresponds to a minimum pressure reading. Hence, provided the wind direction is known approximately (as it generally is even when there is doubt as to the exact direction) the correct presentation of the instrument is easily obtained by means of a search for this pressure minimum. In Prandtl's tube, alignment with the wind direction coincides, according to Kumbruch,‡ with a pressure maximum, but a similar procedure can obviously be adopted.

An experimental investigation of the characteristics of pitot-

† The dotted curve shows the corresponding variation in total-head reading.
‡ *Op. cit.*, pp. 7–14.

static tubes was carried out at the N.P.L. in 1925.† The most important outcome of this work was the information it provided to enable the position of the static holes to be adjusted with respect to

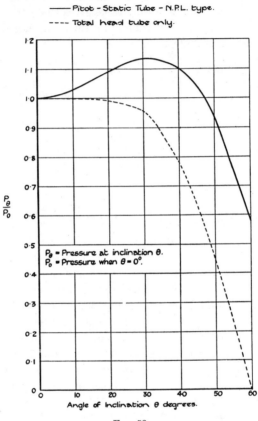

FIG. 58.

the nose and to the stem so that the negative pressure due to the former balances the positive pressure due to the latter and true static pressure is recorded at the static holes. Some previous work by Miss Barker had shown that the total-head tube indicates the true total head provided that qa/ν exceeds 30, where q is the air speed, a the radius of the mouth of the tube, and ν the kinematic

† Ower and Johansen, *A.R.C. Reports and Memoranda*, No. 981 (1926).

viscosity of the air.† Hence the total-head tube of an instrument of the dimensions shown in Figs. 55 and 56, when used in air at ordinary temperatures and pressures, will indicate true total head at all speeds above about 0·7 foot per second, and if in addition the position of the static holes is adjusted in the way just mentioned, it follows that the factor of such an instrument will be unity.

The fundamental calibrations of the pitot-static tube from which the factor k has been determined have invariably been made on whirling arms (§ 110). Thus apart from the swirls set up by the instruments themselves, the motion during calibration has taken place through stationary air. Calibration conditions have therefore been different from those encountered in moving air-streams, where there are, in general, turbulent components of velocity superimposed on the main translational motion. We must therefore consider the effect of these turbulent velocity components on the value of k.

In the first place, it appears that the total-head tube measures $\bar{p} + \frac{1}{2}\rho q^2 + \frac{1}{2}\rho \boldsymbol{q}^2$, where $\bar{p}$ is the mean static pressure, q^2 the square of the mean velocity, and $\boldsymbol{q}^2$ the mean square of the turbulent velocity.‡

The reading of the static-pressure tube gives a measure of the average total pressure inside the tube, and differs from the true average static pressure by a pressure arising from the impact of the fluctuating cross velocities on the tube and its holes. The difference in reading due to this 'impact' pressure depends on the design of the tube, especially on the number, size, and arrangement of the static holes, and on the magnitude and frequency of the cross velocities. If a tube has a large number of small holes equally spaced around its periphery, the reading with the tube aligned in the mean direction of flow is independent of the azimuth position of the holes. It is to be expected that the relation between the reading of the tube $\bar{p}_m$ and the true average static pressure $\bar{p}$ can be written in the form

$$\bar{p}_m = \bar{p} + k_s \rho (\boldsymbol{v}^2 + \boldsymbol{w}^2),$$

where k_s is a numerical factor which has a characteristic value for the same tube in turbulent streams of the same kind, and $\boldsymbol{v}^2$ and $\boldsymbol{w}^2$ are the mean squares of the cross components v and w of the turbulent

† *Proc. Roy. Soc.* A, **101** (1922), 435–445. According to F. Homann (*Forsch. Ingwes.* **7** (1936), 1–10) qa/ν must exceed 125. Corrections to be applied to measured values for small Reynolds numbers are given in the papers cited.

‡ For a theoretical discussion see Goldstein, *Proc. Roy. Soc.* A, **155** (1936), 570, 571.

velocity. Certain theoretical arguments indicate that k_s might be expected to have the value $\frac{1}{4}$, at any rate for isotropic turbulence,[†] but a reliable prediction of k_s can be obtained only by recourse to experiment. Fage[‡] has determined k_s from values of $\bar{p}_m$, v^2 and w^2 measured in turbulent flow in two sets of pipes having in the one case a circular and in the other a very elongated rectangular cross-section (so that in the second case the flow was very nearly two-dimensional). In these cases theoretical relations for $\bar{p}$ in terms of ρv^2 and ρw^2 are known, on the assumption that the stresses due to viscosity are small compared with the Reynolds apparent stresses.

The relations are, for the flat rectangular pipe,

$$\bar{p}/\rho + v^2 = \text{constant},$$

where v^2 is the mean square of the turbulent velocity component at right angles to the wider wall (Chap. V, equation (5)); and for the circular pipe

$$r\frac{\partial}{\partial r}(\bar{p}/\rho + v_r^2) = v_\theta^2 - v_r^2,$$

where v_r^2, v_θ^2 are the mean squares of the radial and circumferential turbulent velocity components at a distance r from the axis of the pipe (Chap. V, the first equation of § 71).

The conclusion obtained from Fage's experiments is that the reading of a static-pressure tube in fully developed turbulence exceeds the true static pressure by an amount given by $\frac{1}{4}\rho(v^2 + w^2)$. In isotropic turbulent flow $v^2 = w^2$ and the measured pressure exceeds the true pressure by $\frac{1}{2}\rho v^2$ or $\frac{1}{6}\rho q^2$. Hence the differential pressure will be $\frac{1}{2}\rho q^2(1 + \frac{2}{3}q^2/q^2)$.

112. Small total-head tubes.

Since very small combined pitot-static tubes are obviously difficult to construct, small total-head tubes are frequently employed for detailed explorations of the flow in the boundary layers of bodies such as cylinders or stream-line solids of revolution, and in transverse sections of pipes. The static pressure, a knowledge of which is required if velocities are to be deduced from the observations, is measured at holes in the surface of the body (see § 113) or in the

[†] Goldstein, *Proc. Roy. Soc.* A, **155** (1936), 571–575.
[‡] *Ibid.*, pp. 576–596. Kumbruch has investigated the effect of large disturbances: *op. cit.*, pp. 19–24.

walls of the pipe. In the case of boundary layer flow along bodies possessing curvature in the direction of motion, the assumption is made that the static pressure is constant through the layer along any normal to the surface, an assumption that ceases to be valid for practical purposes only if the curvature is rapid or the boundary layer unduly thick. Total-head tubes used for explorations of this kind are generally made of hypodermic tubing, nickel being a more suitable metal than steel as it is not liable to become choked by rust after long use. Usually a small diameter of tube is required, and the only limitation to be observed in this respect is that Miss Barker's criterion, $qa/\nu > 30$ (see p. 252), is still fulfilled at the lowest speed it is proposed to measure in any particular case. The tubes are best operated by means of a micrometer arrangement which, for accurate work, should be carried by the body or the pipe itself. In this way the distance of the point of measurement from the surface of the body is easily determined from the micrometer reading and a single measurement of the distance corresponding to one particular reading. The static-pressure observation should be made before the total-head tube is in place, or, at all events, when it is sufficiently distant not to influence the pressure at the surface hole. This is particularly important in measurements of the velocity distribution in pipes of small diameter.

113. Measurement of the distribution of normal pressure on solid bodies.

It has been mentioned in § 112 that the static pressure at a point in the wall of a pipe or in the surface of a body can be measured by boring a small hole in the surface at the point in question and connecting a tube to it by which the pressure acting there is conveyed to a manometer. Such pressure holes should be small in diameter, particularly if they are located in regions of large pressure gradient. About 0·01 to 0·02 inch diameter is a useful average size. The edges of the hole should be flush with the surface at which the pressure is being measured,—it is very important that no protruding burrs be left,—and the axis should be approximately perpendicular to the surface. By using a number of such holes at various points on the body and measuring the pressure at each, the pressure distribution on the surface can be obtained with an accuracy depending on the number of holes.

A convenient practical method of forming the holes in the surface is as follows:—Several soft metal tubes about 0·05 inch internal diameter—'compo' tubing—are let into grooves cut in the surface of the model so that their outer surfaces protrude slightly above that of the model. They are held in place by wax run into the grooves in a molten state, and the whole is then made good by scraping to preserve the designed contours of the model. The tubes are soft and thick-walled, so that there is no difficulty in scraping their slightly projecting exteriors flush with the model surface. One end of each tube is sealed, the other being open and connected by rubber tubing to a manometer. The pressure on the surface of the model at any point along the length of the tube can then be obtained by piercing a hole with a fine drill or needle in the wall of the tube at the point in question. When the pressure there has been observed the hole can be sealed with a special grease mixture or covered with a small piece of thin paper stuck over it, and the pressure at any other point along the tube can then be measured in the same way.

It should perhaps be mentioned that in such work the pressures are almost invariably measured as differences from the static pressure at some conveniently situated section of the tunnel, which is taken as the datum pressure.

114. Forces due to normal pressures.

For a cylinder the lift and drag per unit length due to normal pressures only are given by

$$L = \int p \, dx, \qquad D = \int p \, dy,$$

where the integrations are taken right round the contour of the cylinder. These are the areas of the curves obtained by plotting p against x and y respectively right round the contour. The former gives a single closed curve, the latter two loops whose areas are to be counted of opposite sign. Fig. 59 shows the pressure distribution for an aerofoil plotted in this way.

Another application of the same method arises in the determination of the form drag of stream-line solids of revolution with their axes along the wind direction. In such cases the pressure holes are distributed along a generator, and the form drag—i.e. the resultant drag due to pressure distribution only—is obtained by graphical evaluation of the integral $\pi \int p \, d(r^2)$, where p is the pressure measured at any pressure hole, r is the radius of the body at the hole, and the integration is along the length of the body. The percentage accuracy of the form drag of a stream-line body obtained

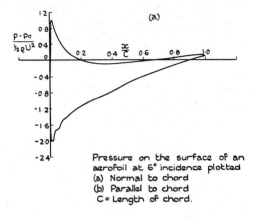

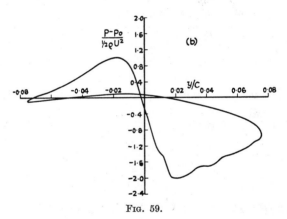

Pressure on the surface of an aerofoil at 6° incidence plotted
(a) Normal to chord
(b) Parallel to chord
C = Length of chord.

FIG. 59.

in this way is generally poor unless a very large number of pressure holes is used. The form drag of a stream-line body is generally small, so that the two loops of the curve of p against r^2 are usually of very nearly the same area. It is therefore difficult to obtain much accuracy in estimating the difference of these areas.

115. Prediction of drag from wake measurements.

The usual method of measuring the total drag of a stream-line body by balance measurements was referred to in § 108, but this force can also be determined directly from total-head losses in the wake, measured at a section at right angles to the general direction of motion and in a region where the velocity changes due to the body are small.† This method has a number of advantages over direct force measurements: it can be used in flight on aeroplanes or airships; there is little interference from wires or supports; and it can be used to find the drag for two-dimensional motion unaffected by end effects.

For an aeroplane wing in flight, measurements have to be taken fairly close to the trailing edge, where the velocity changes are not small, and a method of predicting the drag for this more general case has been developed by Betz.‡ The flow between two parallel planes at right angles to the direction of motion, one in front and the other behind the wing, is considered. The velocities and pressures in the front plane are denoted by U_1, V_1, W_1 and p_1 respectively, and the corresponding values in the rear plane by U_2, V_2, W_2 and p_2. At infinity $U = U_0$, $V = W = 0$, and $p = p_0$. The relation for drag obtained from the momentum equation is

$$D = \iint (p_1 + \rho U_1^2)\, dS - \iint (p_2 + \rho U_2^2)\, dS, \tag{1}$$

where the integrals are surface integrals taken over the entire area of the infinite planes. The merit of Betz's analysis is that he transforms these integrals so that the integration is restricted to the wake.

The total-head relations

$$H_1 = p_1 + \tfrac{1}{2}\rho(U_1^2 + V_1^2 + W_1^2)$$

and

$$H_2 = p_2 + \tfrac{1}{2}\rho(U_2^2 + V_2^2 + W_2^2)$$

are introduced, and on substitution in (1) the drag relation becomes

$$D = \iint (H_1 - H_2)\, dS + \tfrac{1}{2}\rho \iint (U_1^2 - U_2^2)\, dS$$
$$+ \tfrac{1}{2}\rho \iint \{(V_2^2 + W_2^2) - (V_1^2 + W_1^2)\}\, dS. \tag{2}$$

The total head is constant along a stream-line when the effects of viscosity and apparent friction due to turbulence can be neglected, so $(H_1 - H_2)$ is zero except in the wake, and the first integral is confined

---

† Taylor, *Phil. Trans. Roy. Soc.* A, **225** (1925), 238–241; also Fage and Jones, *Proc. Roy. Soc.* A, **111** (1926), 592–603.

‡ *Zeitschr. f. Flugtechn. u. Motorluftschiffahrt*, **16** (1925), 42–44. See also Prandtl, *Aerodynamic Theory* (edited by Durand), **3** (Berlin, 1935), 202–206.

to the wake. To transform the second integral a hypothetical flow is taken, which is the same everywhere as the actual flow except in the wake. In the wake the total head is taken to be H_1, the same as that in the undisturbed stream, the pressure to be p_2, the same as that in the actual flow, and the x-component of the velocity is denoted by U_2^*. The assumption made implies the existence of a distribution of sources at the body and in the wake ahead of the rear measurement plane, of total strength $Q = \int\int^T (U_2^* - U_2)\,dS$: the letter T denotes that the integration is confined to the wake, since everywhere outside $U_2^* = U_2$.† The second integral can be written

$$\tfrac{1}{2}\rho \int\int (U_1^2 - U_2^2)\,dS = \tfrac{1}{2}\rho \int\int (U_1^2 - U_2^{*2})\,dS + \tfrac{1}{2}\rho \int\int (U_2^{*2} - U_2^2)\,dS,$$

and, on the assumptions made, it may be shown by the theory of the stream-line flow of an inviscid fluid that

$$\tfrac{1}{2}\rho \int\int (U_1^2 - U_2^{*2})\,dS = -\rho Q U_0 = -\rho U_0 \int\int^T (U_2^* - U_2)\,dS.$$

The second integral then becomes $\tfrac{1}{2}\rho \int\int^T (U_2^* - U_2)(U_2^* + U_2 - 2U_0)\,dS$, and the drag relation (2) reduces to

$$D = \int\int^T (H_1 - H_2)\,dS + \tfrac{1}{2}\rho \int\int^T (U_2^* - U_2)(U_2^* + U_2 - 2U_0)\,dS$$

$$+ \tfrac{1}{2}\rho \int\int \{(V_2^2 + W_2^2) - (V_1^2 + W_1^2)\}\,dS. \quad (3)$$

For the case of an aerofoil of finite span, the sum of the first two integrals gives the profile drag and the third integral gives the induced drag.

An experimental determination of profile drag by Betz's method involves therefore measurements of both total head and static pressure in the wake. From these measurements the values of U_2 and U_2^* can be deduced from the relations

$$U_2 = \sqrt{\left(\frac{2(H_2 - p_2)}{\rho}\right)}, \qquad U_2^* = \sqrt{\left(\frac{2(H_1 - p_2)}{\rho}\right)}.$$

A value of the profile drag can then be determined graphically from

† $\int\int^T (U_2^* - U_2)\,dS$ will generally have different values at different sections of the wake, so in the hypothetical flow there must also be sources downstream of the measurement plane. The interaction between these sources and those upstream is simply neglected in Betz's method.

the sum of the first two integrals of relation (3). The contribution of the second integral is of the nature of a correction, which is small when the section taken is at great distance from the body, but is important near the body. The method has been used by Weidinger[†] and by M. Schrenk[‡] to measure the profile drag of an aeroplane wing in flight.

An alternative formula in terms of the total head and static pressure in the wake has been obtained and used by B. M. Jones[||] to obtain the profile drag of an aeroplane wing in flight. For an isolated stream-line body, experiencing a drag with no lift, a plane normal to the undisturbed velocity, U_0, can be taken far behind the body where the pressure is sensibly uniform and equal to the pressure in the undisturbed stream, p_0, the velocity being equal to U_0 everywhere in the plane except in the wake. If U_3 is the velocity in the wake and dS_3 an element of area in this plane, the drag, D, is given by the equation

$$D = \rho \iint U_3(U_0 - U_3) \, dS_3, \qquad (4)$$

where the integration is taken over the wake. This relation gives a reliable measurement of drag when applied to a real fluid with a turbulent wake. In flight experiments, however, it is necessary to mount the measuring apparatus fairly close behind the wing in a plane where the static pressure is not equal to the undisturbed pressure. The wake, assumed for the moment to be non-turbulent, can be divided into stream tubes, stretching from the far distant plane to the plane of exploration close behind the body. If dS_2 denotes the element of area cut off from the latter plane by a tube, q_2 the velocity of flow through the element, and ϑ the inclination of the velocity to the perpendicular to the plane, the drag is given by

$$D = \rho \iint q_2 \cos \vartheta (U_0 - U_3) \, dS_2. \qquad (5)$$

With no loss of total head in the tube of flow between the two planes all the quantities on the right-hand side of (5) can be determined from measurements taken in the plane close behind the body. In practice the flow in the wake is turbulent, and it is assumed that differences between the real flow and the assumed hypothetical flow

† *Jahr. Wiss. Gesellsch. Luftfahrt* (Munich, 1926), p. 112.

‡ *Luftfahrtforschung*, **2** (1928), 1–32.

|| 'Measurement of Profile Drag by the Pitot-Traverse Method' by the Cambridge University Aeronautics Laboratory, *A.R.C. Reports and Memoranda*, No. 1688 (1936).

do not affect the drag.† It is also assumed that the angle ϑ is small so that $\cos\vartheta$ can be taken as unity. It should be noted that when the mean direction of flow in the wake is inclined to the direction of the undisturbed stream, as in flow behind a wing exerting a lift, the measurement plane should be taken perpendicular to the mean direction of flow and not to the direction of the undisturbed stream. The relation (5) then gives the profile drag. For a stream-line body the assumption $\cos\vartheta = 1$ is probably sufficiently accurate, but close behind a bluff body may be a source of considerable error.

If H_2 and p_2 are the total head and pressure in the wake at the measurement plane,

$$H_2 = \tfrac{1}{2}\rho q_2^2 + p_2 = \tfrac{1}{2}\rho U_3^2 + p_0.$$

Write

$$g = \left[1 - \frac{(H_0 - H_2)}{\tfrac{1}{2}\rho U_0^2}\right].$$

Then

$$\frac{U_3}{U_0} = g^{\frac{1}{2}}, \qquad \frac{q_2}{U_0} = \left[g - \frac{(p_2 - p_0)}{\tfrac{1}{2}\rho U_0^2}\right]^{\frac{1}{2}},$$

and relations (4) and (5) reduce to the forms

$$D = \tfrac{1}{2}\rho U_0^2 \int\int 2g^{\frac{1}{2}}(1 - g^{\frac{1}{2}})\, dS_3 \tag{6}$$

and

$$D = \tfrac{1}{2}\rho U_0^2 \int\int 2\left[g - \frac{(p_2 - p_0)}{\tfrac{1}{2}\rho U_0^2}\right]^{\frac{1}{2}}[1 - g^{\frac{1}{2}}]\, dS_2 \tag{7}$$

respectively. Jones's relation (7) differs from Betz's relation (3) (in which the first two terms only are to be taken), but for the condition in which the method is likely to be used in practice the two relations become identical to first-order accuracy. The integrands may, in fact, be expanded in powers of $(p_2 - p_0)/(\tfrac{1}{2}\rho U_0^2 g)$, and are found to be identical as regards the first two terms of the expansion: they differ in the term involving the square of $(p_2 - p_0)/(\tfrac{1}{2}\rho U_0^2 g)$.

Values of the profile drag obtained at Cambridge from measurements at four distances behind a smooth aeroplane wing, and calculated according to relations (3), (6) and (7), respectively, are compared in Fig. 60.‡ It is seen that the differences between the drags given by Jones's relation (7) and Betz's relation (3) are negligible except for the observation made very close behind the trailing edge. The drag coefficients which would have been obtained

---

† Taylor (*A.R.C. Reports and Memoranda*, No. 1808 (1937)) has shown theoretically that in the worst case in Jones's measurements the error due to turbulent mixing is only $1\tfrac{1}{2}$ per cent.   ‡ See footnote ‖, p. 260.

if the rise in static pressure behind the wing had been neglected—i.e. from relation (6)—are given for comparison: the results are naturally more accurate the greater the distance behind the wing.

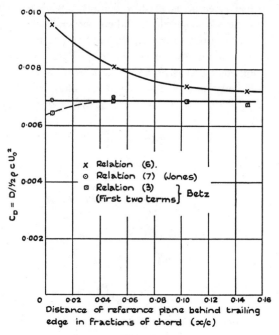

Fig. 60.

At some distance behind the body, g becomes very nearly equal to unity, and (6), which is equivalent to

$$D = \tfrac{1}{2}\rho U_0^2 \iint \left[1 - g - (1 - g^{\frac{1}{2}})^2\right] dS_3,$$

reduces approximately to

$$D = \tfrac{1}{2}\rho U_0^2 \iint (1-g)\, dS_3 = \iint (H_0 - H_2)\, dS_3.$$

Since H_1 in equation (2) can be identified with H_0, this is the result obtained by neglecting the second term in (2). In fact at a section in the wake some distance from the body the second integral of equation (2) is negligibly small, and if there is no lift, the third integral is zero and the drag becomes simply

$$D = \iint (H_1 - H_2)\, dS. \tag{8}$$

PLATE 23

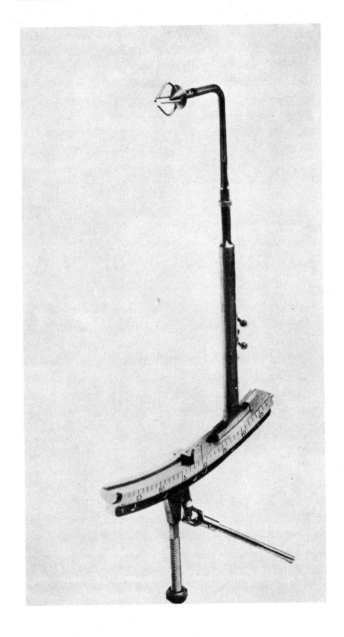

Fage and Jones† have shown that for an aerofoil at a small incidence the simplified expression (8) gives an accurate measure of the drag when the section is as close to the trailing edge as one chord length.

For the drag of a three-dimensional body of revolution the approximate expression corresponding to (8) is

$$D = 2\pi \int_0^{r_0} (H_1 - H_2) r \, dr,$$

where r_0 is the radius of the edge of the wake,—i.e. the radius at which H_2 is equal to H_1.

116. The determination of wind direction.

The mean wind direction at a small region can be determined by means of a pressure direction-meter.‡ This makes use of the experimental fact that the pressure given by a total-head tube falls off as the axis of the head of the tube is given an increasing inclination to the wind (see Fig. 58). When an inclination of about 45° is reached the rate of change of pressure with angle has reached a value not far short of its maximum, so that the sensitivity of a single total-head tube used as a direction meter is a maximum at about 45° inclination to the wind direction.

The direction and velocity meter shown in Fig. 61 and Pl. 23‡ has two pairs of fine total-head tubes, one pair being in a horizontal plane and the other in the vertical plane. The axes of the two members of each pair converge as shown at an angle of 90° towards their mouths, each tube being thus nearly at the angle of maximum sensitivity to the axis of the instrument. In use, the head is rotated about the axis AB until the pressures in the mouths of the two horizontal tubes 1 and 2 are equal, this condition being indicated on a differential manometer to which the tubes are connected. A rotation is then given about the perpendicular axis CD until tubes 3 and 4 also indicate zero pressure difference. If the instrument were perfectly symmetrically constructed, the wind direction would then lie along the common axis of symmetry of the two pairs of tubes forming the direction-head. Actually, however, there will always be a small error on each pair of tubes, and the instrument is really only used to indicate changes of direction from a direction of reference

---

† *Proc. Roy. Soc.* A, **111** (1926), 592–603.
‡ Lavender, *A.R.C. Reports and Memoranda*, No. 844 (1923).

which is generally the axis of the wind tunnel.† The wind direction in the empty tunnel is assumed to be along the axis, and a preliminary adjustment of the instrument to zero pressure difference in the empty tunnel (i.e. before the model is in place) serves to establish the zero for direction changes in the plane of each pair of tubes. These direction changes are read off on two angle scales provided for the purpose.

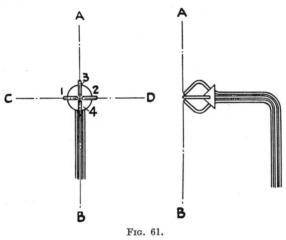

Fig. 61.

Velocity is obtained from a reading of the difference in pressure between the mouth of the fifth central tube and the mouth of any one of the other four, the reading being taken when the head has been adjusted to its null position. In order to increase the velocity reading, tube 5 opens into the space behind a small hollow cone, and is thus in a region of fairly intense suction. A preliminary calibration against a standard pitot tube has to be made to establish the relation between velocity and the differential reading obtained from tube 5 and the selected one of the other four. Tube 5 cannot be seen in Fig. 61; it is a central tube with its opening sheltered by the apex of the cone.

The accuracy of the instrument is about $\frac{1}{10}$ degree on angle and $\frac{1}{2}$ per cent. on velocity.

Hot wire direction-meters are described in § 118 below.

† The instrument would indicate absolute direction if it were reversible. To make it so, however, leads to mechanical complication and the instrument is generally used in the simpler manner described.

117. Electrical methods.   The hot wire anemometer.

A type of instrument especially suitable for use as a low-speed anemometer and for recording the speed variations in turbulent flow consists of a fine electrically heated wire (0·001 to 0·005 inch diameter) stretched across the ends of two prongs. When exposed to an air-stream the wire loses heat by convection, and consequently its temperature, and therefore electrical resistance, varies with the speed and current in accordance with a law which can be established by calibration tests. In one method of using the instrument the wire is heated by a constant current and the speed is deter-mined from a measurement of the resis-tance; in another, the wire is maintained at a constant temperature and the speed is determined from the measured value of the current. Either method can be used for recording low speeds, but the latter is generally used at speeds greater than

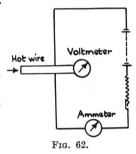

Fig. 62.

about 10 feet per second on account of the increased accuracy obtainable.

The electrical measurements are made with the wire connected to a special circuit. One form, suitable for the constant current method, is shown in Fig. 62. Here the wire is placed in series with a battery and a rheostat, the latter being adjusted to keep the current at a constant average value. A voltmeter is connected across the wire to indicate the potential drop, and so gives a reading which is related to the speed in a manner determinable by calibration. With a fine platinum wire heated to about 500° C. in still air, the method can be used to measure speeds up to 100 feet per second; the accuracy, however, although high at the low end of the range, decreases with increase of speed. If a platinum wire of 0·4 inch length and 0·005 inch diameter, heated by a current of 0·118 ampere, is used, and if measurements of current and voltage are accurate to 1 part in 500, then, from the curve of Fig. 63, it should be possible to determine a speed of 3 feet per second to within ±0·04 foot per second and a speed of 90 feet per second to within ±3·3 feet per second. These figures are not, however, realized in practice, because the cali-bration characteristic is subject to change, partly through the 'ageing' of the wire and partly through the accumulation of dust, which affects the thermal conditions at the surface. For this reason hot wires must be frequently calibrated against a standard instrument.

In the second method the hot wire forms one arm of a Wheatstone bridge (Fig. 64) which has in the other three arms resistances such that the bridge is in balance when the temperature, and consequently the

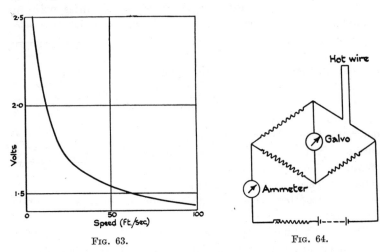

Fig. 63. Fig. 64.

resistance, of the wire reaches some desired value. Any change in the speed necessitates an adjustment of the heating current to restore the wire to its former temperature. This is effected by means of a rheostat in series with the battery, so that when the bridge is again in balance the change in current gives a measure of the speed. For most purposes the current in the external circuit is measured, usually with a reflecting pointer type of ammeter, the readings of which can be related to speed by calibration. A typical calibration curve for the platinum wire previously referred to is shown in Fig. 65: from this it is evident that the changes of resistance resulting from the cooling are most marked at low speeds. The estimated limits of accuracy of measurements made at 3 and 90 feet per second are ± 0.048 and ± 0.65 foot per second respectively. It should be added that, for reasons already stated, these figures are probably unduly favourable.

A more nearly linear calibration curve can be obtained if, in place of the ammeter, a fine wire enclosed in a tube and connected to a voltmeter† is used for measuring current. On the passage of the current the wire is heated to a high temperature. Any change of current affects the resistance, and so produces a proportionately greater change of potential across the wire. Thus, if the wire is appropriately chosen, it is possible to extend the range of the readings for the higher speeds, and thereby to secure a fairly uniform scale.

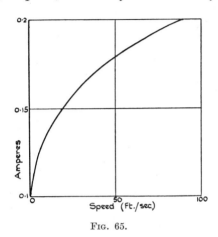

Fig. 65.

118. Electrical methods. Hot wire direction-meters.

Although a hot wire held transversely to the stream is insensitive to direction, a combination of two parallel hot wires placed close together can be used to indicate the direction of flow. The method depends on the fact that the cooling of the second wire is influenced by the wake of the first, and consequently the temperature difference between the two is a maximum when one is shielded by the other. To determine this position the wires are mounted on a support and rotated about a transverse axis until the out-of-balance current of a Wheatstone bridge, of which they constitute two adjacent arms, is a maximum. In general, the accuracy obtainable is not high, being seldom greater than $\pm 0.25°$.

The two-wire direction-meter illustrated in Fig. 66 is a more sensitive instrument.‡ It comprises two short inclined wires fused together to the end of a vertical manganin support, the free ends

† Huguenard, Magnan, and Planiol, *Comptes Rendus*, **176** (1923), 287. Also King, *Engineering*, **117** (1924), 136, 249.

‡ Simmons and Bailey, *A.R.C. Reports and Memoranda*, No. 1019 (1926).

being similarly fused, each to a separate support. In use the wires are set roughly in a plane parallel to the flow with the common point upstream. Under these conditions equal wires, heated by the same current, are equally cooled when the line bisecting the angle between them lies along the direction of flow. To find the wind direction the wires are therefore rotated to a position where the temperature of each wire is the same, as shown by the balance of a Wheatstone

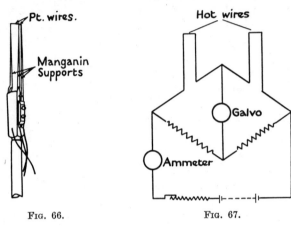

FIG. 66.   FIG. 67.

bridge, to which they are connected in the manner shown in Fig. 67. If, as usually happens, the wires differ slightly in length, in the null position the axis of symmetry will be inclined at a small angle to the stream. The error arising from this cause can be measured in the empty tunnel, wherein the direction of flow is known, and a correction applied to any subsequent measurements made in the neighbourhood of a model.

119. Electrical methods. Measurements of speed variations in turbulent flow.

A hot wire anemometer held transversely to the stream affords a convenient means of recording the variation of longitudinal speed due to turbulence.† In the method most commonly employed it is connected to a Wheatstone bridge similar to Fig. 64, which is balanced in the usual manner by adjusting the heating current until the galvanometer reading is zero. But though the average potential

† Dryden and Kuethe, *N.A.C.A. Report* No. 320 (1929). Also Mock and Dryden, *ibid.*, No. 448 (1932).

across the wire is thus neutralized, there exists a potential varying with the changes of speed. These fluctuations are too fast to be registered by the ordinary galvanometer, and too small to be measured with an A.C. instrument unless first magnified. The bridge is accordingly coupled to a valve amplifier, and the out-of-balance potential measured in terms of the variations of the output current by a thermo-junction type of ammeter or (in cases where the wave form is required) by the cathode-ray oscillograph. The speed variations are then deduced from the electrical constant of the Wheatstone bridge and the amplifier, coupled with a knowledge of the law of cooling of the wire.

Due allowance must be made for the decrease in the response of the wire at high frequencies, since even with the finest wire (of 0·0001 inch diameter) the amplitude of the potential changes are neither proportional to, nor in phase with, the speed variations at frequencies above about 100 cycles per second. Electrical methods of compensating the loss of response have been developed by Dryden and Kuethe,† and, independently, by Ziegler.‡ These, it has been shown, enable a wire to record accurately small changes of speed up to a frequency of 2,000 cycles per second.

Further examples of the applications of the hot wire anemometer are contained in the works cited below.‖

120. Electrical methods. Correlation measurements in turbulent flow.

With the aid of two hot wires it is possible to measure the correlation coefficient, R, between the longitudinal turbulent velocity components at two fixed points in a stream. In the method described by Prandtl and Reichardt†† a cathode-ray oscillograph is provided with two pairs of deflexion plates, and the variable potentials across the wires produced by the fluctuating velocities are applied, after magnification, to the plates of the oscillograph, so that at any instant the horizontal and vertical displacements of the beam represent the longitudinal velocity components at the two points. The beam

---

† *Loc. cit.*

‡ *Proc. Roy. Acad. Sci., Amsterdam,* **34** (1931), 663–672.

‖ Ower, *Measurement of Air Flow* (London, 1933), Chap. X (with bibliography on p. 221); Richardson, *Les appareils à fil chaud. Leurs applications dans la mécanique expérimentale des fluides* (Inst. de Mécanique des Fluides, Paris, 1934).

†† *Deutsche Forschung,* Part **21** (1934), 110–121.

traces out an irregular path of varying size and shape, and a photographic record is taken on a plate exposed to the beam for some time. When developed this reveals a darkened area, roughly elliptical in shape; its outline is ill-defined, but a number of ellipses can be constructed whose boundaries connect points of the same optical density. The axes of the ellipses bisect the angles between axes representing horizontal and vertical displacements; and if R is the correlation coefficient between the longitudinal turbulent velocity components, as above, the ratio of the squares of the lengths of the axes of any ellipse is given by

$$\frac{b^2}{a^2} = \frac{1-R}{1+R},$$

so that

$$R = \frac{a^2-b^2}{a^2+b^2}.$$

This method may be used when the hot wires are close enough together for the correlation to be high, i.e. when $1-R$ is fairly small and the ellipses are elongated in shape. For small correlations it is not so suitable as the electrodynamometer method, described below. A description of an alternative, and very convenient, method of measuring values of R in the neighbourhood of unity follows the description of the electrodynamometer method.

In the electrodynamometer method, two hot wires are arranged in Wheatstone bridge circuits. The out-of-balance potentials (proportional to the longitudinal turbulent velocity components, u_1, u_2, at the two wires) are applied to compensated amplifiers, the output currents from which are indicated by a sensitive electrodynamometer. The quantities $\overline{u_1 u_2}$, $\overline{u_1^2}$, and $\overline{u_2^2}$ are measured separately: $\overline{u_1 u_2}$ by the deflexion, δ_1, of the dynamometer when the moving coil is energized by the output current of the first amplifier and the fixed coil by the current from the second amplifier, and $\overline{u_1^2}$, $\overline{u_2^2}$ by the deflexions, δ_2, δ_3, when the coils of the instrument are joined in series so as to measure, in turn, the mean square value of each output current. The coefficient R is then given by the ratio $\delta_1/(\delta_2 \delta_3)^{\frac{1}{2}}$.

Fig. 68 shows the Wheatstone bridges containing the wires A and B, the amplifiers, and the output circuits arranged for measuring $\overline{u_1 u_2}$. These circuits include the fixed coil of the dynamometer, F, and the moving coil M. The compensating coils M', M'' are each made similar to M, and coils F', F'' similar to F. Accordingly, when the steady drop of potential across $F''M''$ with a small resistance r in series is balanced against the E.M.F. of the battery E, the proportion of the alternating current output (through F in one case and M in the other) remains unchanged over the probable range of frequencies associated with the type of turbulence under examination. The deflexions δ_2 and δ_3 are then observed immediately after δ_1, and are therefore made with the same degree of amplification.

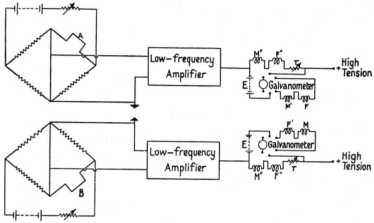

FIG. 68.

When values of R in the neighbourhood of unity are required (i.e. when the wires are near together) $1 - R^2$ may be obtained directly as the ratio of two deflexions of a galvanometer by a method due to Taylor.† Two hot wires, A and B, are used in bridge circuits connected together at DF (see Fig. 69). The steady currents through the hot wires are balanced out in the ordinary way (the bridges and galvanometers used are not shown in Fig. 69), and the mean potentials at all points on the resistances CD and FE across the bridge are then identical. Let a speed variation u_1 at A produce a potential difference E_1 between C and D, and similarly a variation u_2 at B produce a potential difference E_2 between E and F. Then

$$R = \frac{\overline{E_1 E_2}}{(\overline{E_1^2})^{\frac{1}{2}}(\overline{E_2^2})^{\frac{1}{2}}}.$$

By means of sliding contacts P and Q any proportion of either potential difference E_1 or E_2 may be applied to an amplifier and

† *Proc. Roy. Soc.* A, **157** (1936), 537–546.

recorded by the output current passed through a thermo-milliameter.
If $\alpha = PD/DC$, $\beta = FQ/EF$, the potential difference applied to
the input of the amplifier is $\alpha E_1 - \beta E_2$, and its mean square value, to
which the deflexion of the galvanometer is proportional, is

$$\alpha^2 \overline{E_1^2} + \beta^2 \overline{E_2^2} - 2\alpha\beta \overline{E_1 E_2}.$$

With P kept fixed in position, Q is adjusted until a minimum

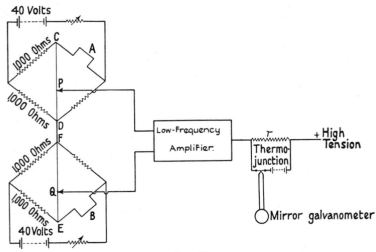

FIG. 69.

deflexion δ_{min} is observed. The minimum value, which occurs when

$$\beta = \alpha \frac{\overline{E_1 E_2}}{\overline{E_2^2}},$$

is proportional to

$$\alpha^2 \left\{ \overline{E_1^2} + \frac{(\overline{E_1 E_2})^2}{\overline{E_2^2}} - 2\frac{(\overline{E_1 E_2})^2}{\overline{E_2^2}} \right\}$$

which is equal to

$$\alpha^2 \overline{E_1^2}(1 - R^2).$$

Finally Q is moved to F (P remaining fixed in position), and the
new deflexion δ_2 is observed with the same amplification as before.
Then δ_2 is proportional to $\alpha^2 \overline{E_1^2}$, and hence

$$1 - R^2 = \frac{\delta_{min}}{\delta_2}.$$

Since both deflexions can usually be read to an accuracy of ± 8
per cent., the error made in estimating $1 - R$ when, say, $R = 0.98$

will not exceed 16 per cent., whereas if R were found by the electro-dynamometer method, an error of 1 per cent. in δ_1, or an error of 2 per cent. in δ_2 or δ_3, would produce an error of 1 per cent. in R and an error of 50 per cent. in $1-R$.

121. Electrical methods. Determination of an energy spectrum in turbulent flow.†

Turbulent motion contains no true periodic components, but (for example) the longitudinal turbulent velocity component u at any point may be subjected to harmonic analysis by Fourier integrals. A definite fraction of the kinetic energy associated with u lies between any given limits of frequency. In this sense we can obtain a spectrum of turbulent motion. By the use of circuits

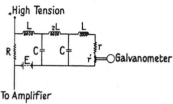

Fig. 70.

called filter circuits, which cut off all frequencies either above or below a certain definite value, it is possible to find the values, $(\overline{u^2})_{n-}$ and $(\overline{u^2})_{n+}$, of $\overline{u^2}$ when all frequencies above n cycles per second in the first case, or below n cycles per second in the second case, are cut off. If these are divided by $(\overline{u^2})_t$, the value of $\overline{u^2}$ without a filter in circuit, the results are equal to $\int_0^n F(n)\, dn$ or $\int_n^\infty F(n)\, dn$, where $F(n)\, dn$ is the fraction of $(\overline{u^2})_t$ for frequencies between n and $n+dn$. Hence by plotting results against n and finding the slopes of the resulting curves, curves of $F(n)$ against n may be obtained.

The filter circuit is inserted in the output lead of an amplifier used in conjunction with a hot wire. Of the two kinds of filters employed that shown in Fig. 70 passes currents of low frequency, but rejects currents whose frequency exceeds a value which is governed by the inductance L and the capacity C. The filter is placed as a shunt across a resistance R in the anode of the power valve of the amplifier, and the current passing through it is measured in the usual way by a thermo-milliameter. The sum of the resistances r and r' is equal to R and is also equal to the characteristic impedance, and the behaviour of the filter approaches closely to the ideal form which gives a uniform

† For references see p. 233.

response up to the critical frequency and zero response beyond. Values of $(\overline{u^2})_{n-}$ are measured in succession with a series of filters of this kind, designed to cut off at different frequencies, and $(\overline{u^2})_t$ is determined without a filter in circuit.

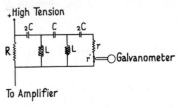

To Amplifier

FIG. 71.

The type of filter shown in Fig. 71 produces no attenuation to currents whose frequency is higher than a critical value, and is more satisfactory than the former type for exploring the high frequency end of the turbulence spectrum.

122. Manometers. The Chattock manometer.

The Chattock manometer[†] is in effect a water U-tube so modified that it enables pressure differences of the order of 0·01 inch of water column to be observed to an accuracy of 1 per cent; that is, the instrument is sensitive to a differential pressure of about 0·0001 inch of water. This degree of sensitivity is achieved as a result of two distinct features. In the first place the pressure difference is not allowed to change the water levels in the two limbs of the U-tube: instead, the tube is tilted in its plane by means of a lever pivoted at one end and operated by a micrometer screw, the tilt given being just sufficient to balance the applied pressure difference. The manner in which balance is indicated is the other feature responsible for the high sensitivity; it can best be explained by reference to Fig. 72, which shows the glass-work of a Chattock manometer. The two cups A and B, which constitute in effect the two vertical limbs of the U-tube, communicate with the central vessel C. Cup A communicates directly with C through its walls, but the tube from cup B enters C from below and passes up the centre as shown, terminating in a ground chamfered end about two-thirds of the height of C from the bottom.

The lower portions of the two cups, the tubes connecting them to the central vessel, and the lower part of the latter itself are filled with distilled water. The remaining space of C is entirely filled with medicinal paraffin admitted from the small reservoir above. Medicinal

† Pannell, *Engineering*, **96** (1913), 343, 344; *A.R.C. Reports and Memoranda*, No. 242 (1915); Duncan, *ibid.* No. 1069 (1927); *Journ. Sci. Insts.* **4** (1927), 376–379.

paraffin does not mix with water, and the levels and the quantities of the two liquids admitted are adjusted so that when the free levels in the two cups are at convenient heights (i.e. about half-way up the cylindrical portions) a surface of separation between the water and the paraffin is formed on the open end of the central vertical tube in C. There will be another surface of separation in the annular space surrounding this tube, but that is incidental. The one formed on the end of the tube has the appearance of a bubble when viewed from

Glass-work for 26 inch Chattock manometer

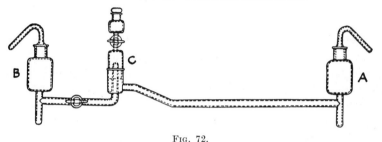

Fig. 72.

outside. If now a pressure difference is applied to the two cups, this bubble tends to become larger or smaller, and its movement, which can be observed by means of a low-power microscope and suitable illumination from behind, is arrested by giving the whole glass-work an appropriate tilt by means of the micrometer. In practice the microscope is carried by the tilting frame on which the glass-work is supported, so that the operation of the instrument merely entails keeping the image of the bubble on a fixed line in the eyepiece of the microscope and observing the applied tilt.

Two types of Chattock manometer are ordinarily employed. These differ only in the distance between the axes of the two cylindrical cups, which is approximately 26 inches in the larger size and 13 inches in the smaller. In both types the length of the lever arm which moves the tilting frame carrying the cups is 10 inches, and the pitch of the micrometer screw is 0·05 inch. About 20 turns of the screw are generally allowed in both types, which gives the larger a pressure range of about 2·6 inches of water and the smaller a range of half this amount.

Manometers having a sensitivity ten or more times that of the

Chattock have been designed for special investigations. For details the reader is referred to the papers cited below.†

123. Manometers. Large-range micromanometers.

It is not practicable to extend the range of the Chattock gauge appreciably without introducing objectionable features. A simple modification of the U-tube principle, however, enables a micromanometer to be made that has a range limited only by the length of micrometer screw that can be cut to the desired accuracy. In this type of instrument the two vertical limbs of the U-tube are connected at their lower ends by a length of flexible rubber tubing, so that one can be moved vertically relatively to the other. One limb is then held fixed, while the other is raised or lowered by means of a micrometer screw on which a special nut travels, the nut carrying the moving limb of the U-tube. A differential pressure applied to the two limbs is balanced by the appropriate vertical displacement, indicated on the micrometer head and scale, of the moving limb. Balance may be indicated in a variety of ways. The fixed limb may take the form of a cup similar to those used on the Chattock gauge, and the moving limb may communicate with it by means of a glass tube passing up the centre, as in the central vessel of the Chattock. If the upper part of the fixed cup is filled with medicinal paraffin, a 'bubble' can be formed on the mouth of the central vertical tube and used to indicate balance in the manner already described. A manometer of this type is in regular use at the N.P.L.‡ It has a range of 4 inches of water and a sensitivity of about 0·001 inch of water. This sensitivity could be increased without difficulty, but is ample for the purpose for which the instrument is used.

Alternatively the moving limb may terminate in an inclined glass tube of adjustable slope, the liquid meniscus being always brought back to a fixed mark etched on this tube. This system has been adopted in an instrument made at the University of Toronto;‖ its sensitivity is stated to be 0·0002 inch of water and its range is 10 inches. Other large-range micromanometers are described in the papers cited below.††

† Fry, *Phil. Mag.* (6), **25** (1913), 494–501; Hodgson, *Journ. Sci. Insts.* **6** (1929), 153–156; Ower, *A.R.C. Reports and Memoranda,* No. 1308 (1930); *Phil. Mag.* (7), **10** (1930), 544–551; Falkner, *A.R.C. Reports and Memoranda,* No. 1589 (1934); Reichardt, *Zeitschr. f. Instrumentenkunde,* **55** (1935), 23–33.

‡ *Report of the National Physical Laboratory* (1921), p. 170.

‖ Parkin, *Bull. School Engrg. Res., Toronto Univ.,* **2**, No. 1 (1921), 49–51.

†† See, for example, Douglas, 'Note on a Large Range Manometer for Wind Tunnel

124. Manometers. The inclined tube manometer.

If one limb of the U-tube is made very large in cross-sectional area compared with the other, virtually all the motion of the liquid takes place in the narrower limb. If, in addition, this limb is inclined at a small angle α to the horizontal the motion is magnified in the ratio $1/\sin\alpha$. Very convenient and robust instruments may be made on this principle; although their sensitivity is not in general as good as that of a micromanometer, being of the order of $0 \cdot 002$ inch of water at $5°$ slope, it is ample for a variety of purposes. Instruments of this kind require calibration against a fundamental standard (such as a micromanometer whose readings depend only on measurable lengths and liquid density) since the motion of the liquid in the inclined tube is governed not only by its density and the slope of the tube, but also by certain other features whose effects cannot easily be determined directly, such as straightness of tube and surface tension as affected by variations of temperature and bore of tube.

125. Manometers. Multitube manometers.

In work involving measurements of the pressure distributions on the surfaces of bodies (see pp. 255, 256) a great saving of time and labour can often be effected by measuring simultaneously the pressure at a number of points on the surface. For this purpose multitube manometers have been designed. A successful type† consists of a manometer with a number of inclined tubes leading out of a common reservoir containing the manometric liquid—in this case alcohol. Each tube is connected to one of the tubes let into the surface of the model (see pp. 255, 256), while the air space above the liquid level in the reservoir is connected either to the atmosphere, or more usually to a source of static pressure at some convenient place in the wind tunnel. The various refinements and special features of construction embodied in the design confer upon this particular multitube manometer an accuracy approaching that of a Chattock gauge with cup centres 26 inches apart.

126. Surface tubes.

The instruments commonly used for the exploration of the flow in a boundary layer are the small pitot tube and the hot wire velocity-meter.

Work', *A.R.C. Reports and Memoranda*, No. 657 (1920); also 'Micrometer Water and Pressure Gauge', *The Engineer*, **151** (1931), 248.

† Warden, *A.R.C. Reports and Memoranda*, No. 1572 (1934).

Instruments of these types are not capable of measuring the velocity very close to a surface with good accuracy. The difficulty with the pitot tube of the ordinary type arises from the fact that a sufficiently close approach to a surface cannot be obtained for models of the size commonly used in wind tunnel experiments, even when the diameter of the tube is small. When an exceedingly fine hot wire is used, and its temperature is kept sufficiently low to avoid radiation loss, the heat conducted across the thin layer between the hot wire and the

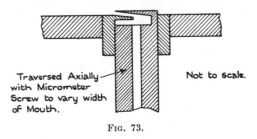

Traversed Axially with Micrometer Screw to vary width of Mouth.

Not to scale.

FIG. 73.

surface considerably modifies the forced convection from the wire due to the wind stream.

To allow measurements of velocity to be made very close to a surface Stanton† designed a special form of total-head tube, shown in Fig. 73, which was such that the inner wall of the tube was formed by the surface itself. The width of the opening could be varied by moving the outer wall. Owing to the extreme smallness of the opening of the tube, the speed deduced from the pressure at its mouth is not the same as that at the geometrical centre of the opening. The tube has therefore to be calibrated to determine the position of the 'effective centre' corresponding to the speed calculated from the measured pressure. This calibration is made in a long pipe of rectangular cross-section, with laminar flow at the section at which the tube is placed. The measurements made in the calibration are the pressure drop down the pipe and the difference between the pressure at the mouth of the tube and the static pressure in the pipe. From the first of these measurements, the mean rate of flow through the pipe and the velocity distribution at the surface are calculated from the known relations for stream-line flow. The second measurement gives the velocity at the mouth of the tube.

† Stanton, Miss Marshall, and Mrs. Bryant, *Proc. Roy. Soc.* A, **97** (1920), 422–434.

The effective distance corresponding to the velocity at the mouth is obtained from the calculated velocity distribution at the surface.

A particular form of surface tube which has been used to measure the distribution of friction on the surface of an aerofoil† is one in

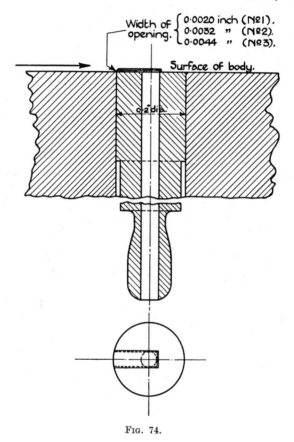

Fɪɢ. 74.

which the tube is constructed on the top of a circular rod designed to pass with a very small clearance through holes drilled in the polished surface of a metal model. The tube is mounted with the top surface of the rod flush with the model surface (see Fig. 74). The widths of the openings of three such tubes used in the research mentioned were 0·0020 inch (No. 1), 0·0032 inch (No. 2), and 0·0044

† Fage and Falkner, *Proc. Roy. Soc.* A, **129** (1930), 378–410.

inch (No. 3). A small hole drilled along the rod axis served to transmit the pressure at the mouth of the tube to a manometer.

Data obtained from the calibrations of the three tubes are given in the following table.

(W = width of the opening of a tube.)

Velocity calculated from the pressure at the mouth of the tube (ft./sec.)	Effective distance (inch)		
	No. 3 W = 0·0044 in.	No. 2 W = 0·0032 in.	No. 1 W = 0·0020 in.
8	0·00320	0·00320	0·00270
11	0·00298	0·00296	0·00253
14	0·00281	0·00276	0·00238
17	0·00268	0·00258	0·00224
20	0·00255	0·00241	0·00217

The effective centre of tube No. 3 is seen to be within the opening, whereas the effective centre of No. 1 is beyond the outer edge of the opening. The ratio of the effective distance to the width of the opening increases therefore as the width is decreased. It will also be observed that there is an outward movement of the effective centre of each tube as the speed at the mouth is decreased. A very interesting characteristic exhibited is that although the opening of tube No. 1 is less than one-half of that of tube No. 3, yet the effective distance is only about 15 per cent. smaller. Tube No. 1 does not, therefore, allow observations to be taken much closer to the surface than either of the tubes No. 2 or No. 3.

SECTION III

VISUALIZATION AND PHOTOGRAPHY OF FLUID MOTION

127. Stream-lines, filament lines, and particle paths.

Various methods are used to reveal to the eye details of fluid motion, and to enable such details to be photographed and analysed. The particular feature of the flow that is observed or recorded depends on the method of visualization and upon the experimental arrangement. Thus a photographic record of a type of fluid motion may show either stream-lines, filament lines, or particle paths. A filament line is the line joining the instantaneous positions of all particles that have passed through a given point in the fluid, while a particle path is the track of any particle of the fluid. In steady motion any stream-line is at the same time a filament line and a particle path, but in unsteady motion this is not so. If we imagine a thin jet of smoke introduced at a certain point into a stream of gas or air, or a jet of an opaque liquid into a stream of colourless liquid, then an instantaneous photograph of the flow, taken under suitable illumination, will reveal a filament line.† If, on the other hand, small puffs of smoke are introduced into the air-stream, or small discrete drops or solid particles into the liquid, a photographic exposure occupying a finite interval will show, in the form of streaks, the paths of the smoke puffs or particles during that interval.

128. Miscellaneous methods of examining flow in a boundary layer. Wool tufts; coating the surface; double refraction.

Before considering the more widely used methods of examining flow by visual means, we mention briefly three methods specially designed for examining flow in a boundary layer (of which the third may also be used for other purposes). The first two methods apply to the flow of air, the third to the flow of certain liquids.

We mention first the method of wool tufts or streamers, a method which has valuable practical applications.‡ Light streamers consisting of threads of fine silk or cotton, attached at one end to a wire support or to a surface near which it is desired to explore the flow, will reveal by their behaviour whether there is present turbulence of the kind associated with separation of the boundary layer from the surface or with an eddying wake. This method is very valuable in searching for regions where the flow has separated from the surface, and has been used both in wind tunnels and on actual aeroplanes in flight. Interesting information on the stalling of aerofoils has been obtained in this way.‖

In another method of examining air flow near a surface, the surface itself is coated with lead hydroxide, and sulphuretted hydrogen is mixed with the air-stream. A brownish stain develops on the surface where the gas flows along it and indicates the average path of the flow.†† Other combinations of chemical coating and vapour may also be used.

---

† Actually, since the jet must have a finite thickness, the picture will show a conglomeration of filament lines.

‡ Clark, *A.R.C. Reports and Memoranda*, No. 1552 (1933). Other references are given on p. 10 of that report.

‖ Cambridge University Aeronautics Laboratory, *A.R.C. Reports and Memoranda*, No. 1588 (1934).   †† Clark, *loc. cit.*

The third method,† of more recent use, is applicable only to certain viscous liquids, namely those which, when in motion, exhibit the property of double refraction. When such a liquid is flowing past a solid boundary the shearing stresses set up produce an effect on the optical properties, analogous to the effect produced in photo-elasticity on a solid material such as glass or bakelite. Measurements of certain optical constants with polarized light enable the velocity distribution in two-dimensional motion to be calculated.†

129. Air flow. Smoke.

The technique involving the use of smoke for examining air flow depends on the particular problem under investigation. Certain features of slow air currents, for example, may be followed by the aid of tobacco smoke introduced into the stream (see § 127). On the other hand, a more elaborate technique is required for studying the motion of large currents in the upper atmosphere, for which purpose shells are exploded and the drift of the smoke is observed. Again, at an aerodrome the smoke obtained from oil sprayed on a hot plate, by revealing the air flow near the ground, proves useful as a direction indicator. All these are examples in which smoke formed by the incomplete combustion of organic matter is used; but when the finer details of the flow structure are under examination, as in many tunnel investigations, because of the different circumstances a more opaque medium is needed. Coloured gases such as chlorine, bromine, and iodine can be used, if safeguards are provided to protect the observer against their toxic effects. The smoke produced by mixing the gases of ammonia and hydrochloric acid, or the smokes generated by hygroscopic salts like titanium tetrachloride or stannic tetra-chloride on exposure to air, are, however, more suitable. All contain a large percentage of small water particles held in suspension, to which they mainly owe their obscuring powers. At the same time the presence of the water makes them heavier than air, causing them to sink under gravity. Therefore, unless allowance is made for the natural motion, observations taken at the slowest rates of flow are apt to prove misleading. At higher speeds, when the rate of descent is small compared with the forward speed, the indications are more reliable. In these circumstances the extreme ease with which a satisfactory source of supply can be maintained, combined

† Alcock and Sadron, *Physics* (U.S.A.), **6** (1935), 92–95.

with the high optical density, are properties which make chemical smoke especially useful in research.

The advantages mentioned apply more particularly to the use of titanium tetrachloride and stannic tetrachloride. Each is liquid at ordinary temperatures, and if brought into contact with the air combines chemically with the moisture present to form fumes containing the oxide of the salt, hydrochloric acid and water, leaving a solid deposit after evaporation. A drop of the liquid at the end of a glass rod emits a cloud of smoke lasting for several minutes in still air. When the rod is held in a reasonably steady air current the cloud is drawn into a thin trail which remains visible for some distance downstream. Persisting as it does for some time, it serves admirably as a streamer for indicating the general direction of flow, and can therefore be used for mapping the lines of flow around models in wind tunnels, and for locating the eddying regions in the wake. Again, by disclosing the changes in the flow pattern following any alteration in the shape, it can be of service in detecting the interference effects between component parts of a model. In these and in similar problems, where the flow conditions at or near the model are under examination, it is more convenient to generate the smoke from a few drops of liquid placed on the surface. This method is also frequently adopted for investigating the flow in the boundary layer, to indicate the extent of the laminar and turbulent regions and the position at which the layer separates from the surface. Care, of course, is taken to remove the solid deposit left after each application of the liquid, as its presence is likely to cause premature turbulence in the boundary layer. The best results are obtained when the models and the surrounding walls of the tunnel are painted black so that the smoke is always viewed against a dark background.

130. Air flow. The smoke tunnel.

A special form of wind tunnel constructed at the N.P.L. for smoke experiments was fitted with an optical system for projecting an enlarged image of the smoke stream on to a screen, in order to render the motion more easily visible. An improved pattern has been designed by Farren,† primarily for obtaining smoke pictures of the flow past small models at low Reynolds numbers. It comprises a

† *Journ. Roy. Aero. Soc.* **36** (1932), 454–460.

wind tunnel (see Fig. 75) fitted with a honeycomb A, a contracting inlet B and D, and guide vanes at C and F to secure a steady and uniform stream through the working section E, where the model is held. This part has a cross-section 3 inches × 3 inches and two glass sides 8 inches long through which the beam of light, used to illuminate

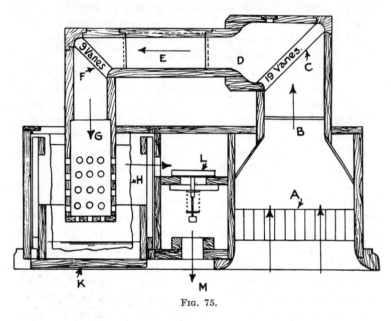

FIG. 75.

the smoke, passes. The flow through the tunnel is maintained by a fan and controlled by valves, one of which, L, can be opened or closed suddenly in order to examine conditions in the neighbourhood of the model when the air flow starts or stops. Titanium tetrachloride, applied on the surface of the model or introduced by a glass rod upstream, is used to make the flow visible. The fact that the smoke contains hydrochloric acid is a great disadvantage; nevertheless, by avoiding as far as possible the use of metal in the construction, the tunnel does not suffer damage. To ensure the steadiest conditions, it is important to exhaust the air into the room instead of into the open. Provision is made for absorbing the acid in the smoke by allowing the air to pass through a gauze curtain, H, surrounding the perforated box G and dipping into the tray K containing a weak solution of ammonia, with the result that the stream emerging from the outlet M on its way to the exhaust fan is hardly more objectionable than tobacco smoke.

Details of the optical system are shown in Fig. 76. Light from a 250-watt metal filament lamp, A, passes through a condensing lens, B, and then to a larger condensing lens, C, supported in contact with one of the glass sides of the working section E. A good quality lens D of about 3 inches aperture is situated on the far side of the tunnel and projects an image of the model and the smoke on to the screen. No difficulty is experienced in obtaining a sharp silhouette of the

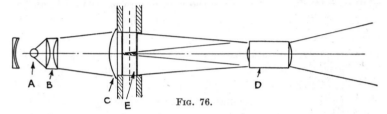

A B
C E   Fig. 76.   D

smoke streams lying in the centre plane of the tunnel, though, owing to its width, the image of the model itself is generally out of focus.

The tunnel can be used to demonstrate some of the fundamental features of fluid motion, such as the change in the character of the flow round circular cylinders between Reynolds numbers of 10 and 1,000, to quote one example. It is also useful for research purposes, constituting a valuable auxiliary to other methods of investigation. One drawback is that tests can only be made at speeds lower than 5 feet a second, since, owing to the vigorous breaking up and mixing of the smoke, it is impossible to follow anything in the nature of turbulent flow at higher speeds. This, added to the small size of the tunnel, restricts its use to Reynolds numbers very considerably less than those of general interest in practical aeronautics. Nevertheless, a critical study of the features of the flow revealed by these small-scale experiments can sometimes afford valuable help in the design of full-scale aircraft, particularly in locating sources of high drag due to breakdown of flow.

131. Air flow. Smoke photography: low and high speeds.

While much valuable information can be obtained by observing air flow in the manner already described, it is impossible, by inspection alone, to detect the finer details of eddying motion. Photography proves an invaluable aid for this purpose by providing permanent records which can be examined at leisure. Attention is drawn to some of the more important methods in use, which, for convenience, are described separately according as they are adapted for photographing air moving at low speeds or at high speeds.

(a) *Low speeds*. The smoke tunnel needs little adaptation to make it suitable for photographic purposes. Instead of the screen and projecting lens, all that is required is a camera fitted with a wide aperture lens together with a subsidiary lens which concentrates a beam of light after it passes through the tunnel, so that when the camera is focused on the central plane it receives the maximum quantity of light. As is to be expected, the best results are obtained in cases where the model extends from wall to wall, the flow at the mid-section being approximately two-dimensional. Successful photographs of the eddying motion in the wakes of cylinders, aerofoils, etc., with time exposures of one-hundredth of a second, have been produced in this way, as well as kinematograph films showing the successive stages of development of the eddies. The records appear identical with those taken at the same Reynolds number in water. Flow pictures at low speeds but at higher Reynolds numbers are obtainable by the same method in ordinary wind tunnels, larger models being used for the purpose. As before, the highest speed at which photographs can be taken is determined by the rate at which the smoke can be supplied. An abundant supply can be secured by blowing air through titanium tetrachloride contained in a flask, but the presence of the tube used for conveying the smoke into the tunnel upstream of the model introduces disturbances which make the method unsuitable for many investigations. Some success has attended efforts to maintain a continuous supply of liquid on the model by means of a tube having its open end flush with the surface. In such cases it is found advisable to add an equal volume of carbon tetrachloride, as the mixture is then less liable to block the mouth of the tube by leaving a solid residue projecting above the surface. The smoke produced by this process, though less effective than that of the undiluted liquid, provides sufficient contrast for photographs taken with relatively long exposures.

Instantaneous photographs are generally more useful for studying vortex motion, because of the improved definition. The technique required is somewhat different from that previously described, since a mechanical shutter cannot give the extremely short exposure

PLATE 24

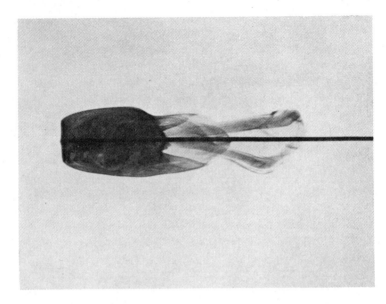

a. Disk normal to wind: $D = 0.6$ inch, $V = 1.25$ feet per second

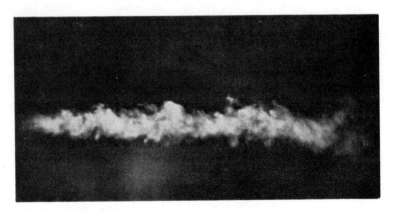

b. Smoke jet at a wind speed of 40 feet per second

necessary. Photographs are therefore taken in a dark room with an open camera exposed to a brilliant light lasting for a brief period of time. The light is produced by the spark discharge of a condenser, placed on the far side of the wind tunnel immediately opposite the camera. A copy of a photograph taken at the N.P.L.† with a spark lasting less than one-millionth of a second for the purpose of tracing the regions of vorticity generated by a disk, is reproduced in Pl. 24a. Such photographs are easily taken by charging an oil insulated condenser of 1 microfarad capacity until the voltage is high enough to cause a spark to jump the small gap between two strips of magnesium ribbon connected across it. A convenient method of charging the condenser is by means of a Ruhmkorff coil, the secondary of which is joined in series with the condenser and to the plate of a 500-watt power valve, the latter serving as a diode to rectify the alternating current in the secondary coil. The time taken before the spark occurs varies with the condition of the points; and though magnesium gives a light rich in actinic value, it oxidizes fairly rapidly, and in consequence the width of the gap changes. Usually, however, it is possible to arrange for the spark to take place from one to one and a half minutes after the coil is started. At low wind speeds this interval is sufficiently long to enable the liquid to be dropped on to the model before the plate is exposed to the flash; but at speeds above about 10 feet per second the smoke disperses too quickly to leave an adequate margin between the application of the liquid and the occurrence of the spark.

(b) *High speeds.* An adequate supply of smoke for the photography of air flow at high speeds cannot easily be maintained without disturbances being introduced into the flow in the form of eddies generated by the tube carrying the smoke into the stream, or without the speed of the smoke issuing from the tube exceeding that of the neighbouring air flow. In some problems the disturbances have little effect. A good example concerns the correct shaping of the roof of a building, in order to reduce the extent of the eddying region over the top. Here it is possible to examine the conditions of flow from photographs recording the path of a smoke stream as it issues from a tube some distance upstream and passes over the model.

Ammonium chloride smoke used in one set of experiments‡ was

---

† Simmons and Dewey, *A.R.C. Reports and Memoranda*, No. 1334 (1931).
‡ Bryant and Williams, *ibid.* No. 962 (1925).

prepared in a flask by the mixing of two air streams, one saturated with hydrochloric acid vapour, the other with ammonia. A pipe connected the flask to a small open-ended tube facing the model; and by means of compressed air a stream of smoke was injected into the wind tunnel, the rate of the supply being adjusted until the jet could be clearly seen after it was deflected by the model. Any change in the rate could easily be detected by the appearance of the stream; for the smoke rapidly became invisible when the speed was too low, and had a feathery appearance when it was too high. The illumination was provided by two arc lamps, and photographs were taken by reflected light, up to wind speeds of 60 feet per second, with a camera mounted so that the optical axis coincided with a line passing through the upper edge of the model. Most of the exposures given were between 2 and 5 seconds, according to the density of the smoke. Thus the photographs recorded the average shape of the discontinuous boundary of the eddying region, but gave no indication of the changes that occur from time to time within that region.

Instantaneous photographs of the jet cannot be taken by the direct illumination of a spark placed behind it and on a level with the camera: attempts to do so invariably lead to negatives which show no trace of the jet. Satisfactory results can, however, be obtained if the spark is placed in a position where the smoke reflects light into the camera and so produces a bright image on the plate. The underlying principle is the same as that whereby smoke, introduced into a beam of light in a dark room, is seen best when the line of vision is inclined at about 45° to the beam. From this it follows that the spark should always be placed on the far side of the smoke, on one or other of two lines inclined at 45° to the axis of the camera. When circumstances permit, it should be held within a few inches of the smoke, with a screen supported near it to intercept the rays which would otherwise enter the camera without illuminating the smoke. Pl. 24b†　is reproduced from a spark photograph taken with a wide aperture lens ($f = 2\cdot8$), and illustrates the billowy appearance of a smoke jet projected into an air current moving at a speed of 40 feet per second.

132. Air flow. Change of refractive index.

Any local change in the refractive index of the air, though not directly visible, may be made so by suitable illumination. A well-

---

†　*Report of the National Physical Laboratory* for the year 1931, Fig. 46d (1932).

PLATE 25

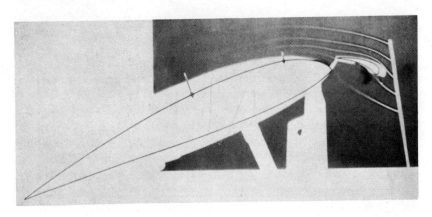

a. Flow round R.A.F. 31 (Slotted) with Hot Wires. $\alpha = 18°$, $V = 40$ feet per second (infinite aspect ratio)

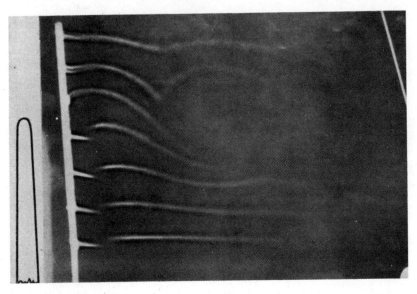

b

known example is that of the photography of sound waves in which
the wave front is revealed by its altered density.

133. Air flow. Hot wire shadows.

The motion of an air-stream may be made visible by mounting
in it a fine wire which is heated by passing an electric current through
it.[†] The filament of heated air in the wake of the wire, though it
cannot be seen directly, may be detected by either the simple shadow
method of Dvořák or by the 'Schlieren' (striae) method.[‡]

In the shadow method the field of flow is illuminated from the
side by a small arc lamp, without any lenses, which casts a shadow
of the heated filament of air on a screen. The temperature of the
wire is unimportant: a platinum wire about $\frac{1}{2}$ inch long and $0 \cdot 002$
inch diameter heated to a dull red is suitable, and produces a filament line several inches in length.

The length of the shadow depends mainly on the degree of turbulence of the stream, and may vary from an inch or two when very
turbulent to 15 inches or more when steady. However, a shadowgraph
made on a process plate with an exposure of about $0 \cdot 001$ second may
give a longer record for turbulent motion than appears to the eye.

There is practically no upper limit to the air speed at which
shadows may be observed, but at very low velocities there is a convection effect, though this is usually negligible above about 2 feet
per second. The method is particularly useful for studying transient
motions, e.g. the early stages of the flow round an aerofoil, etc.

Pl. 25a[†] is a simple shadowgraph, obtained directly on gaslight
printing paper with an exposure of about 7 seconds, of the flow
around a slotted aerofoil at a wind speed of 40 feet per second.
The wires are $\frac{1}{2}$ inch apart.

Pl. 25b[||] shows the flow behind an airscrew 19 inches in diameter
developing a fairly high thrust at a forward speed of 15 feet per
second. This shadowgraph was obtained by light passing through
a slit in a rotating disk driven at airscrew speed, and is equivalent
to a snapshot.

Pl. 26a shows the flow past a rotating cylinder 1 inch in diameter.

† Townend, *A.R.C. Reports and Memoranda*, No. 1349 (1931).
‡ Töpler, *Ann. d. Phys. u. Chem.* **131** (1867), 33–35. See also Wood, *Phil. Mag.*
(5), **48** (1899), 218–227; Taylor and Waldram, *Journ. Sci. Insts.* **10** (1933), 378–389;
Townend, *ibid.* **11** (1934), 184–187; Schardin, *Ver. deutsch. Ing., Forschungsheft* 367
(1934). || Townend, *A.R.C. Reports and Memoranda*, No. 1434 (1932).

In steady motions, such as Pl. 25a, the filament lines obtained by a hot wire shadowgraph are identical with the paths of particles and with the stream-lines, but this is not so in periodic motions such as that in Pl. 25b, where successive particles of air passing the hot wire do not follow the same paths. Thus in Pl. 25b, on account of the thrust of the airscrew, particles passing on opposite sides of a blade receive radial velocity increments of opposite sign, and this causes breaks in the filament lines that widen as the motion proceeds.

134. Air flow. Spark shadows. The 'Schlieren' method. Kinematography. The determination of velocity distributions and measurements of turbulence: accuracy.

In cases of the foregoing kind a hot wire will not yield the path of a particle directly, but this can be obtained if the heat is produced by a periodic electric spark instead of a wire.[†] The possibility of obtaining records of the motions of small masses of air heated in this way enables measurements to be made of the instantaneous velocity at a point in the air-stream.[‡] Pl. 26b[||] shows the flow behind an airscrew. In this photograph shadowgraphs of a hot wire and of a series of sparks may be compared.

Although instantaneous shadowgraphs of the hot spots may be made as described above, much better records are obtained by the use of the 'Schlieren' method. The extra optical sensitivity of this method permits smaller sparks to be used, and this is important when the displacements to be measured are small. The principle of the method may be understood from Fig. 77, which shows the arrangement used for photographing air flow.

An arc lamp is focused on to the straight edge of a stainless steel mirror D. An inverted image of this portion of the mirror is formed, by reflection in the concave mirror M, on the edge of a diaphragm d. The working edges of D and d are close together, and are placed near the centre of curvature of the mirror M. By means of an adjusting screw nearly all the light is intercepted by d, only that from the

---

† Townend, *Phil. Mag.* (7), **14** (1932), 700–712; *Journ. Aero. Sciences,* **3** (1936), 343–352.

‡ Alternatively, when it is desired to determine the velocity of air from kinematograph records, suspended particles may be photographed. See C. Chartier and J. Labat, *Comptes Rendus,* **202** (1936), 729, 730 (aluminium powder); U. Schmieschek, *Zeitschr. f. tech. Physik,* **17** (1936), 98–100 (commercial variety of polymerized acetaldehyde). Soap bubbles have been used by H. Redon and F. Vinsonneau, *Aérotechnique,* **15** (1936), 60–66.

|| Townend, *A.R.C. Reports and Memoranda,* No. 1434 (1932).

PLATE 26

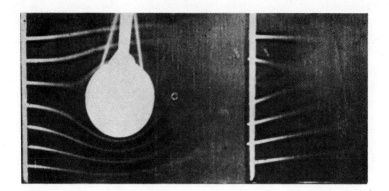

a

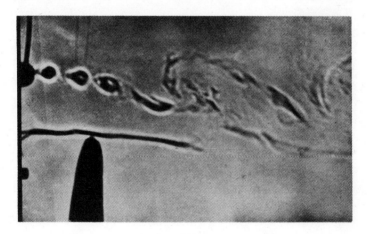

b

extreme edge of D being allowed to pass over into the camera C. This light forms in the camera a uniformly illuminated image of the mirror M. Any optical disturbance in front of the concave mirror, such as that produced by the heating of a small mass of air at a, will deflect some rays of light so that they are intercepted by d, and others which are normally intercepted will be thrown clear of d and pass into the camera. Thus there will be formed on the plate an 'image' of a which is bright on one side and dark on the other. In the arrange-

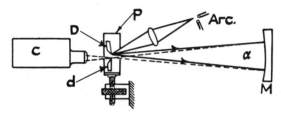

FIG. 77.

ment shown the rays pass through a twice, and this increases the optical sensitivity of the method.

The camera C may be a kinematograph camera, and in that case the light entering it should be intercepted by a rotating disk situated as close behind d as possible, and having a narrow slit near its edge. The speed of the disk should be synchronized with that of the spark generator. It is unnecessary to synchronize the camera, since the exposure is so short (about $\frac{1}{4,000}$ sec.) that the mechanism for moving the film intermittently through the camera may be removed and the film driven at constant speed by a small motor.

A spark may be used as light source instead of an arc lamp, and this spark may be supplied by the same magneto or coil that provides the spark used as heat source in the air-stream. The rotating shutter is then unnecessary.†

The velocity distribution at different points in a flow may be determined by using several spark gaps. Pl. 27 shows the distribution in a 3-inch square pipe using seven spark gaps. The sparks were discharged in series. The following conditions of flow are depicted. (a) and (b) Laminar motion near the entry of the pipe, velocity distribution uniform across the pipe; (c) laminar motion 60 diameters downstream, velocity distribution parabolic; (d) and

† See *Report of the National Physical Laboratory* (1933), pp. 196–198.

(e) turbulent motion 60 diameters downstream. In records (b) and (e) not only are the hot spots due to the sparks visible, but the filament lines springing from the ends of the electrodes themselves, which are kept hot by the stream of sparks, are also apparent. This is because the edge of diaphragm d, Fig. 77, was parallel to the direction of flow. In the other records the edge was at right angles to the direction of flow, and then the filament lines are practically suppressed, because the deflexion of the light rays is mainly transverse to the filament lines themselves and so does not alter the amount of light passing over the edge of d.

Records of the kind shown in Pl. 27 (d) have been used to make a statistical analysis of the turbulent velocities in the flow through a pipe.† By measuring the displacements of a spot relative to the spark gap for several hundred pictures, the mean velocity at the point can be found, and also the root-mean-square values of the lateral and axial components of the turbulence. Quantitative estimates of the turbulence are thus obtainable, and the distribution of turbulence across the field may be measured.‡

In non-turbulent motion the position of the centre of a hot spot may be estimated to about 0·02 inch at a distance of 5 or 6 inches downstream, since the spot does not change its shape. When measuring turbulence much less accuracy is obtainable owing to dispersion of the spot. If, however, the turbulence is small and incidental to the measurements required, as in exploring a steady flow in a normal wind tunnel, the uncertainty introduced is small.

Convection becomes appreciable below 2 feet per second, but can be corrected for, when necessary, by measuring it in a uniform stream.‖

135. Water flow. Water channels and tanks.

The water channel provides a simple method of obtaining pictures of the flow around a body. The body is either held fixed in a moving stream or is moved through stationary water. A common method of making the flow visible is to inject colouring matter, such as red

---

† Townend, Proc. Roy. Soc. A, 145 (1934), 180–211.

‡ Information concerning turbulent fluctuations may also be obtained by utilizing the effect of the air-stream on a glow discharge between two electrodes. See F. C. Lindvall, Electrical Engineering, 53 (1934), 1068–1073.

‖ For later developments of the methods described in this section see Townend, A.R.C. Reports and Memoranda, No. 1803 (1937.)

PLATE 27

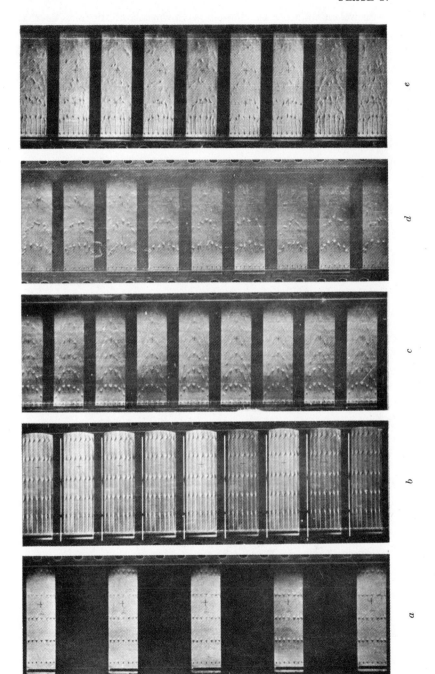

ink, in the form of a fine jet, the velocity of efflux being the same as the local water velocity. Another method is to add to the water small drops of oil, and to illuminate them by a beam of light from an arc lamp. When the drops are viewed at the appropriate angle they appear as bright points of light, which can easily be photographed. If the time of exposure is sufficient, the image of each illuminated particle traces a line on the plate, and the velocity of the particle can be determined from the length of this line and the time of exposure. To eliminate the effects of gravity the drops used are obtained from a mixture of two oils in such proportions that the specific gravity is unity. The best results are obtained when the refractive index of the oil drops is such that the angle between the incident and emergent rays is 90°, for then all the illuminated drops can be brought into focus on the photographic plate at the same time, if the plane of illumination is sufficiently thin. A mixture of olive oil and nitrobenzene has been found suitable for this purpose.†

Minute particles of aluminium or lycopodium powder scattered on the surface of the water have been used to reveal the flow past a two-dimensional obstacle when it projects beyond the surface.‡ Very fine flakes of mica‖ on the surface may also be used to reveal the flow. In such experiments the surface has to be kept very clean to minimize capillary effects. A test for cleanliness is to sprinkle aluminium powder on the surface and to spread the powder by blowing gently on it. If the particles do not collect together, the surface is clean. Movement of the aluminium particles away from the obstacle, under capillary action at the junction, can be prevented by coating the obstacle with a thin layer of paraffin. Motion of a regular pattern is clearly revealed by this method because a great number of the particles have the same orientation.

An apparatus has been designed at Cambridge†† which allows observation of the flow when a model is given an impulsive start from rest. This apparatus consists of an enclosed tank filled with water and having parallel sides 6 inches apart, between which the

---

† Relf, *Adv. Comm. for Aeronautics, Reports and Memoranda*, No. 76 (1913).

‡ Ahlborn, *Abhandl. Gebiete Naturwiss.* **17** (1902), 8–37; Rubach, *Forschungsarbeiten des Ver. deutsch. Ing.*, No. 185 (1916), 1–35.

‖ Prandtl and Tietjens, *Die Naturwissenschaften*, **113** (1925), 1050–1053; Prandtl, *Verhandlungen des dritten internationalen Mathematiker-Kongresses, Heidelberg, 1904* (Leipzig, 1905), pp. 490, 491.

†† Jones, Farren, and Lockyer, *A.R.C. Reports and Memoranda*, No. 1065 (1927). See also Walker, *ibid.*, No. 1402 (1932).

model can be moved through the water, which is at rest apart from the disturbance created by the model. Oil drops suspended in the water reflect light into a camera focused on the plane of flow to be examined, and the movements of the drops due to the disturbance set up by the model are photographically recorded. When the exposure of a plate is of short but finite duration, the photograph records motions relative to the undisturbed water, and a short trace made by a drop can be taken as a vector giving the fluid velocity at its middle point. The energy required to give an impulsive start to the carriage carrying the model is obtained from a flywheel.

136. Water flow. The ultramicroscope. Ultramicroscope photography.

The above methods involve the introduction of particles into the water, and reliable views of the flow are obtained when the motions of relatively large molar masses of water are concerned. Some doubt arises, however, if particles are added for the examination of micro-turbulence, especially near the boundary of the fluid where the scale of the turbulence is small, since such particles may be comparable in size with the molar masses, and then the internal motions of these masses would not be faithfully represented. The ultramicroscope†️ affords a means of obtaining reliable information on minute details of fluid flow without any possible interference with the motion, since neither particles nor measuring instruments are introduced into the fluid.

The principle of the ultramicroscope depends on the fact that very small particles usually present in most fluids, but invisible in ordinary light even under the most powerful microscope, become visible when intensely illuminated provided they are seen against a dark background. Even particles smaller than the wave length of light become visible as bright points of light, if the intensity of the light beam is sufficiently great. A photograph of the ultramicroscope arranged to examine turbulent flow in a square pipe is given in Pl. 28.‡️ The water flowing through the pipe is illuminated through a glass window let into one side of the pipe, and observation is made through a window let into an adjacent side. The light from an arc lamp taking 5 amperes is brought to a focus by a single condensing lens, and

† Fage and Townend, *Proc. Roy. Soc.* A, **135** (1932), 656–677. See also Nisi and Porter, *Phil. Mag.* (6), **46** (1923), 754–768.

‡ Fage, *Journ. Aero. Sci.*, **1** (1934), 37.

PLATE 28

then passed through a compound lens and through the glass window into the water. A small cylindrical lens is interposed between the image of the arc and the compound lens in order to convert the conical incident beam into a wedge-shaped beam: the width of the beam of illumination is thus increased up to the diameter of the field of the microscope without an increase in depth. The illumination of particles well outside the focal plane of the microscope, which would impair the darkness of the background, is thus prevented, and the light available is also conserved. A fine slit placed in the focal plane of the first condensing lens can be used to obtain a very thin illuminating beam. The height of the incident beam can be adjusted by mounting the lens system on an optical bench pivoted at one end and provided with a screw adjustment at the other: this adjustment, used in conjunction with lateral and vertical movements of the microscope, allows observation to be made at any selected point in the fluid. Observation through the microscope can conveniently be made under a magnification of about 50 (except very near a surface, when a higher magnification to increase sensitivity is necessary in order to show the finer details of the motion).

The particles passing through any fixed point in a completely eddying stream move in different directions. When the radii of curvature of the sinuous paths of these particles are large compared with the diameter of the field of the microscope, only short lengths of the paths are seen when the particles are illuminated. These short lengths appear as bright rectilinear streaks inclined at various angles to the mean direction of flow, and at high speeds they appear to intersect each other, owing to persistence of vision. The direction of a path of a particle can be measured by mounting in the focal plane of the eyepiece a fine platinum wire which can be rotated about the axis of the microscope by means of a pointer moving over an angular scale. Observation is facilitated if this wire is rendered luminous by heating it electrically to a dull red glow.

To measure the speed of a particle, use is made of the principle that the particle appears as a bright stationary point when viewed at the speed at which it is moving. Instead of moving the microscope as a whole, the same effect is obtained, over a limited region, if the eyepiece and the microscope tube are held fixed and the objective is moved in the same direction as the particle. The objective is therefore carried on a wheel which is rotated about an offset axis, so that once in every revolution the axis of the objective coincides with the axis of the microscope tube. The position of the axis of rotation is chosen so that at the instant of this coincidence the direction of motion of the objective is parallel to the mean direction of flow. The factor for obtaining the speed of a particle from the speed of rotation is easily obtained by direct calibration. In turbulent flow the successive views seen when the objective rotates differ on account of the fluctuations in the velocity of the stream at any point in the fluid: the velocity component in the direction of mean flow fluctuates continually between minimum and maximum values, so that particles can only appear as points provided that the corresponding speed of the objective lies between these limits. Hence the minimum speed at a point is obtained by slowly increasing the speed of rotation until particles first appear, and the maximum speed until they just cease to appear. The mean velocity is taken as the mean of the maximum and minimum velocities measured at the point, and the maximum velocity fluctuations as one-half the difference between these values.

The maximum lateral components of the turbulent velocity can be deduced from observations of the maximum angular deviations of the particle paths from the mean direction of flow.[†]

It has been found possible to take photographs under a reduced magnification of some of the views seen with an ultramicroscope.[‡] The kind of photograph obtained is illustrated in Pl. 29,[||] where views are given of ordinary tap water (without any particles added) flowing past a long circular cylinder at very low Reynolds numbers $(U_0 d/\nu)$. These photographs were taken with a small camera having an $f/3$ lens ($f = 2$ inches). Photograph (a) shows the steady nature of the flow in the empty tunnel. Photographs (b)–(h) were taken on the median plane at right angles to the axis of the cylinder at values of $U_0 d/\nu$ lying within the range 17·7 to 170. Photographs (i), (j), (k) were taken on the plane passing through the axis of the cylinder: in photograph (j), the flow in the standing vortices at $U_0 d/\nu = 38·0$ is of a spiral character.

† Fage, *Phil. Mag.* (7), **21** (1936), 80–105.
‡ Fage, *Proc. Roy. Soc.* A, **144** (1934), 381–386.
|| *Report of the National Physical Laboratory* for 1933, Fig. 43 (1934).

PLATE 29

Diameter = 0·04 inch

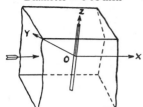

a. Free stream

Views at *O* on Plane *XOY*

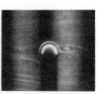

b. $\dfrac{U_0 D}{\nu} = 17\cdot7$ *c.* $= 21$ *d.* $= 27$ *e.* $= 32$

f. $= 47$ *g.* $= 104$ *h.* $= 170$

Views at *O* on Plane *XOZ*

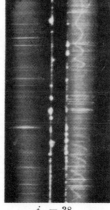

i. $= 24\cdot3$ *j.* $= 38$ *k.* $= 137$

FLOW IN PIPES AND CHANNELS AND ALONG FLAT PLATES

137. Introduction.

THE subject-matter of this and the following chapter may be conveniently divided into three sections:—(i) laminar flow; (ii) the transition from laminar to turbulent flow; (iii) fully developed turbulent flow: (i) and (ii) will be discussed in the present chapter and (iii) in Chapter VIII. In each section those problems which have received theoretical consideration will be discussed first, since they are, in general, fundamental. When theoretical solutions have not been obtained, experimental results will be reduced by dimensional considerations to forms which facilitate application to other problems of the same type.

The Reynolds number is defined for flow in a pipe or channel of any section as $4mu_m/\nu$, where m is the hydraulic mean depth (defined as the area of the cross-section divided by its perimeter), u_m is the average velocity over a section, and ν is the kinematic viscosity. This definition will always be used in the absence of a specific statement to the contrary. (For a circular pipe m is a quarter of the diameter d, and the Reynolds number is $u_m d/\nu$: for two-dimensional flow between parallel walls at a distance $2h$ apart m is h, and the Reynolds number is $4u_m h/\nu$.)

In steady flow along straight pipes and channels, far away from the inlet and the exit (i.e., where the flow at any section is similar to that at any other), the skin-friction τ_0 and the pressure drop† Δp per unit length are related by the equation

$$A\Delta p = L\tau_0, \tag{1}$$

where A is the area of the section and L its perimeter. (For problems of turbulent flow only mean values are considered.) In terms of the hydraulic mean depth m equation (1) may be written

$$m\Delta p = \tau_0. \tag{2}$$

For any length l of a straight pipe or channel a non-dimensional resistance coefficient γ is defined by the equation

$$\gamma = \frac{p_1-p_2}{\tfrac{1}{2}\rho u_m^2}\frac{m}{l}, \tag{3}$$

† The pressure is taken throughout as the difference of the actual pressure and the hydrostatic pressure.

where p_1 and p_2 are the pressures at the end sections of the length considered.

For a fully developed flow (at a sufficient distance from the ends) the pressure gradient is constant, so that $(p_1-p_2)/l$ is Δp and the definition of γ in (3) is equivalent to

$$\gamma = \tau_0/(\tfrac{1}{2}\rho u_m^2). \tag{4}$$

SECTION I
LAMINAR FLOW

138. Flow through a straight pipe of circular cross-section.

The theoretical solution of this problem has been given in Chap. I, § 6 (p. 20). The following results were obtained on the assumption of no slip at the walls:—

(i) The velocity distribution across a section is parabolic and such that the mean velocity, u_m, is half the maximum.

(ii)
$$u_m = -\frac{a^2}{8\mu}\frac{\partial p}{\partial x}, \tag{5}$$

where a is the radius of the pipe, μ is the viscosity, and $-\partial p/\partial x$ is the pressure gradient; the total flux, $\pi a^2 u_m$, therefore varies directly as the fourth power of the radius and the first power of the pressure gradient.

(iii)
$$\gamma = 16/R. \tag{6}$$

It was also pointed out that the velocity distribution is not parabolic all the way from the entry; a certain length—the inlet length—is required before the parabolic distribution is attained. The flow in the inlet length will be considered in § 139.

The theoretical results have been compared with experiment by taking measurements of the flux and obtaining its variation with change of radius and pressure gradient. The easiest way in practice to overcome the difficulty of end effects in the measurement of the pressure gradient is to observe the pressures at holes in the pipe wall in the fully developed region; otherwise the pipe used must either be sufficiently long for the inlet length to be negligible, or some end correction must be applied.

Hagen† and Poiseuille,‡ using water in capillary tubes, found by

† *Poggendorff's Annalen d. Physik u. Chemie* (2), **46** (1839), 423–442.

‡ *Comptes Rendus*, **11** (1840), 961–967; 1041–1048; **12** (1841), 112–115; *Mémoires des Savants Étrangers*, **9** (1846), 433–543.

experiment the proportionality of the flux to the pressure gradient and to the fourth power of the radius; later workers, by applying end corrections to the experimental results of Poiseuille, and also by many further experiments with various fluids in tubes of various materials and widely different radii, have obtained excellent agreement between theory and experiment. Stanton and Pannell,† using water and oil in smooth brass and steel pipes, have made a few velocity measurements and obtained good agreement with the predicted values. Thus the collected results of various experimenters verify the theoretical predictions, and so are in accord with the assumption of no slip at the walls.

139. Flow in the inlet length of a circular pipe.

With a well-designed short trumpet-shaped intake, if care is taken to avoid disturbances‡ the velocity at the entry to a circular pipe will be practically constant over the cross-section. The velocity at the wall is, however, zero, so that an infinitely thin boundary layer is formed round the walls of the pipe; the thickness of this layer increases as we pass downstream until it becomes equal to the radius of the pipe. Until this happens there is a core of fluid practically uninfluenced by viscosity, and in it the total head may be considered constant. Since the flux across any section is constant, and since the boundary layer thickness is increasing, this core is accelerated, and there is a corresponding fall in pressure. The fully developed parabolic distribution is theoretically attained only asymptotically; but we are now interested in the distance which it is necessary to travel downstream before the difference from the parabolic distribution becomes less than the least experimental error. It should be remembered that this state may not be reached simultaneously with the boundary layer thickness becoming equal to the pipe radius: calculations on pp. 304–308 indicate that the whole of the fluid across a section becomes influenced by viscosity some distance before the parabolic distribution is approached.

We require expressions for (i) the pressure difference between any two sections; (ii) the velocity distribution at any section; and (iii) the value of x for which the fully developed parabolic flow may be said to be attained.

---

† *Phil. Trans.* A, **214** (1914), 199–224.
‡ The influence of friction in the intake is neglected.

If the fluid enters the pipe from a cistern in which the pressure P is maintained and in which the velocity is negligible, and if p_L is the pressure at a distance L from the entry to the pipe, at which distance the permanent régime may be considered attained, then a usual approximate result for the pressure difference $P-p_L$ is given by equation (8) below, whilst a more accurate result (but still obtained by neglect of friction in the intake before the entry to the pipe) is given by equation (44) with $x = L$.

We obtain a first approximation to the difference between the pressure at the entry ($x = 0$) and the pressure when the final velocity distribution may be said to be attained ($x = L$) by means of the kinetic energy end-correction.† In this approximation the dissipation of energy in the inlet length is supposed to be equal to the dissipation in the same length when the velocity distribution is parabolic. If p_0, p_L are the pressures at $x = 0$ and at $x = L$, then the rate at which the pressures are doing work is

$$\pi a^2 p_0 u_m - p_L\left[2\pi \int_0^a ur\,dr\right]_{x=L} = \pi a^2 u_m(p_0 - p_L),$$

since the velocity at $x = 0$ is constant and equal to the average velocity, u_m, over a section. The rate of inflow of kinetic energy at $x = 0$ is $\frac{1}{2}\pi a^2 \rho u_m^3$, and the rate of outflow at $x = L$ is

$$2\pi\rho \int_0^a \tfrac{1}{2}u^3 r\,dr = \pi\rho a^2 u_m^3.$$

Thus the difference in the rate of inflow and the rate of outflow of kinetic energy gives rise to an additional pressure drop of $\frac{1}{2}\rho u_m^2$ between $x = 0$ and $x = L$. On these grounds it is assumed that

$$\frac{p_0 - p_L}{\frac{1}{2}\rho u_m^2} = \frac{16\mu u_m L}{\rho u_m^2 a^2} + 1 = \frac{32L}{aR} + 1. \tag{7}$$

If the fluid enters the pipe from a large cistern in which the pressure is P and the velocity is negligible, there is a pressure drop of $\frac{1}{2}\rho u_m^2$ between the cistern and entry (the influence of friction in the intake being neglected), so that

$$\frac{P - p_L}{\frac{1}{2}\rho u_m^2} = \frac{16\mu u_m L}{\rho u_m^2 a^2} + 2 = \frac{32L}{aR} + 2. \tag{8}$$

† Hagenbach, *Poggendorff's Annalen d. Physik u. Chemie* (4), **109** (1860), 385–426; Couette, *Ann. de Chimie et de Physique* (6), **21** (1890), 433–510; Prandtl and Tietjens, *Hydro- und Aeromechanik*, **2** (Berlin, 1931), 25, 26.

An approximation can also be obtained by treating the retarded layer in a manner analogous to that used by Pohlhausen in his discussion of flow in a boundary layer (Chap. IV, §60 (p. 157)). We suppose that the retarded layer has a thickness δ at any cross-section; we write $y = a - r$, and then, following Schiller,[†] we put

$$\frac{u}{u_1} = 2\frac{y}{\delta} - \frac{y^2}{\delta^2} \qquad (9)$$

in the retarded layer, where u_1 is the velocity in the core. It will be noted that the assumption that the velocity distribution becomes parabolic when $\delta = a$ is inherent in this method.

The equation of continuity and the momentum equation give two relations between u_1, x and δ. Elimination of δ leads to a relation between u_1 and x which, with

$$\chi = u_1/u_m - 1, \qquad (10)$$

integrates to $\qquad x/(aR) = f(\chi), \qquad (11)$

where $\qquad R = 2au_m/\nu$

and

$$f(\chi) = \frac{1}{8}\left\{ \frac{58}{15}\chi - \frac{22}{5}\log(1+\chi) - \frac{17}{15}\sqrt{(4+2\chi-2\chi^2)} \right.$$

$$\left. - \frac{16}{5}\left(\frac{4-2\chi}{1+\chi}\right)^{\frac{1}{2}} - \frac{37\sqrt{2}}{10}\sin^{-1}\frac{2\chi-1}{3} + \frac{26}{3} - \frac{37\sqrt{2}}{10}\sin^{-1}\frac{1}{3}\right\}.[‡] \quad (12)$$

A graph of $f(\chi)$ is shown in Fig. 78. In the parabolic flow $u_1 = u_{\max}$, and since $u_{\max} = 2u_m$, $\chi = 1$; this occurs first when

$$x = 0.0575aR;$$

so according to this approximation the permanent régime is established after a finite distance $0.0575aR$. The approximate nature of the calculation is illustrated by the fact that the maximum velocity in the inlet length does not join on smoothly to its final value $2u_m$, since $d\chi/dx$ does not vanish at $\chi = 1$. (Cf. Fig. 80, p. 304.)

If p_1 and p_2 are the pressures at the sections x_1 and x_2, it follows from the constancy of the total head in the core, since

$$u_1 = u_m(\chi+1),$$

that

$$(p_1-p_2)/(\tfrac{1}{2}\rho u_m^2) = [2\chi+\chi^2]_{x_2} - [2\chi+\chi^2]_{x_1} = \Delta(2\chi+\chi^2) \qquad (13)$$

[†] *Zeitschr. f. angew. Math. u. Mech.* **2** (1922), 96–106; *Handbuch der Experimentalphysik*, **4**, part 4 (Leipzig, 1932), 48–57.

[‡] This is a simplified form of Schiller's result.

(say). The resistance coefficient γ defined in equation (3) is therefore equal to
$$\frac{a\Delta(2\chi+\chi^2)}{2(x_2-x_1)}. \tag{14}$$

The theory can be checked against experiment by finding γ for

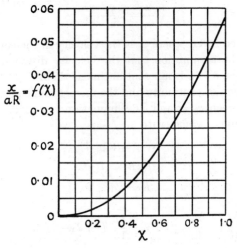

$$\frac{x}{aR} = f(\chi)$$

FIG. 78.

fixed x_1 and x_2 and various values of R. Typical results found by
Schiller are shown in Fig. 79, where the straight line gives the un-
corrected theoretical result.

For $x \leqslant 0.0575aR$,
$$p_0-p = \tfrac{1}{2}\rho u_m^2(2\chi+\chi^2), \tag{15}$$

where p_0 is the pressure at the entry, and p and χ are evaluated at
the section at the distance x from the entry. When $x = 0.0575aR$,
$\chi = 1$ and
$$p_0-p = 1.5\rho u_m^2. \tag{16}$$

For $x > 0.0575aR$,
$$-\partial p/\partial x = 8\mu u_m/a^2 = 16\rho u_m^2/(aR),$$

and hence
$$p_0-p = 1.5\rho u_m^2 + \frac{16\rho u_m^2}{aR}(x-0.0575aR),$$

so that
$$(p_0-p)/(\tfrac{1}{2}\rho u_m^2) = 1.16+32x/(aR). \tag{17}$$

For flow out of a cistern where the pressure is P,
$$(P-p)/(\tfrac{1}{2}\rho u_m^2) = 2.16+32x/(aR), \tag{18}$$

friction in the intake being neglected. The term 2·16 corresponds to
the term 2 of the kinetic energy end-correction.

Schiller† also tested his results by measuring the value of C in
the relation
$$(P-p)/(\tfrac{1}{2}\rho u_m^2) = C+32x/(aR);‡ \tag{19}$$

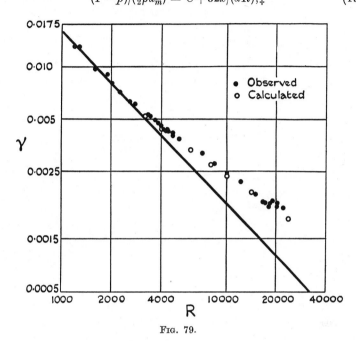

FIG. 79.

he found $C = 2\cdot115$, $2\cdot35$, $2\cdot36$, $2\cdot45$ in four series of experiments.
The mean of these results is 2·32, but Schiller attaches more weight
to the first one than to the other three. It seems, in fact, that no
sufficiently accurate experiments‖ to determine C have yet been
performed; if they are it will be necessary to take into account
friction in the intake. This may be done by assuming an increase in
the length of the pipe and determining this increase together with
C experimentally.

Velocity measurements in the inlet length have been made by

† *Forschungsarbeiten des Ver. deutsch. Ing.*, No. 248 (1922), pp. 29–33; *Handbuch
der Experimentalphysik*, **4**, part 4 (Leipzig, 1932), 56, 57.
‡ The value of C is of importance in the measurement of viscosity of liquids. For
further details see Hatschek, *The Viscosity of Liquids* (London, 1928), chap. II.
‖ Results of other experiments are given by Hatschek, *loc. cit.*

Nikuradse, and the results for $r/a = 0$, $0\cdot2$, $0\cdot4$, $0\cdot6$, $0\cdot7$, $0\cdot8$, and $0\cdot9$ are reproduced in Fig. 80,[†] which also contains results calculated by Schiller's method.

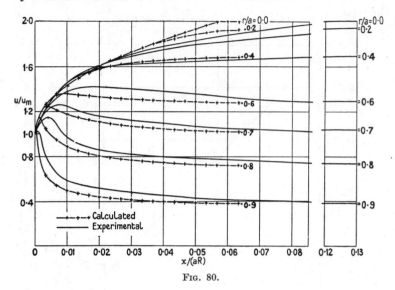

Fig. 80.

A more accurate solution near the pipe entry may be obtained by starting from the equations of motion:[‡]

$$u\frac{\partial u}{\partial x} + v\frac{\partial u}{\partial r} = -\frac{1}{\rho}\frac{\partial p}{\partial x} + \nu\left(\frac{\partial^2 u}{\partial r^2} + \frac{1}{r}\frac{\partial u}{\partial r} + \frac{\partial^2 u}{\partial x^2}\right), \tag{20}$$

$$u\frac{\partial v}{\partial r} + v\frac{\partial v}{\partial r} = -\frac{1}{\rho}\frac{\partial p}{\partial r} + \nu\left(\frac{\partial^2 v}{\partial r^2} + \frac{1}{r}\frac{\partial v}{\partial r} - \frac{v}{r^2} + \frac{\partial^2 v}{\partial x^2}\right), \tag{21}$$

in which use is made of the symmetry of the motion about the axis, and v is the radial component of velocity (which must be present since u changes with x).

The equation of continuity is

$$\frac{\partial}{\partial x}(ru) + \frac{\partial}{\partial r}(rv) = 0, \tag{22}$$

so a stream-function ψ exists such that

$$u = \frac{1}{r}\frac{\partial\psi}{\partial r}, \qquad v = -\frac{1}{r}\frac{\partial\psi}{\partial x}.$$

    † The experimental results in Fig. 80 are reproduced from a small-scale graph in Prandtl and Tietjens, *Hydro- und Aeromechanik*, **2** (Berlin, 1931), 28. Further details do not appear to have been published.

    ‡ Atkinson and Goldstein (unpublished). The method is a variation of a method due to Schlichting for the corresponding problem in two dimensions. See p. 309.

The boundary conditions are

$$u = u_m, \quad v = 0 \quad \text{at} \quad x = 0,$$
$$u = 0, \quad v = 0 \quad \text{at} \quad r = a. \tag{23}$$

We are concerned only with large Reynolds numbers, and the approximations usual in boundary layer theory may be made. The term $\nu \partial^2 u/\partial x^2$ in the first equation of motion may be neglected, and $\rho^{-1} \partial p/\partial x$ may be taken to be a function of x only. So long as there is a core uninfluenced by viscosity we put

$$\xi = \left(\frac{2x}{aR}\right)^{\frac{1}{2}}, \quad y_1 = \frac{1}{2}\left(1 - \frac{r^2}{a^2}\right), \quad \eta = \frac{y_1}{2\xi}, \quad \text{and} \quad -\frac{1}{\rho}\frac{\partial p}{\partial x} = u_1 \frac{du_1}{dx}, \tag{24}$$

where u_1 is the velocity in the core. We assume that

$$u_1 = u_m\{1 + K_1\xi + K_2\xi^2 + \ldots\}, \tag{25}$$

where the K's are constants to be determined: we shall see that with the assumption (25) the K's can be determined so that the flux across a section is constant.

A solution can then be obtained by generalizing Blasius's solution of the two-dimensional boundary layer equation. We put

$$\psi = -a^2 u_m[\xi f_1(\eta) + \xi^2 f_2(\eta) + \ldots], \tag{26}$$

so that $$u = \tfrac{1}{2}u_m[f_1'(\eta) + \xi f_2'(\eta) + \xi^2 f_3'(\eta) + \ldots]. \tag{27}$$

We substitute in the equation of motion and equate coefficients of powers of ξ. This yields the following equations for the f's:

$$f_1''' + f_1 f_1'' = 0, \tag{28}$$

$$f_2''' + f_1 f_2'' - f_1' f_2' + 2f_1'' f_2 = -4K_1 + 4\eta f_1'' + 4f_1', \tag{29}$$

$$f_3''' + f_1 f_3'' - 2f_1' f_3' + 3f_1'' f_3 = -8K_2 - 4K_1^2 + f_2'^2 - 2f_2 f_2'' + 4\eta f_2'' + 4f_2', \tag{30}$$

.   .   .   .

.   .   .   .

where (so long as a core exists)

$$f_n(0) = f_n'(0) = 0, \quad f_1'(\infty) = 2, \quad f_n'(\infty) = 2K_{n-1} \quad (n > 1). \tag{31}$$

The necessary K's can be determined, as below, before the respective f's are calculated.

For large values of η, $f_1 \sim 2\eta + A_1$, $f_2 \sim 2K_1\eta + A_2$, $f_3 \sim 2K_2\eta + A_3,\ldots$, where the A's are determined by the numerical integration of the equations (28), (29), etc.

For constancy of flux the difference in the values of $2\pi\psi$ at $r = a$ (i.e. $\eta = 0$) and at $r = 0$ (i.e. $\eta = 1/(4\xi)$) must be constant and equal to the flux $\pi a^2 u_m$. The stream-function ψ vanishes at $\eta = 0$, and so long as there is a core uninfluenced by viscosity, $1/(4\xi)$ must be sufficiently large for the above approximations to hold in finding the value of ψ at $\eta = 1/(4\xi)$. The condition of constancy of flux therefore becomes

$$\xi\left(\frac{1}{2\xi} + A_1\right) + \xi^2\left(\frac{K_1}{2\xi} + A_2\right) + \xi^3\left(\frac{K_2}{2\xi} + A_3\right) + \ldots = \tfrac{1}{2}. \tag{32}$$

Hence $K_1 = -2A_1,$ $K_2 = -2A_2,$ $K_3 = -2A_3,$ etc.   (33)

Thus a solution is obtained for small values of $x/(aR)$. It is found that the K's increase rapidly ($K_1 = 3{\cdot}4415$, $K_2 = -9{\cdot}0938$, $K_3 = 141{\cdot}982$, $K_4 = -2788$). Beyond about $\xi = 0{\cdot}05$ the series (25) up to the term $K_4 \xi^4$ does not give sufficiently accurate results, whilst some allowance must be made for the following terms even for $\xi = 0{\cdot}05$. It appears that for $\xi \leqslant 0{\cdot}05$ the values of u/u_m calculated by Schiller's method are accurate to within 1 per cent. for $r/a \leqslant 0{\cdot}8$ and to within 5 per cent. for $r/a = 0{\cdot}9$. It follows that the experimental results in Fig. 80 do not agree with the accurate solution for very small values of $x/(aR)$. The singularity in the solution at $x = 0$ will cause some discrepancy very near the entry; whether this is sufficient to explain the actual discrepancy between the observed and calculated values we cannot tell in the absence of further experimental details.

The solution for small values of $x/(aR)$ may be continued by a method due to Boussinesq.† If we write

$$X = 2x/(aR), \quad Y = r^2/a^2, \quad w = Rrv/(2a) \quad \text{and} \quad R = 2u_m a/\nu, \quad (34)$$

the equation of continuity becomes

$$\frac{\partial u}{\partial X} + 2\frac{\partial w}{\partial Y} = 0,$$

so that

$$2w = \int_Y^1 \frac{\partial u}{\partial X} \, dY \quad (35)$$

(since $w = 0$ at $Y = 1$). Hence equation (20) (with $\nu \partial^2 u/\partial x^2$ neglected) becomes

$$u\frac{\partial u}{\partial X} + \frac{\partial u}{\partial Y}\int_Y^1 \frac{\partial u}{\partial X} \, dY = -\frac{1}{\rho}\frac{\partial p}{\partial X} + 4u_m \frac{\partial}{\partial Y}\left(Y\frac{\partial u}{\partial Y}\right). \quad (36)$$

Differentiation with regard to Y gives the equation for u; also, from (36),

$$-\frac{1}{\rho}\frac{\partial p}{\partial X} = \left[u\frac{\partial u}{\partial X} - 4u_m \frac{\partial}{\partial Y}\left(Y\frac{\partial u}{\partial Y}\right)\right]_{Y=0},$$

since $\partial p/\partial X$ is independent of Y and

$$\int_0^1 \frac{\partial u}{\partial X} \, dY = 0$$

$\left(\text{because } \int_0^1 u \, dY \text{ is constant}\right).$

In the permanent régime $u = 2u_m(1-Y),$

so we now put $u = u_m\{2(1-Y) + \varpi\}.$ (37)

For a first approximation, ϖ_1, we suppose ϖ small and neglect squares; we then find that

$$\frac{1-Y}{Y}\frac{\partial}{\partial X}\left(Y\frac{\partial \varpi_1}{\partial Y}\right) = 2\frac{\partial^2}{\partial Y^2}\left(Y\frac{\partial \varpi_1}{\partial Y}\right), \quad (38)$$

which is an equation for $Y\,\partial\varpi_1/\partial Y$.

† *Comptes Rendus*, **113** (1891), 9–15; 49–51. Actually Boussinesq applied his method right from the entry, but it is more accurate when used to continue a solution such as that described above.

Since $\int_0^1 u\, dY$ is constant, $\int_0^1 \varpi_1\, dY = 0$; and since $\varpi_1 = 0$ at $Y = 1$,

$$\int_0^1 Y \frac{\partial \varpi_1}{\partial Y}\, dY = [Y\varpi_1]_0^1 - \int_0^1 \varpi_1\, dY = 0.$$

If we put

$$Y\, \partial\varpi_1/\partial Y = ce^{-2\lambda X}\phi(Y) \tag{39}$$

in (38) we find that

$$\phi'' + \lambda\left(\frac{1-Y}{Y}\right)\phi = 0. \tag{40}$$

The boundary conditions are $\phi(0) = 0$ and $\int_0^1 \phi\, dY = 0$. Equation (40) with these boundary conditions shows that λ has one of a series of characteristic values. If $\lambda_1,\ldots,\lambda_n,\ldots$ are the characteristic values, then the complete solution is

$$Y\, \partial\varpi_1/\partial Y = c_1 e^{-2\lambda_1 X}\phi_1(Y) + c_2 e^{-2\lambda_2 X}\phi_2(Y) + \ldots. \tag{41}$$

Hence

$$-\varpi_1 = c_1 e^{-2\lambda_1 X}\Phi_1(Y) + c_2 e^{-2\lambda_2 X}\Phi_2(Y) + \ldots, \tag{42}$$

where

$$\Phi_r(Y) = \int_Y^1 \phi_r(Y)\frac{dY}{Y}. \tag{43}$$

The condition to determine the c's is that

$$\int_0^1 (c_1\Phi_1 + c_2\Phi_2 + \ldots + c_n\Phi_n + \varpi_0)^2\, dY$$

is a minimum, where ϖ_0 is the value of ϖ_1 when $X = 0$, which we take to be the section from which the solution is started.

Atkinson and Goldstein took into account the terms in c_1 and c_2 in (42), and also found a second approximation by substituting the result so obtained into the neglected terms in (36) and solving again, taking into account in this second approximation only the term in c_1^2. This solution was then joined to the series solution (27) at $\xi = 0.05$ by making the mean-square difference a minimum. The results for $x/(aR) \geqslant 0.015$ are shown in Fig. 81. For smaller values of $x/(aR)$ they are certainly inaccurate.

The calculated values of $(p_0-p)/(\tfrac{1}{2}\rho u_m^2)$ are shown in Table 12 below. The

TABLE 12

$\dfrac{x}{aR}$	$\dfrac{p_0-p}{\frac{1}{2}\rho u_m^2}$	$\dfrac{x}{aR}$	$\dfrac{p_0-p}{\frac{1}{2}\rho u_m^2}$
0	0	0·015	1·36
0·001	0·32	0·020	1·63
0·002	0·46	0·025	1·88
0·003	0·56	0·030	2·10
0·004	0·65	0·040	2·51
0·005	0·73	0·05	2·88
0·007	0·87	0·06	3·24
0·009	1·00	0·07	3·59
0·011	1·11	0·08	3·93
0·013	1·22	0·09	4·26
0·015	1·33	0·10	4·59
		0·11	4·92

values in the first two columns are found by Schiller's method; those in the third and fourth by Atkinson and Goldstein's extension of Boussinesq's method. At $x/(aR) = 0\cdot015$ the results differ by about 2 per cent. For more accurate results the values of u/u_m found from the series (27) would have to be continued for larger values of $x/(aR)$ by step-by-step calculations, and the

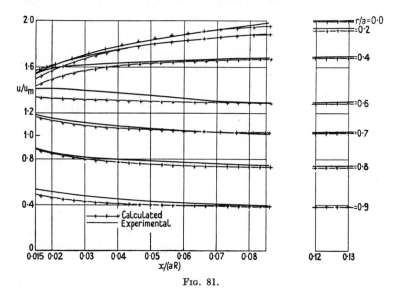

Fig. 81.

extension of Boussinesq's solution joined to the values so found at a larger value of $x/(aR)$ than is at present possible.

For larger values of $x/(aR)$ than those shown in the table

$$\frac{p_0-p}{\frac{1}{2}\rho u_m^2} = \frac{32x}{aR} + 1\cdot41,$$

and for flow out of a cistern where the pressure is P

$$\frac{P-p}{\frac{1}{2}\rho u_m^2} = \frac{32x}{aR} + 2\cdot41. \tag{44}$$

140. Two-dimensional flow through a straight channel.

At sections far from the ends the velocity distribution for steady flow in a channel of breadth $2h$ may be obtained by integrating the equation of momentum for a symmetrically situated rectangular slab of fluid of breadth $2y$, with the boundary condition $u = 0$ at $y = h$: the result is

$$u = -\frac{1}{2\mu}\frac{\partial p}{\partial x}(h^2-y^2),$$

where y is the distance from the middle of the channel. The mean velocity over a section is

$$u_m = -\frac{h^2}{3\mu}\frac{\partial p}{\partial x}. \tag{45}$$

The mean velocity is two-thirds the maximum, and the velocity distribution is parabolic.

The hydraulic mean depth, m, is equal to the half-width, h. As Reynolds number we therefore take

$$R = 4hu_m/\nu,$$

and for the resistance coefficient γ we obtain the equation

$$\gamma = \tau_0/\tfrac{1}{2}\rho u_m^2 = 24/R, \tag{46}$$

where τ_0 is the shearing stress at a wall.

141. Two-dimensional flow in the inlet length of a straight channel.

By calculations similar to those in § 139 the velocity distribution, the pressure drop and the skin-friction in the inlet length may be determined for two-dimensional pressure flow between parallel walls. The equation for the pressure drop from the entry to any section where the parabolic flow is fully established, when calculated by Schiller's method, is

$$(p_0-p)/(\tfrac{1}{2}\rho u_m^2) = 24x/(hR)+0{\cdot}626.\dagger \tag{47}$$

The corresponding result from the kinetic energy end-correction is

$$(p_0-p)/(\tfrac{1}{2}\rho u_m^2) = 24x/(hR)+0{\cdot}543. \tag{48}$$

A solution‡ by a method similar to that described on pp. 304–308 for a circular pipe leads to the result

$$(p_0-p)/(\tfrac{1}{2}\rho u_m^2) = 24x/(hR)+0{\cdot}601: \tag{49}$$

the velocity distributions calculated by this method are shown in Figs. 82 and 83. The broken line in Fig. 82 is the Poiseuille parabola: the broken lines in Fig. 83 give the asymptotic values for the parabolic flow. In Table 13, $(p_0-p)/(\tfrac{1}{2}\rho u_m^2)$ is tabulated against $\nu x/(h^2 u_m)$, where p_0 is the pressure at the entry and p is the pressure at a section distant x downstream.

---

† Schiller gave $0{\cdot}614$ in place of $0{\cdot}626$. See Schlichting, *Zeitschr. f. angew. Math. u. Mech.* **14** (1934), 372.

‡ Schlichting, *op. cit*, pp. 368–373.

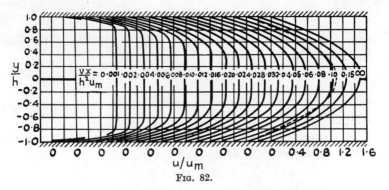

FIG. 82.

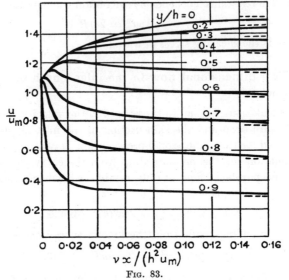

FIG. 83.

TABLE 13

$\dfrac{\nu x}{h^2 u_m}$	$\dfrac{p_0-p}{\frac{1}{2}\rho u_m^2}$	$\dfrac{\nu x}{h^2 u_m}$	$\dfrac{p_0-p}{\frac{1}{2}\rho u_m^2}$
0	0	0·040	0·688
0·001	0·1100	0·050	0·772
0·002	0·1600	0·060	0·850
0·004	0·2322	0·080	1·002
0·006	0·291	0·100	1·145
0·008	0·338	0·125	1·315
0·010	0·378	0·150	1·478
0·012	0·411	0·250	2·101
0·016	0·466	0·500	3·601
0·020	0·510	1·000	6·601
0·025	0·558	∞	∞
0·032	0·620		

142. The effect of roughness on laminar flow in pipes and channels.

We can estimate the order of magnitude of the maximum size of protuberances which will not alter the character of the flow in a circular pipe.[†] If ϵ is the maximum permissible height of a protuberance, then (ϵ being small) the velocity at its tip is

$$u_\epsilon = 2u_m\{1-(1-\epsilon/a)^2\} \doteqdot 4u_m\,\epsilon/a$$

to the first order. (It is assumed that the presence of the roughness has not altered the character of the flow.) Therefore

$$R_\epsilon\,(= \epsilon u_\epsilon/\nu) = 2(\epsilon/a)^2 R, \quad \text{where} \quad R = 2au_m/\nu.$$

For uniform flow past an obstacle a critical Reynolds number R_c exists such that for $R > R_c$ a vortex wake forms behind the obstacle, whereas for $R < R_c$ the flow closes up behind. If the flow past the protuberances which form the roughness in the pipe is such as to cause the production of vortex wakes, then the form of the flow in the pipe will be considerably different from the flow in a smooth pipe. In order to obtain an order of magnitude for the size of the protuberances which do not produce great variation in the flow we may therefore express the condition that R_ϵ should be less than the value of R_c for flow past an obstacle of the shape of the protuberances. For a circular cylinder, for example, we may take $R_c = 50$,[‡] and this value leads to the condition

$$\epsilon/a < 5/R^{\frac{1}{2}}.$$

If for a flat plate normal to a disturbed stream we assume that $R_c = 30$, we obtain $\epsilon/a < 4/R^{\frac{1}{2}}$ as the condition for sharp-edged roughnesses.

If we write U_τ for $\sqrt{(\tau_0/\rho)}$, where τ_0 is the shearing stress at the wall, and if we assume that τ_0 is unaltered, then the condition can be expressed in the form that $\epsilon U_\tau/\nu$ must be less than $\sqrt{R_c}$, or, with $R_c = 30$, less than about 5·5. This order of magnitude appears to be in satisfactory agreement with experiment.[∥]

For a channel $R_\epsilon = \frac{3}{4}R(\epsilon/h)^2$, and ϵ/h must be less than about $6/R^{\frac{1}{2}}$ for sharp-edged roughnesses to be without effect. $\epsilon U_\tau/\nu$ must again be less than $\sqrt{R_c}$.

[†] Schiller, *Handbuch der Experimentalphysik*, **4**, part 4 (Leipzig, 1932), 191, 192.
[‡] Cf. Chap. IX, § 184.
[∥] Schiller, *op. cit.*, pp. 189–192; see also p. 377 and Nikuradse, *Ver. deutsch. Ing.*, *Forschungsheft* 361 (1933). It should be observed that, with a disturbed entry, the above estimate will not apply till the disturbance has died down.

143. Flow through curved pipes.

We confine our attention to flow through pipes of circular cross-section whose axes are bent into circles. We take coordinates as shown in Fig. 84 (O being the centre of curvature of the axis of the pipe), and denote by L the radius of curvature of the axis, by a the radius of the pipe, and by U, V, and W the velocities in the directions of r, ϕ, and θ increasing. In the region where the flow is fully developed U, V and W are independent of θ. The equations of motion referred to this system of coordinates are to be found in a paper by Dean;[†] they are complicated. If a/L is small and if terms of order $1/L$ are neglected compared with terms of order $1/r$, the equations simplify. By reducing these simplified equations to non-dimensional form it may be shown that dynamical similarity depends on the parameter

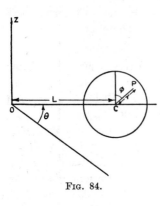

FIG. 84.

$$K' = \left(\frac{a}{L}\right)^{\frac{1}{2}}\left(\frac{2W_0 a}{\nu}\right) \qquad (50)$$

only, where W_0 is the mean velocity in flow through a straight pipe under the same pressure gradient as that along the pipe axis in the curved pipe. Thus the ratio of the flux F_c through the curved pipe to the flux F_s through a straight pipe under the same pressure gradient is a function of K' only for small values of a/L; further, if γ_c and γ_s are the resistance coefficients in the curved pipe[‡] and in a straight pipe when the flux is F_s in both cases, it may be shown that $F_c/F_s = \gamma_s/\gamma_c$. Expanding in powers of K', Dean finds that

$$\frac{\gamma_s}{\gamma_c} = \frac{F_c}{F_s} = 1 - 0.03058\left(\frac{K'^2}{1152}\right)^2 + 0.01195\left(\frac{K'^2}{1152}\right)^4 + \dots. \qquad (51)$$

The error when only the three terms shown are taken into account increases with K'. It is probably not serious at any rate for $K' < 30$.

To a first approximation the parameter K' is equal to K, defined as $(a/L)^{\frac{1}{2}}(2W_m a/\nu)$, where W_m is the mean velocity in the flow through

† *Phil. Mag.* (7), **4** (1927), 208–223; **5** (1928), 673–695.
‡ γ_c has a definition equivalent to the definition (3) for γ_s, viz.

$$\gamma_c = -\frac{1}{L}\frac{\partial p}{\partial \theta}\frac{a}{\rho W_m^2}.$$

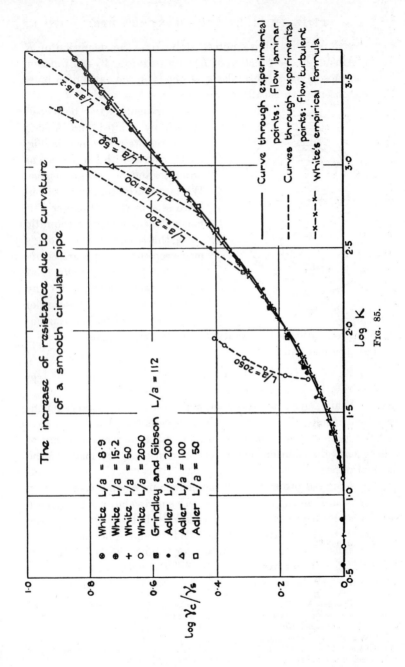

The increase of resistance due to curvature of a smooth circular pipe

⊗ White $L/a = 8.9$
⊛ White $L/a = 15.2$
+ White $L/a = 50$
○ White $L/a = 2050$
▣ Grindley and Gibson $L/a = 112$
● Adler $L/a = 200$
△ Adler $L/a = 100$
□ Adler $L/a = 50$

$\log \gamma_c / \gamma_s$

Log K

—— Curve through experimental points: Flow laminar
– – – Curves through experimental points: Flow turbulent
—×—×— White's empirical formula

Fig. 85.

the curved pipe: it follows immediately from the definition of K that it is in any case a function of K' only (since W_m/W_0 is a function of K' only), so dynamical similarity depends on the value of K only. Experimenters have usually preferred to use K instead of K'.

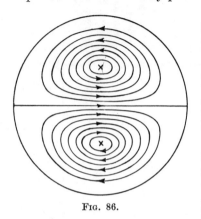

FIG. 86.

Experiments have been performed by White[†] and Adler,[‡] whose results are shown in Fig. 85 by curves with $\log_{10}(\gamma_c/\gamma_s)$ as ordinates and $\log_{10} K$ as abscissae. White remarks that once turbulence sets in the parameter K is not sufficient to define the ratio γ_c/γ_s; this is supported by Adler's measurements. It appears, therefore, that the value of $\log K$ at which turbulence sets in for any particular pipe is the abscissa of the point where the corresponding observed curve in Fig. 85 leaves the universal curve.

The empirical equation

$$\frac{\gamma_c}{\gamma_s} = \left[1 - \left\{ 1 - \left(\frac{11 \cdot 6}{K} \right)^{0 \cdot 45} \right\}^{2 \cdot 22} \right]^{-1} \quad (11 \cdot 6 < K < 3000), \qquad (52)$$

due to White, gives a good representation of the observed non-turbulent results. The corresponding curve is included in Fig. 85.

Adler (*loc. cit.*) has made a large number of measurements of the velocity distribution, for which reference may be made to the original paper.

The calculated projections of the particle paths on a cross-section of the pipe are shown in Fig. 86 for a very small value of K; they were calculated by neglecting terms of order K^4, but serve to show the secondary motion which is set up.[||] White and Adler both found this secondary motion experimentally for laminar flow:[††] the former observed that it was by no means as evident once the flow became turbulent. This he ascribed to the fact that in turbulent flow the

---

[†] *Proc. Roy. Soc.* A, **123** (1929), 645–663. The results when $L/a = 8 \cdot 9$ were obtained after the publication of the paper, and kindly communicated to us by Prof. White.

[‡] *Zeitschr. f. angew. Math. u. Mech.* **14** (1934), 257–275.

[||] Dean, *loc. cit.* For a qualitative explanation, see Chap. II, § 28 (p. 84).

[††] This secondary flow has also been confirmed in a striking manner by Taylor using a colour thread (*Proc. Roy. Soc.* A, **124** (1929), 243–249).

velocity distribution is much more nearly uniform than in laminar flow, and correspondingly the pressure gradients producing the secondary motion are less.

144. Two-dimensional flow through curved channels.

We confine our attention to a channel formed by two coaxial cylindrical walls, and consider two-dimensional flow perpendicular to the common axis due to a pressure gradient parallel to the walls and perpendicular to the common axis.

If we denote by W the velocity parallel to the walls and perpendicular to the common axis, and by W_m the mean value of W, we find from the equations of motion that

$$W = -\frac{1}{2\mu}\frac{\partial p}{\partial \theta}\left[\frac{(b^2\log b - a^2\log a)}{(b^2-a^2)}r - \frac{a^2b^2}{(b^2-a^2)}\left(\log\frac{b}{a}\right)\frac{1}{r} - r\log r\right], \quad (53)$$

and

$$(b-a)W_m = -\frac{1}{2\mu}\frac{\partial p}{\partial \theta}\left[\frac{(b^2-a^2)}{4} - \frac{a^2b^2}{(b^2-a^2)}\left(\log\frac{b}{a}\right)^2\right], \quad (54)$$

where r is distance measured from the common axis, θ is angular distance measured round the common axis, the walls are at $r = a$ and $r = b$ $(b > a)$, and p is the pressure. ($\partial p/\partial \theta$ may be shown to be a constant independent of r and θ.) The other velocity components vanish: there is a pressure gradient across the channel which just balances the centrifugal force.

We may obtain alternative forms for (53) and (54) by writing $b = a+2h$, $r = a+h+y$, $h/a = \alpha$. These forms are

$$W = -\frac{1}{2\mu}\frac{\partial p}{\partial \theta}\frac{h}{\alpha}\left\{\left[\frac{(1+2\alpha)^2\log(1+2\alpha)}{4\alpha+4\alpha^2}\right]\left[1+\alpha+\frac{\alpha y}{h}-\frac{1}{1+\alpha+\alpha y/h}\right]\right.$$
$$\left. -(1+\alpha+\alpha y/h)\log(1+\alpha+\alpha y/h)\right\}, \quad (55)$$

$$W_m = -\frac{1}{4\mu}\frac{\partial p}{\partial \theta}\frac{h}{\alpha^2}\left\{\alpha+\alpha^2-\frac{(1+2\alpha)^2}{4(\alpha+\alpha^2)}\left[\log(1+2\alpha)\right]^2\right\}. \quad (56)$$

Curves in Fig. 87 show W/W_m plotted against y/h for $\alpha = 2$, $0\cdot 5$, $0\cdot 1$, and 0 (straight channel). The effect of the curvature is very small when $\alpha = 0\cdot 1$.

The fact that no secondary flow occurs has been pointed out previously.† The pressure gradient across the channel due to

---

† Chap. II, § 28 (p. 87).

centrifugal force produces no secondary flow in the absence of walls parallel to it, no retarded layers being produced on which the pressure gradient could act.

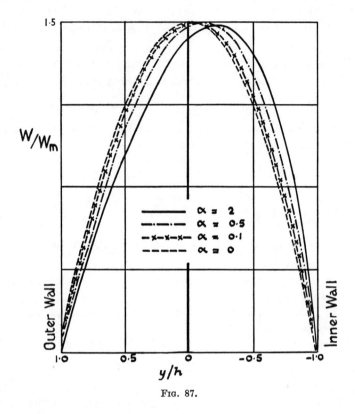

Fig. 87.

145. Flow along a flat plate. Roughness.

The laminar flow along a flat plate placed edgeways to a steady stream has been calculated on the assumptions of the boundary layer theory in Chap. IV, §53 (pp. 135, 136). The velocity distribution has been measured experimentally by Hansen† in an open jet wind tunnel, and his results are compared with theory in Fig. 88: there is quite good agreement. (In Fig. 88, u_1 is the velocity outside the boundary layer, x is distance from the leading edge, and u the forward velocity at a distance y from the plate.) The experimental

† *Zeitschr. f. angew. Math. u. Mech.* **8** (1928), 185–199.

values of u/u_1 obtained by Dryden[†] in a closed tunnel, when plotted against $y\sqrt{(u_1/\nu x)}$, are also in very satisfactory agreement with the theoretical curve; whereas the results of measurements in a closed tunnel by Burgers and Van der Hegge Zijnen[‡] are consistently greater than those of theory. Burgers attributes the discrepancy to the fact that the main stream may not have been quite steady,

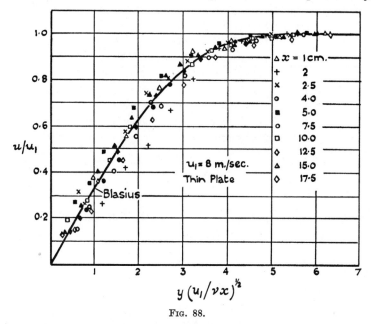

Fig. 88.

and suggests that the interchange which subsequently arises in the boundary layer would lead to these increased values: on the other hand, it is possible that the acceleration of the main stream due to the growth of the boundary layer along both the plate and the channel walls would account for the discrepancy.||

In Chapter IV it was pointed out that for flow along a cylinder open at both ends (with generators parallel to the main flow) the same results should hold as for a flat plate provided that the cylinder is

---

† *N.A.C.A. Report* No. 562 (1936). See especially Fig. 17.

‡ *Proc. 1st Internat. Congress for Applied Mechanics, Delft,* 1924 (Delft, 1925), pp. 113–128.

|| Due account was taken of the pressure gradient in the direction of flow in reducing the observations, but no account was taken of the pressure gradient in the theoretical calculations.

short enough. Experiments have been carried out on small rings of this type by Miss Marshall,[†] who obtained the skin-friction from measurements in the wake; the results were larger than those of theory.

The resistance of a flat plate has been obtained by Fage[‡] by measurements in the wake in an open jet tunnel; he too finds values which are larger than those calculated.

It may be remarked that considerable fluctuations in the velocity in the 'laminar' portion of the boundary layer along a flat plate have been observed.[||] These fluctuations are due to fluctuations in the main flow. The fluctuating components of the velocities are uncorrelated, and so do not give rise to any transfer of momentum or 'apparent stresses'. The fluctuations are of amplitude several times the amplitude in the main stream, but are much slower.

A limit can be set to the permissible height of roughnesses in order that they may not materially affect the flow. From equations (44) and (46) of Chapter IV

$$u = \tfrac{1}{2}u_1\left(\alpha\eta - \frac{\alpha^2\eta^4}{4!} + \dots\right),$$

where $\qquad\qquad \alpha = 1{\cdot}32824, \qquad \eta = \tfrac{1}{2}\left(\frac{u_1}{\nu x}\right)^{\frac{1}{2}}y,$

so that at the tip of a projection of height ϵ,

$$u_\epsilon = \frac{\alpha}{4}\frac{u_1^{\frac{3}{2}}}{\nu^{\frac{1}{2}}}\frac{\epsilon}{x^{\frac{1}{2}}}$$

to the first order. Thus

$$R_\epsilon\left(= \frac{\epsilon u_\epsilon}{\nu}\right) = \frac{\alpha}{4}\frac{u_1^{\frac{3}{2}}\epsilon^2}{\nu^{\frac{3}{2}}x^{\frac{1}{2}}} = R_x^{\frac{3}{2}}\left(\frac{\epsilon}{x}\right)^2\frac{\alpha}{4},$$

where $R_x = u_1 x/\nu$.

Using the same estimates of the critical value (R_c) of R as in § 142, namely $R_c = 50$ for rounded roughnesses and 30 for sharp ones, we see that we require $\qquad, \; R_x^{\frac{3}{2}}(\epsilon/x)^2 \leqslant 200/\alpha \doteqdot 150$

or $\qquad\qquad\qquad\qquad \epsilon/x \leqslant 12{\cdot}2(R_x)^{-\frac{3}{4}}$

for the former, and

$$R_x^{\frac{3}{2}}(\epsilon/x)^2 \leqslant 120/\alpha \doteqdot 90$$

or $\qquad\qquad\qquad\qquad \epsilon/x \leqslant 9{\cdot}5(R_x)^{-\frac{3}{4}}$

† A.R.C. Reports and Memoranda, No. 1004 (1926).
‡ A.R.C. Reports and Memoranda, No. 1580 (1934), pp. 1–7.
|| Dryden, Proc. Fourth Internat. Congress for Applied Mechanics, Cambridge, 1934 (Cambridge, 1935), p. 175; Journal of the Washington Academy of Sciences, 25 (1935), 106; N.A.C.A. Report No. 562 (1936).

for the latter, if the effect of the roughness is to be inappreciable. It is evident that a given size of roughness is more likely to have a disturbing effect near the leading edge than elsewhere. In terms of U_τ the condition is $\epsilon U_\tau/\nu < \sqrt{R_c}$, exactly as for pipes and channels (§ 142).

SECTION II
THE TRANSITION FROM LAMINAR TO TURBULENT FLOW

146. The transition to turbulence in smooth pipes and channels.

The phenomena in a pipe or channel are closely associated with the entry conditions. With disturbed conditions at entry the disturbances die out after a certain length if R is small enough. As R is increased a critical value R_{crit} is reached such that for $R > R_{\text{crit}}$ the disturbances are no longer damped out and the flow in the pipe is turbulent. There is a minimum value of R_{crit} such that for R less than this minimum value all disturbances, however great, are damped out sufficiently far downstream. This minimum value of R_{crit} is determined experimentally by imposing very disturbed conditions at entry: the values obtained by various experimenters are shown in the following tables for straight and for curved pipes.

Straight Pipes

R_{crit}	Shape of cross-section	Experimenter	Method
2000	Smooth circular	Reynolds†	pressure drop and flux (water)
2100	,, ,,	Ruckes‡	,, ,, ,, ,, (air)
2100	,, ,,	Stanton and Pannel‖	,, ,, ,, ,, (air and water)
2000	,, ,,		$u_m/u_{\max}$ and $au_{\max}/\nu$ (air and water)
1900	,, ,,	Barnes and Coker††	axial temperature (with pipe surrounded by jacket) and flux (water)
2800	Rectangular pipe: ratio of sides 104:1–165:1	White and Davies‡‡	resistance and flux (water)
2100	Square	Schiller‖‖	,, ,, ,, ,,
1600	Rectangular pipe: ratio of sides 2·83:1	Schiller‖‖	,, ,, ,, ,,
2400	Annular pipe: ratio of radii 0·818:1	Fage†††	pressure and flux (water)

† *Phil. Trans.* **174** (1883), 935–982; *Scientific Papers*, **2**, 51–105.
‡ *Ann. d. Phys.* (4), **25** (1908), 983–1021.
‖ *Phil. Trans.* A, **214** (1914), 199–224.
†† *Proc. Roy. Soc.* A, **74** (1905), 341–356.   ‡‡ *Ibid.* **119** (1928), 92–107.
‖‖ *Zeitschr. f. angew. Math. u. Mech.* **3** (1923), 2–13.
††† *Proc. Roy. Soc.* A, **165** (1938), 520–525.

The two quantities mentioned in the last column were in each instance plotted against each other, and a sudden change in the relationship was taken to indicate the onset of turbulence. The resistance was obtained, in those methods where it was used, from pressure measurements; there is therefore effectively no difference between the two methods. The experimental fluid is mentioned in brackets.

Curved Pipes of Circular Cross-Section

R_{crit}	a/L	Experimenter	Method
7590†	0·066	White‡	Curves of γ_c/γ_s plotted against K (see
6020†	0·020	White‡	pp. 313, 314). Point where particular
5620	0·020	Adler‖	curve leaves universal one taken to
4730	0·010	Adler‖	indicate onset of turbulence.
3980	0·005	Adler‖	
2270†	0·00049	White‡	

White (loc. cit.) remarks that turbulence arises, in all his experiments, when $\gamma_c = 0.0090$. It is rather difficult to take values accurately from Adler's graph; it appears that, in the order given in the table, his results give $\gamma_c = 0.0095, 0.0090, 0.0084$. The difference between 0·0090 and the first and last of these results is probably greater than the error in estimating values from the graphs. Even so, $\gamma_c = 0.0090$ gives a rough idea of the value of R_{crit}.

147. The effect of roughness on the critical Reynolds number.

If the disturbances produced by the roughnesses are less than those introduced in the entry, roughness may be expected to have no effect on R_{crit}: if they are bigger, roughness will certainly affect R_{crit}. No systematic effects of roughness on the minimum value of R_{crit} are apparent from experimental data available, and no great differences between the minimum values of R_{crit} for smooth and rough pipes have been obtained.

148. The entry length. Experimental results for smooth entry conditions in straight pipes.

In determining the values of R_{crit} experimentally a sufficient entry length must be allowed in order to determine whether an initial disturbance will increase or be damped out. This length depends

---

† These figures are given by Taylor (Proc. Roy. Soc. A, **124** (1929), 243–249), who took them from White's results. He also confirmed these values of R_{crit} by means of colour threads.

‡ Loc. cit. ante (p. 314).   ‖ Loc. cit. ante (p. 314).

largely on the nature of the disturbances. Schiller† found that a length of 130 diameters was sufficient, whereas one of 65 diameters was not. For flow in a channel (a rectangular pipe of large breadth/depth ratio) Davies and White‡ found that 54 times the depth was a sufficient entry length.

As the disturbances at entry decrease, R_{crit} increases. (There does not seem to be any evidence concerning a possible systematic dependence of R_{crit} on the *form* of the disturbances.) Reynolds believed

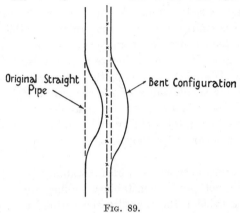

Original Straight Pipe

Bent Configuration

FIG. 89.

that an upper critical number exists for flow in pipes such that for greater numbers the flow is necessarily turbulent: experimentally, using a colour thread, he found a value 6,000 for such a number. The available evidence seems to show, however, that R_{crit} could be increased indefinitely if the disturbances present could be decreased indefinitely. Barnes and Coker (*loc. cit.*) obtained laminar flow at a Reynolds number greater than 2×10^4, and Schiller‖ reached about the same value: Ekman,†† using Reynolds's original apparatus, obtained laminar flow in one case at a Reynolds number as high as 5×10^4. Taylor, in some unpublished experiments with a very long inlet, found that laminar flow was possible up to a Reynolds number of $3 \cdot 2 \times 10^4$, and also showed that when the pipe was bent by an amount nearly equal to the diameter, the flow still remained laminar. Moreover, a filament line (shown $--\times--\times--$ in Fig. 89) appeared nearly straight.

† *Zeitschr. f. angew. Math. u. Mech.* 1 (1921), 436–444.
‡ *Proc. Roy. Soc.* A, 119 (1928), 99.   ‖ *Op. cit.*, p. 442.
†† *Ark. f. mat., astr. och. fys.* 6 (1910), No. 12.

149. The instability of laminar flow in curved channels.

The theoretical and experimental results obtained by Taylor for the stability of the flow between two rotating cylinders were described in Chap. V, § 75 (pp. 196, 197).[†] Taylor's experimental work was confined to water and glass surfaces; Lewis[‡] has covered a larger range by using xylene, nitrobenzene, and a mixture of the two as experimental fluids and by using a lead or silver inner surface together with a glass outer tube.

We discussed steady laminar flow in a curved channel on pp. 315, 316: Dean[||] has made calculations concerning its stability, assuming infinitesimal disturbances symmetrical about the common axis and periodic along it. If $2h$ and a denote respectively the distance between the walls and the radius of the inner wall, as before, then Dean found for small values of h/a a critical Reynolds number given by $2W_m h/\nu = 25\cdot45(a/h)^{\frac{1}{2}}$. For greater Reynolds numbers the system is unstable, the instability first manifesting itself for a disturbance with a particular wave-length in the direction parallel to the axis.

The type of disturbance for which instability is produced in this problem does not produce instability in flow through a straight channel. It is evident, therefore, that curvature has a marked effect on the stability of steady flow.[††] This result is borne out by experiments on flow in straight and curved pipes. When turbulence appears in straight pipes there is a sudden increase in the loss of head, which is not observed in curved pipes. A possible explanation is that curved flow becomes unstable for infinitesimal disturbances, whereas straight flow becomes unstable for finite disturbances only.

The stability of the flow due to a pressure gradient parallel to their common axis between two rotating cylinders has been investigated theoretically[‡‡] and experimentally.[||||] If the radii of the cylinders are a, $a+2h$ and their angular velocities Ω_1, Ω_2, where $\Omega_2/\Omega_1 = \alpha$, then for small values of h/a stability depends, for a given value of the Reynolds number R of the flow parallel to the axis, on the value of

$$(1+\alpha)\frac{\Omega_1^2 h^3}{\nu^2}\frac{a^2-\alpha(a+2h)^2}{a+h}.$$

[†] For further information concerning critical speeds for flow between rotating cylinders see also pp. 388–390.   [‡] *Proc. Roy. Soc.* A, **117** (1928), 388–407.
[||] *Ibid.* **121** (1928), 402–420.   [††] Cf. also pp. 388–390.
[‡‡] Goldstein, *Proc. Camb. Phil. Soc.* **33** (1937), 41–61.
[||||] Cornish, *Proc. Roy. Soc.* A, **140** (1933), 227–240; Fage, *ibid.* **165** (1938), 513–517.

If α is not nearly equal to unity, this reduces approximately for small values of h/a to

$$\frac{(1-\alpha^2)\Omega_1^2 h^3 a}{\nu^2}.$$

The theoretical numerical results have been evaluated for the outer cylinder at rest and for small values of R: for $R = 0$ they agree with Taylor's result. The experiments also were performed with the outer cylinder at rest. Apart from a rapid fall in the calculated value of the critical rotational speed Ω_c near the highest value of R at which calculations were made (which was probably due to too drastic mathematical approximations), the calculated results are consistent with the results of Fage's experiments. These experiments show a continual increase in Ω_c with increasing R. The value of Ω_c was found by measurements of the pressure drop down a test length, and the results of these measurements, at each fixed value of R, show that as Ω_1 is increased beyond Ω_c the difference of the pressure drop from its theoretical value for laminar flow is at first very small and increases very slowly, and that this stage is followed by a much more rapid increase at higher speeds.

150. Phenomena associated with a disturbed entry. Schiller's theory of the transition to turbulence in straight pipes and channels.

The form of the disturbances associated with the transition from laminar to turbulent flow in a straight pipe of circular cross-section with various types of entry has been examined experimentally[†] by introducing a coloured indicator. Three distinct types of flow were observed.

(i) For the smallest Reynolds numbers, even though the flow before entering the pipe is disturbed, the flow in the pipe is smooth and the colour thread straight right from the entry. For a straight circular pipe with a sharp entry Naumann gives $R = 280$ as the Reynolds number at which this régime breaks down when the water from the reservoir is very disturbed.

(ii) At higher Reynolds numbers the colour filament assumes a wave-like form in what is roughly the inlet length as calculated by Schiller (see p. 301), but becomes rectilinear farther downstream.

---

† Schiller, *Proc. 3rd Internat. Congress for Applied Mechanics, Stockholm*, 1930, **1**, 226–233; *Zeitschr. f. angew. Math. u. Mech.* **14** (1934), 36–42; Naumann, *Forsch. Ingwes.* **2** (1931), 85–98; Kurzweg, *Ann. d. Phys.* **18** (1933), 193–216.

Apparently a vortex-sheet, arising from the edge of the entry to the pipe, encloses with the wall a dead water region. It seems probable that this vortex-sheet is unstable for sufficiently high speeds and that the wave-like form is due to this instability. When the colour filament is moved towards the centre of the pipe the point at which waves begin moves continuously farther from the entry.

With increasing velocity the amplitudes of the waves increase. Finally, with still further increase of velocity, the vortex-sheet rolls up periodically and discrete eddies are formed. The disturbances still die away downstream and the flow is laminar sufficiently far from the entry. This type of flow continues for a sharp entry until R is between 1,600 and 1,700. The greater the value of R in the range 280–1,600 the greater the distance the disturbances travel before being damped out: this distance is always roughly the same as the inlet length found by Schiller.

(iii) When R is between 1,600 and 1,700 a second critical stage is reached. The vortex-sheet rolls up into a single large stationary cylindrical eddy which extends from the pipe entry to a distance L downstream and is of thickness d ($L \gg d$). At a distance of about

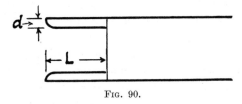

Fig. 90.

$\frac{2}{3} L$ from the entry this elongated eddy exhibits a gradually increasing constriction which leads finally to the separation of a disturbance eddy passing off downstream. This casting off occurs periodically. The distance between consecutive eddies is much greater than in stage (ii).

With the formation of this elongated eddy damping-out of the initial disturbances no longer occurs and the flow is wholly turbulent.

Similar results were found for a circular pipe with an annular cover—i.e. a plane annulus placed over the entry, effectively reducing the diameter there—and also with a semicircular cover.

In the neighbourhood of the critical Reynolds number, Schiller and Naumann observed (as did Reynolds) that the laminar flow was occasionally interrupted for a short distance by a vigorous eddying motion. Reynolds called such regions of turbulence 'flashes', but no explanation of them has yet been given.

Naumann† has discussed two-dimensional flow in a straight channel, and finds results of the same kind as for a pipe. White and Davies, independently of Schiller, discovered by means of pressure measurements the existence of the three separate régimes (i), (ii), and (iii) for a rectangular channel of great breadth/depth ratio.‡ They also found 280 as the Reynolds number at which the first régime breaks down.

In a circular pipe with a sharp entry the vorticity ζ in the disturbance is about circles round the axis of the pipe. The circulation Γ per unit length in the disturbance is defined as $\int \zeta \, dS$, the integral being taken over the area enclosed by the rectangular circuit which is formed by a line of unit length along the axis, two parallel radii at its ends, and the intercept they make on the pipe wall. Schiller and Kurzweg suggest that turbulence sets in when

$$a\Gamma = 1{,}170\nu,$$

where a is the radius of the pipe.‖ Naumann† obtained analogous results for flow in a channel.

151. The transition to turbulence in flow along a flat plate.

For sufficiently high velocities or sufficiently long plates laminar flow in the boundary layer near the leading edge of a plate at zero incidence is followed by a transition to turbulence farther downstream. The flow does not become a fully developed turbulent flow immediately it ceases to follow the laws of laminar flow: there is a finite transition region. The shearing stress at the plate decreases with increasing distance downstream both in the laminar and in the fully developed turbulent regions; in the transition region, however, the shearing stress at the upstream end is considerably less than that at the downstream end. General statements concerning the length of the transition region, or any of the average conditions within it, cannot yet be made with confidence. Burgers and van der Hegge Zijnen†† have investigated the conditions experimentally, and Fig. 91

---

† *Forsch. Ingwes.* **6** (1935), 139–145.

‡ *Proc. Roy. Soc.* A, **119** (1928), 92–107.

‖ Hahnemann (*Forsch. Ingwes.* **8** (1937), 226–237) has verified this criterion for sufficiently small disturbances at entry, such that R_{crit} is greater than 3,200. When the entry disturbances are increased, so that R_{crit} falls from 3,200 to the lower critical value 2,320, $(a\Gamma/\nu)_{\text{crit}}$ rises considerably.

†† *Proc. 1st Internat. Congress for Applied Mechanics*, Delft, 1924, pp. 113–128.

gives their measured values of the velocity gradient α at the surface of a glass plate in the transition region, plotted against the distance x from the leading edge for various values of U_1, the stream velocity outside the boundary layer.

Dimensional considerations suggest that in any particular experi-

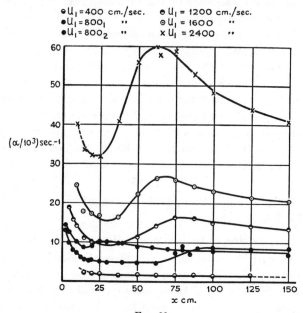

FIG. 91.

ment the transition region starts when R_x ($= U_1 x/\nu$) reaches a certain value dependent on the turbulence in the main stream. Since R_x and R_δ ($= U_1 \delta/\nu$, where δ is the thickness of the boundary layer) are related, any particular value of R_x corresponds to a particular value of R_δ. The values found experimentally for R_{xT}, the value of R_x at the commencement of the transition region, vary between 9×10^4 and $1 \cdot 1 \times 10^6$;† the corresponding range for $R_{\delta T}$ is about 1,650

† Dryden (*Journ. Aero. Sciences*, **1** (1934), 71, 72; *Proc. 4th Internat. Congress for Applied Mechanics, Cambridge*, 1934, p. 175: *N.A.C.A. Report* No. 562 (1936), p. 21) has reported that as a result of experiments in the Bureau of Standards tunnel he found that $R_{xT} = 1 \cdot 1 \times 10^6$ for $u/U_1 = 0 \cdot 005$ (free tunnel) and $R_{xT} = 10^5$ for $u/U_1 = 0 \cdot 03$ (stream behind wire screen of $\frac{1}{2}$-in. mesh). u denotes the root-mean-square of the turbulent velocity component in the direction of the main stream. The corresponding values of $U_1 \delta_1/\nu$ were 1,700 and 560, where δ_1 denotes the displacement thickness (Chap. IV, eqn. (15), p. 123). See p. 330 for recent results.

to 5,750. There is no evidence that these numbers are upper and lower limits to R_{xT} or $R_{\delta T}$, or that such limits exist.

Small pressure gradients in the air-stream greatly affect the value of $U_1 x/\nu$ at transition, an accelerating gradient delaying the transition.† The value of $U_1 \delta_1/\nu$ is, however, less sensitive. (δ_1 denotes the displacement thickness: see Chap. IV, equation (15), p. 123.)

Prandtl‡ observes that the point where transition starts oscillates with time. Cathode ray oscillograph records‖ of the fluctuations of the velocity component parallel to the stream show that transition is actually a sudden phenomenon, with an intermittent change from laminar to eddying flow in the transition region, eddying flow occurring at infrequent intervals and for only a short fraction of the time near the beginning of the region and at more and more frequent intervals and for an increasing fraction of the time as the downstream end of the region is approached. Near the downstream end there are only short, infrequent occurrences of flow of the type in the laminar portion of the boundary layer (with slow, uncorrelated fluctuations: see p. 318).

If transition is controlled by variations in the pressure gradient due to turbulence in the main stream, then fluctuations in the pressure distribution will cause fluctuations in transition; but turbulence will occur more frequently the thicker the boundary layer and so the farther downstream the section we are considering, until, sufficiently far downstream, it will be practically permanent. A satisfactory definition of a point of transition can, then, be given only on a statistical basis. The ideas described below furnish a beginning in this direction.

We have remarked that the value of $U_1 x/\nu$ or $U_1 \delta/\nu$ at the commencement of the transition region depends on the turbulence in the main stream. It appears, however, that the value of $U_1 \delta/\nu$ at transition is not a function of u/U_1 only (where u is the root-mean-square of the turbulent velocity component in the direction of the main stream) but depends also on the scale of the turbulence-producing mechanism. G. I. Taylor†† seeks to find the correct functional relation by associating the two suggestions that the disturbance necessary to produce turbulence is a function of $U_1 \delta/\nu$ and that

---

† Dryden, *loc. cit.*
‡ *Aerodynamic Theory* (edited by Durand), 3 (Berlin, 1935), 152.
‖ Dryden, *Journal of the Washington Academy of Sciences*, 25 (1935), 105–107; *N.A.C.A. Report* No. 562 (1936).   †† *Proc. Roy. Soc.* A, 156 (1936), 307–310.

transition is controlled by variations in the pressure gradient due to turbulence in the main stream. If $\partial u/\partial x$ is the root-mean-square of the x-derivative of the turbulent velocity component along the plate, $\partial p/\partial x$ the root-mean-square of the x-derivative of the turbulent variation in static pressure, Taylor argues that, with isotropic turbulence, $\partial p/\partial x$ is of the same order of magnitude as $\rho u\,\partial u/\partial x$, and puts these two expressions proportional to one another.[†] From Chap. V, § 91, equations (76), (79) and (80), we see that $\partial u/\partial x$ is u/λ; and if M is a characteristic length of the turbulence-producing mechanism, then (Chap. V, § 92, equation (84)) λ is proportional to $\nu^{\frac{1}{2}}M^{\frac{1}{2}}u^{-\frac{1}{2}}$ for sufficiently large values of Mu/ν. Hence

$$\frac{\partial p}{\partial x} = \text{constant}\,\rho u^{\frac{3}{2}}M^{-\frac{1}{2}}\nu^{-\frac{1}{2}}. \tag{57}$$

Now in the Kármán-Pohlhausen approximate method of considering flow in a laminar boundary layer (Chap. IV, § 60), the velocity distribution at any section depends only on the parameter

$$\Lambda = -\frac{\delta^2}{\rho\nu U_1}\frac{\partial p}{\partial x}, \tag{58}$$

where U_1 is the velocity in the main stream just outside the boundary layer, and $\partial p/\partial x$ is the pressure gradient. This result (which rests on approximations of a rather drastic nature) makes the velocity distribution depend only on the pressure gradient at the section considered and not on the state of affairs upstream (except in so far as this affects δ): it seems reasonable to suppose that for fluctuating pressure gradients the result may still be applied with the same degree of approximation as before, and that the velocity distribution depends on $\Lambda+\Lambda'$, where

$$\Lambda' = -\frac{\delta^2}{\rho\nu U_1}\frac{\partial p}{\partial x}. \tag{59}$$

For a flat plate $\Lambda = 0$, and δ^2 is proportional to $\nu x/U_1$. Hence

$$\Lambda' = \text{constant}\left(\frac{u}{U_1}\right)^{\frac{5}{2}}\left(\frac{xU_1}{\nu}\right)^{\frac{1}{2}}\left(\frac{x}{M}\right)^{\frac{1}{2}}. \tag{60}$$

If it is supposed that the critical value of Λ' necessary to produce turbulence is a function of $\delta U_1/\nu$ or xU_1/ν, it follows that xU_1/ν at the point of transition to turbulence is a function of $(u/U_1)(x/M)^{\frac{1}{2}}$.

Owing to its complexity, we cannot formulate a mathematical

[†] See *Proc. Roy. Soc.* A, **151** (1935), 476, 477; *Proc. Camb. Phil. Soc.* **32** (1936), 382–384.

theory of the flow in the transition region. In problems where it is necessary to consider a boundary layer containing both laminar and turbulent portions it is customary to neglect the length of the transition region. The point where, for mathematical purposes, the instantaneous transition is imagined to take place (say $x = X$) will presumably lie within the actual transition region. Suppose now that the actual flow is fully turbulent for $x \geqslant L$: the problem arises as to how X and the conditions at $x = X$ may be determined in order that calculated and observed values of the velocity and of the wall friction may agree for $x \geqslant L$. We assume that X is determined by a condition $U_1 x / \nu = C$, where C depends on the turbulence in the main flow. The equation of momentum may be written†

$$\frac{d\vartheta}{dx} = \frac{\tau_0}{\rho U_1^2}, \qquad (61)$$

where τ_0 is the wall friction and ϑ the 'momentum thickness' (Chap. IV, eqn. (37)). For an instantaneous transition ϑ is therefore continuous at $x = X$. If we take the flow as laminar on one side of a sudden transition, and as the completely developed turbulent flow on the other side, then if we calculate ϑ in terms of the boundary layer thickness δ for the laminar flow by the Kármán-Pohlhausen approximate theory (Chap. IV, §60) and for the turbulent flow by means of formulae given in Chap. VIII, §163, we find that making ϑ continuous implies a fairly small discontinuity in δ. On the other hand, it implies a very large increase in τ_0—a much larger increase than is usually observed between the beginning and the end of the transition region. It may be possible, then, to obtain better agreement with observed values, especially for the wall friction, by making a different *ad hoc* assumption at a point where transition is assumed to take place. Prandtl's assumption,‡ that for $x \geqslant X$ the turbulent layer behaves as though it had been turbulent right from the leading edge, implies a considerably greater discontinuity in δ and consequently a much smaller discontinuity in τ_0 than making ϑ continuous; and if X is taken as the abscissa of the point where the flow ceases to be laminar this assumption seems to give fairly good agreement with experiment in the fully developed turbulent region. When some assumption is required we shall then, for flow along a flat plate, use Prandtl's condition.

† Chap. IV, equation (38), p. 133.
‡ *Ergebnisse der Aerodynamischen Versuchsanstalt zu Göttingen*, **3** (1927), 1–5.

ADDITIONAL REFERENCES

Treatises and Collected Works.

SCHILLER, *Handbuch der Experimentalphysik,* **4**, part 4 (Leipzig, 1932).

DRYDEN, MURNAGHAN, and BATEMAN, *Hydrodynamics* (Bulletin No. 84 of the National Research Council, Washington, 1932), pp. 438–492.

Laminar Flow in Convergent and Divergent Pipes.

GIBSON, *Phil. Mag.* (6), **18** (1909), 36–38.

HARRISON, *Proc. Camb. Phil. Soc.* **19** (1919), 307–312.

BOND, *Phil. Mag.* (6), **50** (1925), 1058–1066.

Laminar Flow in Straight Pipes of other than Circular Section.

LAMB, *Hydrodynamics* (1932), chap. xi, § 332, pp. 586, 587.

BOUSSINESQ, *Journ. de Math. pur. et appl.* (2), **13** (1868), 377–421.

CORNISH, *Proc. Roy. Soc.* A, **120** (1928), 691–700 (Rectangular pipes).

ALLEN and GRUNBERG, *Phil. Mag.* (7), **23** (1937), 490–503 (Rectangular pipes).

For other references see SCHILLER, *Handbuch der Experimentalphysik,* **4**, part 4 (1932), 138–152.

Laminar and Turbulent Flow in Inclined Open Rectangular Channels.

HOPF, *Ann. d. Phys.* (4), **32** (1910), 777–808.

JEFFREYS, *Phil. Mag.* (6), **49** (1925), 793–807.

Inlet Length in Rectangular Pipes.

FRANKL and BALANOV, *Trans. Centr. Aero-Hydrodyn. Inst.,* Moscow, No. 176 (1934), 19–32.

Laminar and Turbulent Flow in Curved Pipes.

NIPPERT, *Forschungsarbeiten des Ver. deutsch. Ing.,* No. 320 (1929).

RICHTER, *ibid.,* No. 338 (1930).

GREGORIG, *Zürich Dissertation,* 1933.

KEULEGAN and BEIJ, *Journ. Res. Nat. Bur. Stand.* **18** (1937), 89–114.

Laminar and Turbulent Flow at a Surface formed by two Intersecting Walls.

LOYTZANSKY, *Trans. Centr. Aero-Hydrodyn. Inst.,* Moscow, No. 249 (1936).

LOYTZANSKY and BOLSHAKOV, *ibid.,* No. 279 (1936).

Transition to Turbulence in Flow along along a Flat Plate.

B. M. JONES, *Journ. Aero. Sciences,* **5** (1938), 94, reports that in the unusually smooth air-stream of the new wind tunnel at Cambridge R_x has reached the value 3×10^6 without transition to the turbulent régime.

CATALOGUE OF DOVER BOOKS

BOOKS EXPLAINING SCIENCE AND MATHEMATICS

General

WHAT IS SCIENCE?, Norman Campbell. This excellent introduction explains scientific method, role of mathematics, types of scientific laws. Contents: 2 aspects of science, science & nature, laws of science, discovery of laws, explanation of laws, measurement & numerical laws, applications of science. 192pp. 5⅜ x 8. **S43 Paperbound $1.25**

THE COMMON SENSE OF THE EXACT SCIENCES, W. K. Clifford. Introduction by James Newman, edited by Karl Pearson. For 70 years this has been a guide to classical scientific and mathematical thought. Explains with unusual clarity basic concepts, such as extension of meaning of symbols, characteristics of surface boundaries, properties of plane figures, vectors, Cartesian method of determining position, etc. Long preface by Bertrand Russell. Bibliography of Clifford. Corrected, 130 diagrams redrawn. 249pp. 5⅜ x 8.
T61 Paperbound $1.60

SCIENCE THEORY AND MAN, Erwin Schrödinger. This is a complete and unabridged reissue of SCIENCE AND THE HUMAN TEMPERAMENT plus an additional essay: "What is an Elementary Particle?" Nobel laureate Schrödinger discusses such topics as nature of scientific method, the nature of science, chance and determinism, science and society, conceptual models for physical entities, elementary particles and wave mechanics. Presentation is popular and may be followed by most people with little or no scientific training. "Fine practical preparation for a time when laws of nature, human institutions . . . are undergoing a critical examination without parallel," Waldemar Kaempffert, N. Y. TIMES. 192pp. 5⅜ x 8.
T428 Paperbound $1.35

FADS AND FALLACIES IN THE NAME OF SCIENCE, Martin Gardner. Examines various cults, quack systems, frauds, delusions which at various times have masqueraded as science. Accounts of hollow-earth fanatics like Symmes; Velikovsky and wandering planets; Hoerbiger; Bellamy and the theory of multiple moons; Charles Fort; dowsing, pseudoscientific methods for finding water, ores, oil. Sections on naturopathy, iridiagnosis, zone therapy, food fads, etc. Analytical accounts of Wilhelm Reich and orgone sex energy; L. Ron Hubbard and Dianetics; A. Korzybski and General Semantics; many others. Brought up to date to include Bridey Murphy, others. Not just a collection of anecdotes, but a fair, reasoned appraisal of eccentric theory. Formerly titled IN THE NAME OF SCIENCE. Preface. Index. x + 384pp. 5⅜ x 8. **T394 Paperbound $1.50**

A DOVER SCIENCE SAMPLER, edited by George Barkin. 64-page book, sturdily bound, containing excerpts from over 20 Dover books, explaining science. Edwin Hubble, George Sarton, Ernst Mach, A. d'Abro, Galileo, Newton, others, discussing island universes, scientific truth, biological phenomena, stability in bridges, etc. Copies limited; no more than 1 to a customer,
FREE

POPULAR SCIENTIFIC LECTURES, Hermann von Helmholtz. Helmholtz was a superb expositor as well as a scientist of genius in many areas. The seven essays in this volume are models of clarity, and even today they rank among the best general descriptions of their subjects ever written. "The Physiological Causes of Harmony in Music" was the first significant physiological explanation of musical consonance and dissonance. Two essays, "On the Interaction of Natural Forces" and "On the Conservation of Force," were of great importance in the history of science, for they firmly established the principle of the conservation of energy. Other lectures include "On the Relation of Optics to Painting," "On Recent Progress in the Theory of Vision," and "On Goethe's Scientific Researches," and "On the Origin and Significance of Geometrical Axioms." Selected and edited with an introduction by Professor Morris Kline. xii + 286pp. 5⅜ x 8½. **T799 Paperbound $1.45**

BOOKS EXPLAINING SCIENCE AND MATHEMATICS

Physics

CONCERNING THE NATURE OF THINGS, Sir William Bragg. Christmas lectures delivered at the Royal Society by Nobel laureate. Why a spinning ball travels in a curved track; how uranium is transmuted to lead, etc. Partial contents: atoms, gases, liquids, crystals, metals, etc. No scientific background needed; wonderful for intelligent child. 32pp. of photos, 57 figures. xii + 232pp. 5⅜ x 8. **T31 Paperbound $1.35**

THE RESTLESS UNIVERSE, Max Born. New enlarged version of this remarkably readable account by a Nobel laureate. Moving from sub-atomic particles to universe, the author explains in very simple terms the latest theories of wave mechanics. Partial contents: air and its relatives, electrons & ions, waves & particles, electronic structure of the atom, nuclear physics. Nearly 1000 illustrations, including 7 animated sequences. 325pp. 6 x 9.
T412 Paperbound $2.00

FROM EUCLID TO EDDINGTON: A STUDY OF THE CONCEPTIONS OF THE EXTERNAL WORLD, Sir Edmund Whittaker. A foremost British scientist traces the development of theories of natural philosophy from the western rediscovery of Euclid to Eddington, Einstein, Dirac, etc. The inadequacy of classical physics is contrasted with present day attempts to understand the physical world through relativity, non-Euclidean geometry, space curvature, wave mechanics, etc. 5 major divisions of examination: Space; Time and Movement; the Concepts of Classical Physics; the Concepts of Quantum Mechanics; the Eddington Universe. 212pp. 5⅜ x 8.   T491 Paperbound **$1.35**

PHYSICS, THE PIONEER SCIENCE, L. W. Taylor. First thorough text to place all important physical phenomena in cultural-historical framework; remains best work of its kind. Exposition of physical laws, theories developed chronologically, with great historical, illustrative experiments diagrammed, described, worked out mathematically. Excellent physics text for self-study as well as class work. Vol. 1: Heat, Sound: motion, acceleration, gravitation, conservation of energy, heat engines, rotation, heat, mechanical energy, etc. 211 illus. 407pp. 5⅜ x 8. Vol. 2: Light, Electricity: images, lenses, prisms, magnetism, Ohm's law, dynamos, telegraph, quantum theory, decline of mechanical view of nature, etc. Bibliography. 13 table appendix. Index. 551 illus. 2 color plates. 508pp. 5⅜ x 8.
Vol. 1 S565 Paperbound **$2.00**
Vol. 2 S566 Paperbound **$2.00**
The set **$4.00**

A SURVEY OF PHYSICAL THEORY, Max Planck. One of the greatest scientists of all time, creator of the quantum revolution in physics, writes in non-technical terms of his own discoveries and those of other outstanding creators of modern physics. Planck wrote this book when science had just crossed the threshold of the new physics, and he communicates the excitement felt then as he discusses electromagnetic theories, statistical methods, evolution of the concept of light, a step-by-step description of how he developed his own momentous theory, and many more of the basic ideas behind modern physics. Formerly "A Survey of Physics." Bibliography. Index. 128pp. 5⅜ x 8.   S650 Paperbound **$1.15**

THE ATOMIC NUCLEUS, M. Korsunsky. The only non-technical comprehensive account of the atomic nucleus in English. For college physics students, etc. Chapters cover: Radioactivity, the Nuclear Model of the Atom, the Mass of Atomic Nuclei, the Disintegration of Atomic Nuclei, the Discovery of the Positron, the Artificial Transformation of Atomic Nuclei, Artificial Radioactivity, Mesons, the Neutrino, the Structure of Atomic Nuclei and Forces Acting Between Nuclear Particles, Nuclear Fission, Chain Reaction, Peaceful Uses, Thermonuclear Reactions. Slightly abridged edition. Translated by G. Yankovsky. 65 figures. Appendix includes 45 photographic illustrations. 413 pp. 5⅜ x 8.   S1052 Paperbound **$2.00**

PRINCIPLES OF MECHANICS SIMPLY EXPLAINED, Morton Mott-Smith. Excellent, highly readable introduction to the theories and discoveries of classical physics. Ideal for the layman who desires a foundation which will enable him to understand and appreciate contemporary developments in the physical sciences. Discusses: Density, The Law of Gravitation, Mass and Weight, Action and Reaction, Kinetic and Potential Energy, The Law of Inertia, Effects of Acceleration, The Independence of Motions, Galileo and the New Science of Dynamics, Newton and the New Cosmos, The Conservation of Momentum, and other topics. Revised edition of "This Mechanical World." Illustrated by E. Kosa, Jr. Bibliography and Chronology. Index. xiv + 171pp. 5⅜ x 8½.   T1067 Paperbound **$1.00**

THE CONCEPT OF ENERGY SIMPLY EXPLAINED, Morton Mott-Smith. Elementary, non-technical exposition which traces the story of man's conquest of energy, with particular emphasis on the developments during the nineteenth century and the first three decades of our own century. Discusses man's earlier efforts to harness energy, more recent experiments and discoveries relating to the steam engine, the engine indicator, the motive power of heat, the principle of excluded perpetual motion, the bases of the conservation of energy, the concept of entropy, the internal combustion engine, mechanical refrigeration, and many other related topics. Also much biographical material. Index. Bibliography. 33 illustrations. ix + 215pp. 5⅜ x 8½.   T1071 Paperbound **$1.25**

HEAT AND ITS WORKINGS, Morton Mott-Smith. One of the best elementary introductions to the theory and attributes of heat, covering such matters as the laws governing the effect of heat on solids, liquids and gases, the methods by which heat is measured, the conversion of a substance from one form to another through heating and cooling, evaporation, the effects of pressure on boiling and freezing points, and the three ways in which heat is transmitted (conduction, convection, radiation). Also brief notes on major experiments and discoveries. Concise, but complete, it presents all the essential facts about the subject in readable style. Will give the layman and beginning student a first-rate background in this major topic in physics. Index. Bibliography. 50 illustrations. x + 165pp. 5⅜ x 8½. T978 Paperbound **$1.00**

THE STORY OF ATOMIC THEORY AND ATOMIC ENERGY, J. G. Feinberg. Wider range of facts on physical theory, cultural implications, than any other similar source. Completely non-technical. Begins with first atomic theory, 600 B.C., goes through A-bomb, developments to 1959. Avogadro, Rutherford, Bohr, Einstein, radioactive decay, binding energy, radiation danger, future benefits of nuclear power, dozens of other topics, told in lively, related, informal manner. Particular stress on European atomic research. "Deserves special mention . . . authoritative," Saturday Review. Formerly "The Atom Story." New chapter to 1959. Index. 34 illustrations. 251pp. 5⅜ x 8.   T625 Paperbound **$1.45**

THE STRANGE STORY OF THE QUANTUM, AN ACCOUNT FOR THE GENERAL READER OF THE GROWTH OF IDEAS UNDERLYING OUR PRESENT ATOMIC KNOWLEDGE, B. Hoffmann. Presents lucidly and expertly, with barest amount of mathematics, the problems and theories which led to modern quantum physics. Dr. Hoffmann begins with the closing years of the 19th century, when certain trifling discrepancies were noticed, and with illuminating analogies and examples takes you through the brilliant concepts of Planck, Einstein, Pauli, de Broglie, Bohr, Schroedinger, Heisenberg, Dirac, Sommerfeld, Feynman, etc. This edition includes a new, long postscript carrying the story through 1958. "Of the books attempting an account of the history and contents of our modern atomic physics which have come to my attention, this is the best," H. Margenau, Yale University, in "American Journal of Physics.", 32 tables and line illustrations. Index. 275pp. 5⅜ x 8. T518 Paperbound **$1.50**

THE EVOLUTION OF SCIENTIFIC THOUGHT FROM NEWTON TO EINSTEIN, A. d'Abro. Einstein's special and general theories of relativity, with their historical implications, are analyzed in non-technical terms. Excellent accounts of the contributions of Newton, Riemann, Weyl, Planck, Eddington, Maxwell, Lorentz and others are treated in terms of space and time, equations of electromagnetics, finiteness of the universe, methodology of science. 21 diagrams. 482pp. 5⅜ x 8. T2 Paperound **$2.00**

THE RISE OF THE NEW PHYSICS, A. d'Abro. A half-million word exposition, formerly titled THE DECLINE OF MECHANISM, for readers not versed in higher mathematics. The only thorough explanation, in everyday language, of the central core of modern mathematical physical theory, treating both classical and modern theoretical physics, and presenting in terms almost anyone can understand the equivalent of 5 years of study of mathematical physics. Scientifically impeccable coverage of mathematical-physical thought from the Newtonian system up through the electronic theories of Dirac and Heisenberg and Fermi's statistics. Combines both history and exposition; provides a broad yet unified and detailed view, with constant comparison of classical and modern views on phenomena and theories. "A must for anyone doing serious study in the physical sciences," JOURNAL OF THE FRANKLIN INSTITUTE. "Extraordinary faculty . . . to explain ideas and theories of theoretical physics in the language of daily life," ISIS. First part of set covers philosophy of science, drawing upon the practice of Newton, Maxwell, Poincaré, Einstein, others, discussing modes of thought, experiment, interpretations of causality, etc. In the second part, 100 pages explain grammar and vocabulary of mathematics, with discussions of functions, groups, series, Fourier series, etc. The remainder is devoted to concrete, detailed coverage of both classical and quantum physics, explaining such topics as analytic mechanics, Hamilton's principle, wave theory of light, electromagnetic waves, groups of transformations, thermodynamics, phase rule, Brownian movement, kinetics, special relativity, Planck's original quantum theory, Bohr's atom, Zeeman effect, Broglie's wave mechanics, Heisenberg's uncertainty, Eigen-values, matrices, scores of other important topics. Discoveries and theories are covered for such men as Alembert, Born, Cantor, Debye, Euler, Foucault, Galois, Gauss, Hadamard, Kelvin, Kepler, Laplace, Maxwell, Pauli, Rayleigh, Volterra, Weyl, Young, more than 180 others. Indexed. 97 illustrations. ix + 982pp. 5⅜ x 8.
T3 Volume 1, Paperbound **$2.00**
T4 Volume 2, Paperbound **$2.00**

SPINNING TOPS AND GYROSCOPIC MOTION, John Perry. Well-known classic of science still unsurpassed for lucid, accurate, delightful exposition. How quasi-rigidity is induced in flexible and fluid bodies by rapid motions; why gyrostat falls, top rises; nature and effect on climatic conditions of earth's precessional movement; effect of internal fluidity on rotating bodies, etc. Appendixes describe practical uses to which gyroscopes have been put in ships, compasses, monorail transportation. 62 figures. 128pp. 5⅜ x 8. T416 Paperbound **$1.00**

THE UNIVERSE OF LIGHT, Sir William Bragg. No scientific training needed to read Nobel Prize winner's expansion of his Royal Institute Christmas Lectures. Insight into nature of light, methods and philosophy of science. Explains lenses, reflection, color, resonance, polarization, x-rays, the spectrum, Newton's work with prisms, Huygens' with polarization, Crookes' with cathode ray, etc. Leads into clear statement of 2 major historical theories of light, corpuscle and wave. Dozens of experiments you can do. 199 illus., including 2 full-page color plates. 293pp. 5⅜ x 8. S538 Paperbound **$1.85**

THE STORY OF X-RAYS FROM RÖNTGEN TO ISOTOPES, A. R. Bleich. Non-technical history of x-rays, their scientific explanation, their applications in medicine, industry, research, and art, and their effect on the individual and his descendants. Includes amusing early reactions to Röntgen's discovery, cancer therapy, detections of art and stamp forgeries, potential risks to patient and operator, etc. Illustrations show x-rays of flower structure, the gall bladder, gears with hidden defects, etc. Original Dover publication. Glossary. Bibliography. Index. 55 photos and figures. xiv + 186pp. 5⅜ x 8. T662 Paperbound **$1.35**

ELECTRONS, ATOMS, METALS AND ALLOYS, Wm. Hume-Rothery. An introductory-level explanation of the application of the electronic theory to the structure and properties of metals and alloys, taking into account the new theoretical work done by mathematical physicists. Material presented in dialogue-form between an "Old Metallurgist" and a "Young Scientist." Their discussion falls into 4 main parts: the nature of an atom, the nature of a metal, the nature of an alloy, and the structure of the nucleus. They cover such topics as the hydrogen atom, electron waves, wave mechanics, Brillouin zones, co-valent bonds, radioactivity and natural disintegration, fundamental particles, structure and fission of the nucleus, etc. Revised, enlarged edition. 177 illustrations. Subject and name indexes. 407pp. 5⅜ x 8½. S1046 Paperbound **$2.25**

OUT OF THE SKY, H. H. Nininger. A non-technical but comprehensive introduction to "meteoritics", the young science concerned with all aspects of the arrival of matter from outer space. Written by one of the world's experts on meteorites, this work shows how, despite difficulties of observation and sparseness of data, a considerable body of knowledge has arisen. It defines meteors and meteorites; studies fireball clusters and processions, meteorite composition, size, distribution, showers, explosions, origins, craters, and much more. A true connecting link between astronomy and geology. More than 175 photos, 22 other illustrations. References. Bibliography of author's publications on meteorites. Index. viii + 336pp. 5⅜ x 8.　　　　　　　　　　　　　　　　　　　　T519 Paperbound **$1.85**

SATELLITES AND SCIENTIFIC RESEARCH, D. King-Hele. Non-technical account of the manmade satellites and the discoveries they have yielded up to the autumn of 1961. Brings together information hitherto published only in hard-to-get scientific journals. Includes the life history of a typical satellite, methods of tracking, new information on the shape of the earth, zones of radiation, etc. Over 60 diagrams and 6 photographs. Mathematical appendix. Bibliography of over 100 items. Index. xii + 180pp. 5⅜ x 8½.　　　　　　　T703 Paperbound **$2.00**

BOOKS EXPLAINING SCIENCE AND MATHEMATICS

Mathematics

CHANCE, LUCK AND STATISTICS: THE SCIENCE OF CHANCE, Horace C. Levinson. Theory of probability and science of statistics in simple, non-technical language. Part I deals with theory of probability, covering odd superstitions in regard to "luck," the meaning of betting odds, the law of mathematical expectation, gambling, and applications in poker, roulette, lotteries, dice, bridge, and other games of chance. Part II discusses the misuse of statistics, the concept of statistical probabilities, normal and skew frequency distributions, and statistics applied to various fields—birth rates, stock speculation, insurance rates, advertising, etc. "Presented in an easy humorous style which I consider the best kind of expository writing," Prof. A. C. Cohen, Industry Quality Control. Enlarged revised edition. Formerly titled "The Science of Chance." Preface and two new appendices by the author. Index. xiv + 365pp. 5⅜ x 8.　　　　　　　　　　　　　　　　　　T1007 Paperbound **$1.85**

PROBABILITIES AND LIFE, Emile Borel. Translated by M. Baudin. Non-technical, highly readable introduction to the results of probability as applied to everyday situations. Partial contents: Fallacies About Probabilities Concerning Life After Death; Negligible Probabilities and the Probabilities of Everyday Life; Events of Small Probability; Application of Probabilities to Certain Problems of Heredity; Probabilities of Deaths, Diseases, and Accidents; On Poisson's Formula. Index. 3 Appendices of statistical studies and tables. vi + 87pp. 5⅜ x 8½.　　　　　　　　　　　　　　　　　　　　　　T121 Paperbound **$1.00**

GREAT IDEAS OF MODERN MATHEMATICS: THEIR NATURE AND USE, Jagjit Singh. Reader with only high school math will understand main mathematical ideas of modern physics, astronomy, genetics, psychology, evolution, etc., better than many who use them as tools, but comprehend little of their basic structure. Author uses his wide knowledge of non-mathematical fields in brilliant exposition of differential equations, matrices, group theory, logic, statistics, problems of mathematical foundations, imaginary numbers, vectors, etc. Original publication. 2 appendices. 2 indexes. 65 illustr. 322pp. 5⅜ x 8.　　S587 Paperbound **$1.75**

MATHEMATICS IN ACTION, O. G. Sutton. Everyone with a command of high school algebra will find this book one of the finest possible introductions to the application of mathematics to physical theory. Ballistics, numerical analysis, waves and wavelike phenomena, Fourier series, group concepts, fluid flow and aerodynamics, statistical measures, and meteorology are discussed with unusual clarity. Some calculus and differential equations theory is developed by the author for the reader's help in the more difficult sections. 88 figures. Index. viii + 236pp. 5⅜ x 8.　　　　　　　　　　　　　　　T440 Clothbound **$3.50**

THE FOURTH DIMENSION SIMPLY EXPLAINED, edited by H. P. Manning. 22 essays, originally Scientific American contest entries, that use a minimum of mathematics to explain aspects of 4-dimensional geometry: analogues to 3-dimensional space, 4-dimensional absurdities and curiosities (such as removing the contents of an egg without puncturing its shell), possible measurements and forms, etc. Introduction by the editor. Only book of its sort on a truly elementary level, excellent introduction to advanced works. 82 figures. 251pp. 5⅜ x 8.　　　　　　　　　　　　　　　　　　　　　　　　　　T711 Paperbound **$1.35**

MATHEMATICS—INTERMEDIATE TO ADVANCED

General

INTRODUCTION TO APPLIED MATHEMATICS, Francis D. Murnaghan. A practical and thoroughly sound introduction to a number of advanced branches of higher mathematics. Among the selected topics covered in detail are: vector and matrix analysis, partial and differential equations, integral equations, calculus of variations, Laplace transform theory, the vector triple product, linear vector functions, quadratic and bilinear forms, Fourier series, spherical harmonics, Bessel functions, the Heaviside expansion formula, and many others. Extremely useful book for graduate students in physics, engineering, chemistry, and mathematics. Index. 111 study exercises with answers. 41 illustrations. ix + 389pp. 5⅜ x 8½.
S1042 Paperbound **$2.00**

OPERATIONAL METHODS IN APPLIED MATHEMATICS, H. S. Carslaw and J. C. Jaeger. Explanation of the application of the Laplace Transformation to differential equations, a simple and effective substitute for more difficult and obscure operational methods. Of great practical value to engineers and to all workers in applied mathematics. Chapters on: Ordinary Linear Differential Equations with Constant Coefficients;; Electric Circuit Theory; Dynamical Applications; The Inversion Theorem for the Laplace Transformation; Conduction of Heat; Vibrations of Continuous Mechanical Systems; Hydrodynamics; Impulsive Functions; Chains of Differential Equations; and other related matters. 3 appendices. 153 problems, many with answers. 22 figures. xvi + 359pp. 5⅜ x 8½.
S1011 Paperbound **$2.25**

APPLIED MATHEMATICS FOR RADIO AND COMMUNICATIONS ENGINEERS, C. E. Smith. No extraneous material here!—only the theories, equations, and operations essential and immediately useful for radio work. Can be used as refresher, as handbook of applications and tables, or as full home-study course. Ranges from simplest arithmetic through calculus, series, and wave forms, hyperbolic trigonometry, simultaneous equations in mesh circuits, etc. Supplies applications right along with each math topic discussed. 22 useful tables of functions, formulas, logs, etc. Index. 166 exercises, 140 examples, all with answers. 95 diagrams. Bibliography. x + 336pp. 5⅜ x 8.
S141 Paperbound **$1.75**

Algebra, group theory, determinants, sets, matrix theory

ALGEBRAS AND THEIR ARITHMETICS, L. E. Dickson. Provides the foundation and background necessary to any advanced undergraduate or graduate student studying abstract algebra. Begins with elementary introduction to linear transformations, matrices, field of complex numbers; proceeds to order, basal units, modulus, quaternions, etc.; develops calculus of linears sets, describes various examples of algebras including invariant, difference, nilpotent, semi-simple. "Makes the reader marvel at his genius for clear and profound analysis," Amer. Mathematical Monthly. Index. xii + 241pp. 5⅜ x 8.
S616 Paperbound **$1.50**

THE THEORY OF EQUATIONS WITH AN INTRODUCTION TO THE THEORY OF BINARY ALGEBRAIC FORMS, W. S. Burnside and A. W. Panton. Extremely thorough and concrete discussion of the theory of equations, with extensive detailed treatment of many topics curtailed in later texts. Covers theory of algebraic equations, properties of polynomials, symmetric functions, derived functions, Horner's process, complex numbers and the complex variable, determinants and methods of elimination, invariant theory (nearly 100 pages), transformations, introduction to Galois theory, Abelian equations, and much more. Invaluable supplementary work for modern students and teachers. 759 examples and exercises. Index in each volume. Two volume set. Total of xxiv + 604pp. 5⅜ x 8.
S714 Vol I Paperbound **$1.85**
S715 Vol II Paperbound **$1.85**
The set **$3.70**

COMPUTATIONAL METHODS OF LINEAR ALGEBRA, V. N. Faddeeva, translated by **C. D. Benster.** First English translation of a unique and valuable work, the only work in English presenting a systematic exposition of the most important methods of linear algebra—classical and contemporary. Shows in detail how to derive numerical solutions of problems in mathematical physics which are frequently connected with those of linear algebra. Theory as well as individual practice. Part I surveys the mathematical background that is indispensable to what follows. Parts II and III, the conclusion, set forth the most important methods of solution, for both exact and iterative groups. One of the most outstanding and valuable features of this work is the 23 tables, double and triple checked for accuracy. These tables will not be found elsewhere. Author's preface. Translator's note. New bibliography and index. x + 252pp. 5⅜ x 8.
S424 Paperbound **$1.95**

ALGEBRAIC EQUATIONS, E. Dehn. Careful and complete presentation of Galois' theory of algebraic equations; theories of Lagrange and Galois developed in logical rather than historical form, with a more thorough exposition than in most modern books. Many concrete applications and fully-worked-out examples. Discusses basic theory (very clear exposition of the symmetric group); isomorphic, transitive, and Abelian groups; applications of Lagrange's and Galois' theories; and much more. Index. List of Theorems. Newly revised by the author. xi + 208pp. 5⅜ x 8.
S697 Paperbound **$1.45**

Differential equations, ordinary and partial; integral equations

INTRODUCTION TO THE DIFFERENTIAL EQUATIONS OF PHYSICS, L. Hopf. Especially valuable to the engineer with no math beyond elementary calculus. Emphasizing intuitive rather than formal aspects of concepts, the author covers an extensive territory. Partial contents: Law of causality, energy theorem, damped oscillations, coupling by friction, cylindrical and spherical coordinates, heat source, etc. Index. 48 figures. 160pp. 5⅜ x 8.
S120 Paperbound **$1.25**

INTRODUCTION TO THE THEORY OF LINEAR DIFFERENTIAL EQUATIONS, E. G. Poole. Authoritative discussions of important topics, with methods of solution more detailed than usual, for students with background of elementary course in differential equations. Studies existence theorems, linearly independent solutions; equations with constant coefficients; with uniform analytic coefficients; regular singularities; the hypergeometric equation; conformal representation; etc. Exercises. Index. 210pp. 5⅜ x 8.
S629 Paperbound **$1.65**

DIFFERENTIAL EQUATIONS FOR ENGINEERS, P. Franklin. Outgrowth of a course given 10 years at M. I. T. Makes most useful branch of pure math accessible for practical work. Theoretical basis of D.E.'s; solution of ordinary D.E.'s and partial derivatives arising from heat flow, steady-state temperature of a plate, wave equations; analytic functions; convergence of Fourier Series. 400 problems on electricity, vibratory systems, other topics. Formerly "Differential Equations for Electrical Engineers." Index 41 illus. 307pp. 5⅜ x 8.
S601 Paperbound **$1.65**

DIFFERENTIAL EQUATIONS, F. R. Moulton. A detailed, rigorous exposition of all the non-elementary processes of solving ordinary differential equations. Several chapters devoted to the treatment of practical problems, especially those of a physical nature, which are far more advanced than problems usually given as illustrations. Includes analytic differential equations; variations of a parameter; integrals of differential equations; analytic implicit functions; problems of elliptic motion; sine-amplitude functions; deviation of formal bodies; Cauchy-Lipschitz process; linear differential equations with periodic coefficients; differential equations in infinitely many variations; much more. Historical notes. 10 figures. 222 problems. Index. xv + 395pp. 5⅜ x 8.
S451 Paperbound **$2.00**

DIFFERENTIAL AND INTEGRAL EQUATIONS OF MECHANICS AND PHYSICS (DIE DIFFERENTIAL-UND INTEGRALGLEICHUNGEN DER MECHANIK UND PHYSIK), edited by P. Frank and R. von Mises. Most comprehensive and authoritative work on the mathematics of mathematical physics available today in the United States: the standard, definitive reference for teachers, physicists, engineers, and mathematicians—now published (in the original German) at a relatively inexpensive price for the first time! Every chapter in this 2,000-page set is by an expert in his field: Carathéodory, Courant, Frank, Mises, and a dozen others. Vol I, on mathematics, gives concise but complete coverages of advanced calculus, differential equations, integral equations, and potential, and partial differential equations. Index. xxiii + 916pp. Vol. II (physics): classical mechanics, optics, continuous mechanics, heat conduction and diffusion, the stationary and quasi-stationary electromagnetic field, electromagnetic oscillations, and wave mechanics. Index. xxiv + 1106pp. Two volume set. Each volume available separately. 5⅝ x 8⅜.
S787 Vol I Clothbound **$7.50**
S788 Vol II Clothbound **$7.50**
The set **$15.00**

LECTURES ON CAUCHY'S PROBLEM, J. Hadamard. Based on lectures given at Columbia, Rome, this discusses work of Riemann, Kirchhoff, Volterra, and the author's own research on the hyperbolic case in linear partial differential equations. It extends spherical and cylindrical waves to apply to all (normal) hyperbolic equations. Partial contents: Cauchy's problem, fundamental formula, equations with odd number, with even number of independent variables; method of descent. 32 figures. Index. iii + 316pp. 5⅜ x 8.
S105 Paperbound **$1.75**

THEORY OF DIFFERENTIAL EQUATIONS, A. R. Forsyth. Out of print for over a decade, the complete 6 volumes (now bound as 3) of this monumental work represent the most comprehensive treatment of differential equations ever written. Historical presentation includes in 2500 pages every substantial development. Vol. 1, 2: EXACT EQUATIONS, PFAFF'S PROBLEM; ORDINARY EQUATIONS, NOT LINEAR: methods of Grassmann, Clebsch, Lie, Darboux; Cauchy's theorem; branch points; etc. Vol. 3, 4: ORDINARY EQUATIONS, NOT LINEAR; ORDINARY LINEAR EQUATIONS: Zeta Fuchsian functions, general theorems on algebraic integrals, Brun's theorem, equations with uniform periodic coefficients, etc. Vol. 4, 5: PARTIAL DIFFERENTIAL EQUATIONS: 2 existence-theorems, equations of theoretical dynamics, Laplace transformations, general transformation of equations of the 2nd order, much more. Indexes. Total of 2766pp. 5⅜ x 8.
S576-7-8 Clothbound: the set **$15.00**

PARTIAL DIFFERENTIAL EQUATIONS OF MATHEMATICAL PHYSICS, A. G. Webster. A keystone work in the library of every mature physicist, engineer, researcher. Valuable sections on elasticity, compression theory, potential theory, theory of sound, heat conduction, wave propagation, vibration theory. Contents include: deduction of differential equations, vibrations, normal functions, Fourier's series, Cauchy's method, boundary problems, method of Riemann-Volterra. Spherical, cylindrical, ellipsoidal harmonics, applications, etc. 97 figures. vii + 440pp. 5⅜ x 8.
S263 Paperbound **$2.00**

ELEMENTARY CONCEPTS OF TOPOLOGY, P. Alexandroff. First English translation of the famous brief introduction to topology for the beginner or for the mathematician not undertaking extensive study. This unusually useful intuitive approach deals primarily with the concepts of complex, cycle, and homology, and is wholly consistent with current investigations. Ranges from basic concepts of set-theoretic topology to the concept of Betti groups. "Glowing example of harmony between intuition and thought," David Hilbert. Translated by A. E. Farley. Introduction by D. Hilbert. Index. 25 figures. 73pp. 5⅜ x 8.   S747 Paperbound **$1.00**

Number theory

INTRODUCTION TO THE THEORY OF NUMBERS, L. E. Dickson. Thorough, comprehensive approach with adequate coverage of classical literature, an introductory volume beginners can follow. Chapters on divisibility, congruences, quadratic residues & reciprocity, Diophantine equations, etc. Full treatment of binary quadratic forms without usual restriction to integral coefficients. Covers infinitude of primes, least residues, Fermat's theorem, Euler's phi function, Legendre's symbol, Gauss's lemma, automorphs, reduced forms, recent theorems of Thue & Siegel, many more. Much material not readily available elsewhere. 239 problems. Index. I figure. viii + 183pp. 5⅜ x 8.   S342 Paperbound **$1.65**

ELEMENTS OF NUMBER THEORY, I. M. Vinogradov. Detailed 1st course for persons without advanced mathematics; 95% of this book can be understood by readers who have gone no farther than high school algebra. Partial contents: divisibility theory, important number theoretical functions, congruences, primitive roots and indices, etc. Solutions to both problems and exercises. Tables of primes, indices, etc. Covers almost every essential formula in elementary number theory! Translated from Russian. 233 problems, 104 exercises. viii + 227pp. 5⅜ x 8.   S259 Paperbound **$1.60**

THEORY OF NUMBERS and DIOPHANTINE ANALYSIS, R. D. Carmichael. These two complete works in one volume form one of the most lucid introductions to number theory, requiring only a firm foundation in high school mathematics. "Theory of Numbers," partial contents: Eratosthenes' sieve, Euclid's fundamental theorem, G.C.F. and L.C.M. of two or more integers, linear congruences, etc "Diophantine Analysis": rational triangles, Pythagorean triangles, equations of third, fourth, higher degrees, method of functional equations, much more. "Theory of Numbers": 76 problems. Index. 94pp. "Diophantine Analysis": 222 problems. Index. 118pp. 5⅜ x 8.   S529 Paperbound **$1.35**

Numerical analysis, tables

MATHEMATICAL TABLES AND FORMULAS, Compiled by Robert D. Carmichael and Edwin R. Smith. Valuable collection for students, etc. Contains all tables necessary in college algebra and trigonometry, such as five-place common logarithms, logarithmic sines and tangents of small angles, logarithmic trigonometric functions, natural trigonometric functions, four-place antilogarithms, tables for changing from sexagesimal to circular and from circular to sexagesimal measure of angles, etc. Also many tables and formulas not ordinarily accessible, including powers, roots, and reciprocals, exponential and hyperbolic functions, ten-place logarithms of prime numbers, and formulas and theorems from analytical and elementary geometry and from calculus. Explanatory introduction. viii + 269pp. 5⅜ x 8½.   S111 Paperbound **$1.00**

MATHEMATICAL TABLES, H. B. Dwight. Unique for its coverage in one volume of almost every function of importance in applied mathematics, engineering, and the physical sciences. Three extremely fine tables of the three trig functions and their inverse functions to thousandths of radians; natural and common logarithms; squares, cubes; hyperbolic functions and the inverse hyperbolic functions; $(a^2 + b^2)$ exp. ½a; complete elliptic integrals of the 1st and 2nd kind; sine and cosine integrals; exponential integrals Ei(x) and Ei($-x$); binomial coefficients; factorials to 250; surface zonal harmonics and first derivatives; Bernoulli and Euler numbers and their logs to base of 10; Gamma function; normal probability integral; over 60 pages of Bessel functions; the Riemann Zeta function. Each table with formulae generally used, sources of more extensive tables, interpolation data, etc. Over half have columns of differences, to facilitate interpolation. Introduction. Index. viii + 231pp. 5⅜ x 8.   S445 Paperbound **$1.75**

TABLES OF FUNCTIONS WITH FORMULAE AND CURVES, E. Jahnke & F. Emde. The world's most comprehensive 1-volume English-text collection of tables, formulae, curves of transcendent functions. 4th corrected edition, new 76-page section giving tables, formulae for elementary functions—not in other English editions. Partial contents: sine, cosine, logarithmic integral; factorial function; error integral; theta functions; elliptic integrals, functions; Legendre, Bessel, Riemann, Mathieu, hypergeometric functions, etc. Supplementary books. Bibliography. Indexed. "Out of the way functions for which we know no other source," SCIENTIFIC COMPUTING SERVICE, Ltd. 212 figures. 400pp. 5⅜ x 8.   S133 Paperbound **$2.00**

CHEMISTRY AND PHYSICAL CHEMISTRY

ORGANIC CHEMISTRY, F. C. Whitmore. The entire subject of organic chemistry for the practicing chemist and the advanced student. Storehouse of facts, theories, processes found elsewhere only in specialized journals. Covers aliphatic compounds (500 pages on the properties and synthetic preparation of hydrocarbons, halides, proteins, ketones, etc.), alicyclic compounds, aromatic compounds, heterocyclic compounds, organophosphorus and organometallic compounds. Methods of synthetic preparation analyzed critically throughout. Includes much of biochemical interest. "The scope of this volume is astonishing," INDUSTRIAL AND ENGINEERING CHEMISTRY. 12,000-reference index. 2387-item bibliography. Total of x + 1005pp. 5⅜ x 8.
Two volume set. S700 Vol I Paperbound **$2.00**
S701 Vol II Paperbound **$2.00**
The set **$4.00**

THE MODERN THEORY OF MOLECULAR STRUCTURE, Bernard Pullman. A reasonably popular account of recent developments in atomic and molecular theory. Contents: The Wave Function and Wave Equations (history and bases of present theories of molecular structure); The Electronic Structure of Atoms (Description and classification of atomic wave functions, etc.); Diatomic Molecules; Non-Conjugated Polyatomic Molecules; Conjugated Polyatomic Molecules; The Structure of Complexes. Minimum of mathematical background needed. New translation by David Antin of "La Structure Moleculaire." Index. Bibliography. vii + 87pp. 5⅜ x 8½. S987 Paperbound **$1.00**

CATALYSIS AND CATALYSTS, Marcel Prettre, Director, Research Institute on Catalysis. This brief book, translated into English for the first time, is the finest summary of the principal modern concepts, methods, and results of catalysis. Ideal introduction for beginning chemistry and physics students. Chapters: Basic Definitions of Catalysis (true catalysis and generalization of the concept of catalysis); The Scientific Bases of Catalysis (Catalysis and chemical thermodynamics, catalysis and chemical kinetics); Homogeneous Catalysis (acid-base catalysis, etc.); Chain Reactions; Contact Masses; Heterogeneous Catalysis (Mechanisms of contact catalyses, etc.); and Industrial Applications (acids and fertilizers, petroleum and petroleum chemistry, rubber, plastics, synthetic resins, and fibers). Translated by David Antin. Index. vi + 88pp. 5⅜ x 8½. S998 Paperbound **$1.00**

POLAR MOLECULES, Pieter Debye. This work by Nobel laureate Debye offers a complete guide to fundamental electrostatic field relations, polarizability, molecular structure. Partial contents: electric intensity, displacement and force, polarization by orientation, molar polarization and molar refraction, halogen-hydrides, polar liquids, ionic saturation, dielectric constant, etc. Special chapter considers quantum theory. Indexed. 172pp. 5⅜ x 8.
S64 Paperbound **$1.50**

THE ELECTRONIC THEORY OF ACIDS AND BASES, W. F. Luder and Saverio Zuffanti. The first full systematic presentation of the electronic theory of acids and bases—treating the theory and its ramifications in an uncomplicated manner. Chapters: Historical Background; Atomic Orbitals and Valence; The Electronic Theory of Acids and Bases; Electrophilic and Electrodotic Reagents; Acidic and Basic Radicals; Neutralization; Titrations with Indicators; Displacement; Catalysis; Acid Catalysis; Base Catalysis; Alkoxides and Catalysts; Conclusion. Required reading for all chemists. Second revised (1961) eidtion, with additional examples and references. 3 figures. 9 tables. Index. Bibliography xii + 165pp. 5⅜ x 8.
S201 Paperbound **$1.50**

KINETIC THEORY OF LIQUIDS, J. Frenkel. Regarding the kinetic theory of liquids as a generalization and extension of the theory of solid bodies, this volume covers all types of arrangements of solids, thermal displacements of atoms, interstitial atoms and ions, orientational and rotational motion of molecules, and transition between states of matter. Mathematical theory is developed close to the physical subject matter. 216 bibliographical footnotes. 55 figures. xi + 485pp. 5⅜ x 8. S95 Paperbound **$2.55**

THE PRINCIPLES OF ELECTROCHEMISTRY, D. A. MacInnes. Basic equations for almost every subfield of electrochemistry from first principles, referring at all times to the soundest and most recent theories and results; unusually useful as text or as reference. Covers coulometers and Faraday's Law, electrolytic conductance, the Debye-Hueckel method for the theoretical calculation of activity coefficients, concentration cells, standard electrode potentials, thermodynamic ionization constants, pH, potentiometric titrations, irreversible phenomena, Planck's equation, and much more. "Excellent treatise," AMERICAN CHEMICAL SOCIETY JOURNAL. "Highly recommended," CHEMICAL AND METALLURGICAL ENGINEERING. 2 Indices. Appendix. 585-item bibliography. 137 figures. 94 tables. ii + 478pp. 5⅝ x 8⅜.
S52 Paperbound **$2.45**

THE PHASE RULE AND ITS APPLICATION, Alexander Findlay. Covering chemical phenomena of 1, 2, 3, 4, and multiple component systems, this "standard work on the subject" (NATURE, London), has been completely revised and brought up to date by A. N. Campbell and N. O. Smith. Brand new material has been added on such matters as binary, tertiary liquid equilibria, solid solutions in ternary systems, quinary systems of salts and water. Completely revised to triangular coordinates in ternary systems, clarified graphic representation, solid models, etc. 9th revised edition. Author, subject indexes. 236 figures. 505 footnotes, mostly bibliographic. xii + 494pp. 5⅜ x 8. S91 Paperbound **$2.45**

PHYSICS

General physics

FOUNDATIONS OF PHYSICS, R. B. Lindsay & H. Margenau. Excellent bridge between semi-popular works & technical treatises. A discussion of methods of physical description, construction of theory; valuable for physicist with elementary calculus who is interested in ideas that give meaning to data, tools of modern physics. Contents include symbolism, mathematical equations; space & time foundations of mechanics; probability; physics & continua; electron theory; special & general relativity; quantum mechanics; causality. "Thorough and yet not overdetailed. Unreservedly recommended," NATURE (London). Unabridged, corrected edition. List of recommended readings. 35 illustrations. xi + 537pp. 5⅜ x 8.
S377 Paperbound $2.75

FUNDAMENTAL FORMULAS OF PHYSICS, ed. by D. H. Menzel. Highly useful, fully inexpensive reference and study text, ranging from simple to highly sophisticated operations. Mathematics integrated into text—each chapter stands as short textbook of field represented. Vol. 1: Statistics, Physical Constants, Special Theory of Relativity, Hydrodynamics, Aerodynamics, Boundary Value Problems in Math. Physics; Viscosity, Electromagnetic Theory, etc. Vol. 2: Sound, Acoustics, Geometrical Optics, Electron Optics, High-Energy Phenomena, Magnetism, Biophysics, much more. Index. Total of 800pp. 5⅜ x 8.   Vol. 1 S595 Paperbound $2.00
Vol. 2 S596 Paperbound $2.00

MATHEMATICAL PHYSICS, D. H. Menzel. Thorough one-volume treatment of the mathematical techniques vital for classic mechanics, electromagnetic theory, quantum theory, and relativity. Written by the Harvard Professor of Astrophysics for junior, senior, and graduate courses, it gives clear explanations of all those aspects of function theory, vectors, matrices, dyadics, tensors, partial differential equations, etc., necessary for the understanding of the various physical theories. Electron theory, relativity, and other topics seldom presented appear here in considerable detail. Scores of definitions, conversion factors, dimensional constants, etc. "More detailed than normal for an advanced text . . . excellent set of sections on Dyadics, Matrices, and Tensors," JOURNAL OF THE FRANKLIN INSTITUTE. Index. 193 problems, with answers. x + 412pp. 5⅜ x 8.   S56 Paperbound $2.00

THE SCIENTIFIC PAPERS OF J. WILLARD GIBBS. All the published papers of America's outstanding theoretical scientist (except for "Statistical Mechanics" and "Vector Analysis"). Vol I (thermodynamics) contains one of the most brilliant of all 19th-century scientific papers—the 300-page "On the Equilibrium of Heterogeneous Substances," which founded the science of physical chemistry, and clearly stated a number of highly important natural laws for the first time; 8 other papers complete the first volume. Vol II includes 2 papers on dynamics, 8 on vector analysis and multiple algebra, 5 on the electromagnetic theory of light, and 6 miscellaneous papers. Biographical sketch by H. A. Bumstead. Total of xxxvi + 718pp. 5⅜ x 8⅜.
S721 Vol I Paperbound $2.00
S722 Vol II Paperbound $2.00
The set $4.00

BASIC THEORIES OF PHYSICS, Peter Gabriel Bergmann. Two-volume set which presents a critical examination of important topics in the major subdivisions of classical and modern physics. The first volume is concerned with classical mechanics and electrodynamics: mechanics of mass points, analytical mechanics, matter in bulk, electrostatics and magnetostatics, electromagnetic interaction, the field waves, special relativity, and waves. The second volume (Heat and Quanta) contains discussions of the kinetic hypothesis, physics and statistics, stationary ensembles, laws of thermodynamics, early quantum theories, atomic spectra, probability waves, quantization in wave mechanics, approximation methods, and abstract quantum theory. A valuable supplement to any thorough course or text.
Heat and Quanta: Index. 8 figures. x + 300pp. 5⅜ x 8½.   S968 Paperbound $1.75
Mechanics and Electrodynamics: Index. 14 figures. vii + 280pp. 5⅜ x 8½.
S969 Paperbound $1.75

THEORETICAL PHYSICS, A. S. Kompaneyets. One of the very few thorough studies of the subject in this price range. Provides advanced students with a comprehensive theoretical background. Especially strong on recent experimentation and developments in quantum theory. Contents: Mechanics (Generalized Coordinates, Lagrange's Equation, Collision of Particles, etc.), Electrodynamics (Vector Analysis, Maxwell's equations, Transmission of Signals, Theory of Relativity, etc.), Quantum Mechanics (the Inadequacy of Classical Mechanics, the Wave Equation, Motion in a Central Field, Quantum Theory of Radiation, Quantum Theories of Dispersion and Scattering, etc.), and Statistical Physics (Equilibrium Distribution of Molecules in an Ideal Gas, Boltzmann statistics, Bose and Fermi Distribution, Thermodynamic Quantities, etc.). Revised to 1961. Translated by George Yankovsky, authorized by Kompaneyets. 137 exercises. 56 figures. 529pp. 5⅜ x 8½. S972 Paperbound $2.50

ANALYTICAL AND CANONICAL FORMALISM IN PHYSICS, André Mercier. A survey, in one volume, of the variational principles (the key principles—in mathematical form—from which the basic laws of any one branch of physics can be derived) of the several branches of physical theory, together with an examination of the relationships among them. Contents: the Lagrangian Formalism, Lagrangian Densities, Canonical Formalism, Canonical Form of Electrodynamics, Hamiltonian Densities, Transformations, and Canonical Form with Vanishing Jacobian Determinant. Numerous examples and exercises. For advanced students, teachers, etc. 6 figures. Index. viii + 222pp. 5⅜ x 8½.   S1077 Paperbound $1.75

MATHEMATICAL PUZZLES AND RECREATIONS

AMUSEMENTS IN MATHEMATICS, Henry Ernest Dudeney. The foremost British originator of mathematical puzzles is always intriguing, witty, and paradoxical in this classic, one of the largest collections of mathematical amusements. More than 430 puzzles, problems, and paradoxes. Mazes and games, problems on number manipulation, unicursal and other route problems, puzzles on measuring, weighing, packing, age, kinship, chessboards, joining, crossing river, plane figure dissection, and many others. Solutions. More than 450 illustrations. vii + 258pp. 5⅜ x 8. **T473 Paperbound $1.25**

SYMBOLIC LOGIC and THE GAME OF LOGIC, Lewis Carroll. "Symbolic Logic" is not concerned with modern symbolic logic, but is instead a collection of over 380 problems posed with charm and imagination, using the syllogism, and a fascinating diagrammatic method of drawing conclusions. In "The Game of Logic," Carroll's whimsical imagination devises a logical game played with 2 diagrams and counters (included) to manipulate hundreds of tricky syllogisms. The final section, "Hit or Miss" is a lagniappe of 101 additional puzzles in the delightful Carroll manner. Until this reprint edition, both of these books were rarities costing up to $15 each. Symbolic Logic: Index, xxxi + 199pp. The Game of Logic: 96pp. Two vols. bound as one. 5⅜ x 8. **T492 Paperbound $1.50**

MAZES AND LABYRINTHS: A BOOK OF PUZZLES, W. Shepherd. Mazes, formerly associated with mystery and ritual, are still among the most intriguing of intellectual puzzles. This is a novel and different collection of 50 amusements that embody the principle of the maze: mazes in the classical tradition; 3-dimensional, ribbon, and Möbius-strip mazes; hidden messages; spatial arrangements; etc.—almost all built on amusing story situations. 84 illustrations. Essay on maze psychology. Solutions. xv + 122pp. 5⅜ x 8. **T731 Paperbound $1.00**

MATHEMATICAL RECREATIONS, M. Kraitchik. Some 250 puzzles, problems, demonstrations of recreational mathematics for beginners & advanced mathematicians. Unusual historical problems from Greek, Medieval, Arabic, Hindu sources: modern problems based on "mathematics without numbers," geometry, topology, arithmetic, etc. Pastimes derived from figurative numbers, Mersenne numbers, Fermat numbers; fairy chess, latruncles, reversi, many topics. Full solutions. Excellent for insights into special fields of math. 181 illustrations. 330pp. 5⅜ x 8. **T163 Paperbound $1.75**

MATHEMATICAL PUZZLES OF SAM LOYD, Vol. I, selected and edited by M. Gardner. Puzzles by the greatest puzzle creator and innovator. Selected from his famous "Cyclopedia of Puzzles," they retain the unique style and historical flavor of the originals. There are posers based on arithmetic, algebra, probability, game theory, route tracing, topology, counter, sliding block, operations research, geometrical dissection. Includes his famous "14-15" puzzle which was a national craze, and his "Horse of a Different Color" which sold millions of copies. 117 of his most ingenious puzzles in all, 120 line drawings and diagrams. Solutions. Selected references. xx + 167pp. 5⅜ x 8. **T498 Paperbound $1.00**

MY BEST PUZZLES IN MATHEMATICS, Hubert Phillips ("Caliban"). Caliban is generally considered the best of the modern problemists. Here are 100 of his best and wittiest puzzles, selected by the author himself from such publications as the London Daily Telegraph, and each puzzle is guaranteed to put even the sharpest puzzle detective through his paces. Perfect for the development of clear thinking and a logical mind. Complete solutions are provided for every puzzle. x + 107pp. 5⅜ x 8½. **T91 Paperbound $1.00**

MY BEST PUZZLES IN LOGIC AND REASONING, H. Phillips ("Caliban"). 100 choice, hitherto unavailable puzzles by England's best-known problemist. No special knowledge needed to solve these logical or inferential problems, just an unclouded mind, nerves of steel, and fast reflexes. Data presented are both necessary and just sufficient to allow one unambiguous answer. More than 30 different types of puzzles, all ingenious and varied, many one of a kind, that will challenge the expert, please the beginner. Original publication. 100 puzzles, full solutions. x + 107pp. 5⅜ x 8½. **T119 Paperbound $1.00**

MATHEMATICAL PUZZLES FOR BEGINNERS AND ENTHUSIASTS, G. Mott-Smith. 188 mathematical puzzles to test mental agility. Inference, interpretation, algebra, dissection of plane figures, geometry, properties of numbers, decimation, permutations, probability, all enter these delightful problems. Puzzles like the Odic Force, How to Draw an Ellipse, Spider's Cousin, more than 180 others. Detailed solutions. Appendix with square roots, triangular numbers, primes, etc. 135 illustrations. 2nd revised edition. 248pp. 5⅜ x 8. **T198 Paperbound $1.00**

MATHEMATICS, MAGIC AND MYSTERY, Martin Gardner. Card tricks, feats of mental mathematics, stage mind-reading, other "magic" explained as applications of probability, sets, theory of numbers, topology, various branches of mathematics. Creative examination of laws and their applications with scores of new tricks and insights. 115 sections discuss tricks wtih cards, dice, coins; geometrical vanishing tricks, dozens of others. No sleight of hand needed; mathematics guarantees success. 115 illustrations. xii + 174pp. 5⅜ x 8. **T335 Paperbound $1.00**

RECREATIONS IN THE THEORY OF NUMBERS: THE QUEEN OF MATHEMATICS ENTERTAINS, Albert H. Beiler. The theory of numbers is often referred to as the "Queen of Mathematics." In this book Mr. Beiler has compiled the first English volume to deal exclusively with the recreational aspects of number theory, an inherently recreational branch of mathematics. The author's clear style makes for enjoyable reading as he deals with such topics as: perfect numbers, amicable numbers, Fermat's theorem, Wilson's theorem, interesting properties of digits, methods of factoring, primitive roots, Euler's function, polygonal and figurate numbers, Mersenne numbers, congruence, repeating decimals, etc. Countless puzzle problems, with full answers and explanations. For mathematicians and mathematically-inclined laymen, etc. New publication. 28 figures. 9 illustrations. 103 tables. Bibliography at chapter ends. vi + 247pp. 5⅜ x 8½. T1096 Paperbound **$1.85**

PAPER FOLDING FOR BEGINNERS, W. D. Murray and F. J. Rigney. A delightful introduction to the varied and entertaining Japanese art of origami (paper folding), with a full crystal-clear text that anticipates every difficulty; over 275 clearly labeled diagrams of all important stages in creation. You get results at each stage, since complex figures are logically developed from simpler ones. 43 different pieces are explained: place mats, drinking cups, bonbon boxes, sailboats, frogs, roosters, etc. 6 photographic plates. 279 diagrams. 95pp. 5⅝ x 8⅜. T713 Paperbound **$1.00**

1800 RIDDLES, ENIGMAS AND CONUNDRUMS, Darwin A. Hindman. Entertaining collection ranging from hilarious gags to outrageous puns to sheer nonsense—a welcome respite from sophisticated humor. Children, toastmasters, and practically anyone with a funny bone will find these zany riddles tickling and eminently repeatable. Sample: "Why does Santa Claus always go down the chimney?" "Because it soots him." Some old, some new—covering a wide variety of subjects. New publication. iii + 154pp. 5⅜ x 8½. T1059 Paperbound **$1.00**

EASY-TO-DO ENTERTAINMENTS AND DIVERSIONS WITH CARDS, STRING, COINS, PAPER AND MATCHES, R. M. Abraham. Over 300 entertaining games, tricks, puzzles, and pastimes for children and adults. Invaluable to anyone in charge of groups of youngsters, for party givers, etc. Contains sections on card tricks and games, making things by paperfolding—toys, decorations, and the like; tricks with coins, matches, and pieces of string; descriptions of games; toys that can be made from common household objects; mathematical recreations; word games; and 50 miscellaneous entertainments. Formerly "Winter Nights Entertainments." Introduction by Lord Baden Powell. 329 illustrations. v + 186pp. 5⅜ x 8. T921 Paperbound **$1.00**

DIVERSIONS AND PASTIMES WITH CARDS, STRING, PAPER AND MATCHES, R. M. Abraham. Another collection of amusements and diversion for game and puzzle fans of all ages. Many new paperfolding ideas and tricks, an extensive section on amusements with knots and splices, two chapters of easy and not-so-easy problems, coin and match tricks, and lots of other parlor pastimes from the agile mind of the late British problemist and gamester. Corrected and revised version. Illustrations. 160pp. 5⅜ x 8½. T1127 Paperbound **$1.00**

STRING FIGURES AND HOW TO MAKE THEM: A STUDY OF CAT'S-CRADLE IN MANY LANDS, Caroline Furness Jayne. In a simple and easy-to-follow manner, this book describes how to make 107 different string figures. Not only is looping and crossing string between the fingers a common youthful diversion, but it is an ancient form of amusement practiced in all parts of the globe, especially popular among primitive tribes. These games are fun for all ages and offer an excellent means for developing manual dexterity and coordination. Much insight also for the anthropological observer on games and diversions in many different cultures. Index. Bibliography. Introduction by A. C. Haddon, Cambridge University. 17 full-page plates. 950 illustrations. xxiii + 407pp. 5⅜ x 8½. T152 Paperbound **$2.00**

CRYPTANALYSIS, Helen F. Gaines. (Formerly ELEMENTARY CRYPTANALYSIS.) A standard elementary and intermediate text for serious students. It does not confine itself to old material, but contains much that is not generally known, except to experts. Concealment, Transposition, Substitution ciphers; Vigenere, Kasiski, Playfair, multafid, dozens of other techniques. Appendix with sequence charts, letter frequencies in English, 5 other languages, English word frequencies. Bibliography. 167 codes. New to this edition: solution to codes. vi + 230pp. 5⅜ x 8. T97 Paperbound **$1.95**

MAGIC SQUARES AND CUBES, W. S. Andrews. Only book-length treatment in English, a thorough non-technical description and analysis. Here are nasik, overlapping, pandiagonal, serrated squares; magic circles, cubes, spheres, rhombuses. Try your hand at 4-dimensional magical figures! Much unusual folklore and tradition included. High school algebra is sufficient. 754 diagrams and illustrations. viii + 419pp. 5⅜ x 8. T658 Paperbound **$1.85**

CALIBAN'S PROBLEM BOOK: MATHEMATICAL, INFERENTIAL, AND CRYPTOGRAPHIC PUZZLES, H. Phillips ("Caliban"), S. T. Shovelton, G. S. Marshall. 105 ingenious problems by the greatest living creator of puzzles based on logic and inference. Rigorous, modern, piquant, and reflecting their author's unusual personality, these intermediate and advanced puzzles all involve the ability to reason clearly through complex situations; some call for mathematical knowledge, ranging from algebra to number theory. Solutions. xi + 180pp. 5⅜ x 8. T736 Paperbound **$1.25**

FICTION

THE LAND THAT TIME FORGOT and THE MOON MAID, Edgar Rice Burroughs. In the opinion of many, Burroughs' best work. The first concerns a strange island where evolution is individual rather than phylogenetic. Speechless anthropoids develop into intelligent human beings within a single generation. The second projects the reader far into the future and describes the first voyage to the Moon (in the year 2025), the conquest of the Earth by the Moon, and years of violence and adventure as the enslaved Earthmen try to regain possession of their planet. "An imaginative tour de force that keeps the reader keyed up and expectant," NEW YORK TIMES. Complete, unabridged text of the original two novels (three parts in each). 5 illustrations by J. Allen St. John. vi + 552pp. 5⅜ x 8½.

T1020 Clothbound **$3.75**
T358 Paperbound **$2.00**

AT THE EARTH'S CORE, PELLUCIDAR, TANAR OF PELLUCIDAR: THREE SCIENCE FICTION NOVELS BY EDGAR RICE BURROUGHS. Complete, unabridged texts of the first three Pellucidar novels. Tales of derring-do by the famous master of science fiction. The locale for these three related stories is the inner surface of the hollow Earth where we discover the world of Pellucidar, complete with all types of bizarre, menacing creatures, strange peoples, and alluring maidens—guaranteed to delight all Burroughs fans and a wide circle of adventure lovers. Illustrated by J. Allen St. John and P. F. Berdanier. vi + 433pp. 5⅜ x 8½.

T1051 Paperbound **$2.00**

THE PIRATES OF VENUS and LOST ON VENUS: TWO VENUS NOVELS BY EDGAR RICE BURROUGHS. Two related novels, complete and unabridged. Exciting adventure on the planet Venus with Earthman Carson Napier broken-field running through one dangerous episode after another. All lovers of swashbuckling science fiction will enjoy these two stories set in a world of fascinating societies, fierce beasts, 5000-ft. trees, lush vegetation, and wide seas. Illustrations by Fortunino Matania. Total of vi + 340pp. 5⅜ x 8½.   T1053 Paperbound **$1.75**

A PRINCESS OF MARS and A FIGHTING MAN OF MARS: TWO MARTIAN NOVELS BY EDGAR RICE BURROUGHS. "Princess of Mars" is the very first of the great Martian novels written by Burroughs, and it is probably the best of them all; it set the pattern for all of his later fantasy novels and contains a thrilling cast of strange peoples and creatures and the formula of Olympian heroism amidst ever-fluctuating fortunes which Burroughs carries off so successfully. "Fighting Man" returns to the same scenes and cities—many years later. A mad scientist, a degenerate dictator, and an indomitable defender of the right clash—with the fate of the Red Planet at stake! Complete, unabridged reprinting of original editions. Illustrations by F. E. Schoonover and Hugh Hutton. v + 356pp. 5⅜ x 8½.

T1140 Paperbound **$1.75**

THREE MARTIAN NOVELS, Edgar Rice Burroughs. Contains: Thuvia, Maid of Mars; The Chessmen of Mars; and The Master Mind of Mars. High adventure set in an imaginative and intricate conception of the Red Planet. Mars is peopled with an intelligent, heroic human race which lives in densely populated cities and with fierce barbarians who inhabit dead sea bottoms. Other exciting creatures abound amidst an inventive framework of Martian history and geography. Complete unabridged reprintings of the first edition. 16 illustrations by J. Allen St. John. vi + 499pp. 5⅜ x 8½.   T39 Paperbound **$1.85**

THREE PROPHETIC NOVELS BY H. G. WELLS, edited by E. F. Bleiler. Complete texts of "When the Sleeper Wakes" (1st book printing in 50 years), "A Story of the Days to Come," "The Time Machine" (1st complete printing in book form). Exciting adventures in the future are as enjoyable today as 50 years ago when first printed. Predict TV, movies, intercontinental airplanes, prefabricated houses, air-conditioned cities, etc. First important author to foresee problems of mind control, technological dictatorships. "Absolute best of imaginative fiction," N. Y. Times. Introduction. 335pp. 5⅜ x 8.   T605 Paperbound **$1.50**

28 SCIENCE FICTION STORIES OF H. G. WELLS. Two full unabridged novels, MEN LIKE GODS and STAR BEGOTTEN, plus 26 short stories by the master science-fiction writer of all time. Stories of space, time, invention, exploration, future adventure—an indispensable part of the library of everyone interested in science and adventure. PARTIAL CONTENTS: Men Like Gods, The Country of the Blind, In the Abyss, The Crystal Egg, The Man Who Could Work Miracles, A Story of the Days to Come, The Valley of Spiders, and 21 more! 928pp. 5⅜ x 8.

T265 Clothbound **$4.50**

THE WAR IN THE AIR, IN THE DAYS OF THE COMET, THE FOOD OF THE GODS: THREE SCIENCE FICTION NOVELS BY H. G. WELLS. Three exciting Wells offerings bearing on vital social and philosophical issues of his and our own day. Here are tales of air power, strategic bombing, East vs. West, the potential miracles of science, the potential disasters from outer space, the relationship between scientific advancement and moral progress, etc. First reprinting of "War in the Air" in almost 50 years. An excellent sampling of Wells at his storytelling best. Complete, unabridged reprintings. 16 illustrations. 645pp. 5⅜ x 8½.

T1135 Paperbound **$2.00**

SEVEN SCIENCE FICTION NOVELS, H. G. Wells. Full unabridged texts of 7 science-fiction novels of the master. Ranging from biology, physics, chemistry, astronomy to sociology and other studies, Mr. Wells extrapolates whole worlds of strange and intriguing character. "One will have to go far to match this for entertainment, excitement, and sheer pleasure . . . ," NEW YORK TIMES. Contents: The Time Machine, The Island of Dr. Moreau, First Men in the Moon, The Invisible Man, The War of the Worlds, The Food of the Gods, In the Days of the Comet. 1015pp. 5⅜ x 8. T264 Clothbound **$4.50**

BEST GHOST STORIES OF J. S. LE FANU, Selected and introduced by E. F. Bleiler. LeFanu is deemed the greatest name in Victorian supernatural fiction. Here are 16 of his best horror stories, including 2 nouvelles: "Carmilla," a classic vampire tale couched in a perverse eroticism, and "The Haunted Baronet." Also: "Sir Toby's Will," "Green Tea," "Schalken the Painter," "Ultor de Lacy," "The Familiar," etc. The first American publication of about half of this material: a long-overdue opportunity to get a choice sampling of LeFanu's work. New selection (1964). 8 illustrations. 5⅜ x 8⅜. T415 Paperbound **$1.85**

THE WONDERFUL WIZARD OF OZ, L. F. Baum. Only edition in print with all the original W. W. Denslow illustrations in full color—as much a part of "The Wizard" as Tenniel's drawings are for "Alice in Wonderland." "The Wizard" is still America's best-loved fairy tale, in which, as the author expresses it, "The wonderment and joy are retained and the heartaches and nightmares left out." Now today's young readers can enjoy every word and wonderful picture of the original book. New introduction by Martin Gardner. A Baum bibliography. 23 full-page color plates. viii + 268pp. 5⅜ x 8. T691 Paperbound **$1.45**

GHOST AND HORROR STORIES OF AMBROSE BIERCE, Selected and introduced by E. F. Bleiler. 24 morbid, eerie tales—the cream of Bierce's fiction output. Contains such memorable pieces as "The Moonlit Road," "The Damned Thing," "An Inhabitant of Carcosa," "The Eyes of the Panther," "The Famous Gilson Bequest," "The Middle Toe of the Right Foot," and other chilling stories, plus the essay, "Visions of the Night" in which Bierce gives us a kind of rationale for his aesthetic of horror. New collection (1964). xxii + 199pp. 5⅜ x 8⅜. T767 Paperbound **$1.00**

HUMOR

MR. DOOLEY ON IVRYTHING AND IVRYBODY, Finley Peter Dunne. Since the time of his appearance in 1893, "Mr. Dooley," the fictitious Chicago bartender, has been recognized as America's most humorous social and political commentator. Collected in this volume are 102 of the best Dooley pieces—all written around the turn of the century, the height of his popularity. Mr. Dooley's Irish brogue is employed wittily and penetratingly on subjects which are just as fresh and relevant today as they were then: corruption and hypocrisy of politicans, war preparations and chauvinism, automation, Latin American affairs, superbombs, etc. Other articles range from Rudyard Kipling to football. Selected with an introduction by Robert Hutchinson. xii + 244pp. 5⅜ x 8½. T626 Paperbound **$1.00**

RUTHLESS RHYMES FOR HEARTLESS HOMES and MORE RUTHLESS RHYMES FOR HEARTLESS HOMES, Harry Graham ("Col. D. Streamer"). A collection of Little Willy and 48 other poetic "disasters." Graham's funniest and most disrespectful verse, accompanied by original illustrations. Nonsensical, wry humor which employs stern parents, careless nurses, uninhibited children, practical jokers, single-minded golfers, Scottish lairds, etc. in the leading roles. A precursor of the "sick joke" school of today. This volume contains, bound together for the first time, two of the most perennially popular books of humor in England and America. Index. vi + 69pp. 5⅜ x 8. T930 Paperbound **75¢**

A WHIMSEY ANTHOLOGY, Collected by Carolyn Wells. 250 of the most amusing rhymes ever written. Acrostics, anagrams, palindromes, alphabetical jingles, tongue twisters, echo verses, alliterative verses, riddles, mnemonic rhymes, interior rhymes, over 40 limericks, etc. by Lewis Carroll, Edward Lear, Joseph Addison, W. S. Gilbert, Christina Rossetti, Chas. Lamb, James Boswell, Hood, Dickens, Swinburne, Leigh Hunt, Harry Graham, Poe, Eugene Field, and many others. xiv + 221pp. 5⅜ x 8½. T195 Paperbound **$1.25**

MY PIOUS FRIENDS AND DRUNKEN COMPANIONS and MORE PIOUS FRIENDS AND DRUNKEN COMPANIONS, Songs and ballads of Conviviality Collected by Frank Shay. Magnificently illuminated by John Held, Jr. 132 ballads, blues, vaudeville numbers, drinking songs, cowboy songs, sea chanties, comedy songs, etc. of the Naughty Nineties and early 20th century. Over a third are reprinted with music. Many perennial favorites such as: The Band Played On, Frankie and Johnnie, The Old Grey Mare, The Face on the Bar-room Floor, etc. Many others unlocatable elsewhere: The Dog-Catcher's Child, The Cannibal Maiden, Don't Go in the Lion's Cage Tonight, Mother, etc. Complete verses and introductions to songs. Unabridged republication of first editions, 2 Indexes (song titles and first lines and choruses). Introduction by Frank Shay. 2 volumes bounds as 1. Total of xvi + 235pp. 5⅜ x 8½. T946 Paperbound **$1.00**

MAX AND MORITZ, Wilhelm Busch. Edited and annotated by H. Arthur Klein. Translated by H. Arthur Klein, M. C. Klein, and others. The mischievous high jinks of Max and Moritz, Peter and Paul, Ker and Plunk, etc. are delightfully captured in sketch and rhyme. (Companion volume to "Hypocritical Helena.") In addition to the title piece, it contians: Ker and Plunk; Two Dogs and Two Boys; The Egghead and the Two Cut-ups of Corinth; Deceitful Henry; The Boys and the Pipe; Cat and Mouse; and others. (Original German text with accompanying English translations.) Afterword by H. A. Klein. vi + 216pp. 5⅜ x 8½.
T181 Paperbound **$1.00**

THROUGH THE ALIMENTARY CANAL WITH GUN AND CAMERA: A FASCINATING TRIP TO THE INTERIOR, Personally Conducted by George S. Chappell. In mock-travelogue style, the amusing account of an imaginative journey down the alimentary canal. The "explorers" enter the esophagus, round the Adam's Apple, narrowly escape from a fierce Amoeba, struggle through the impenetrable Nerve Forests of the Lumbar Region, etc. Illustrated by the famous cartoonist, Otto Soglow, the book is as much a brilliant satire of academic pomposity and professional travel literature as it is a clever use of the facts of physiology for supremely comic purposes. Preface by Robert Benchley. Author's Foreword. 1 Photograph. 17 illustrations by O. Soglow. xii + 114pp. 5⅜ x 8½.
T376 Paperbound **$1.00**

THE BAD CHILD'S BOOK OF BEASTS, MORE BEASTS FOR WORSE CHILDREN, and A MORAL ALPHABET, H. Belloc. Hardly an anthology of humorous verse has appeared in the last 50 years without at least a couple of these famous nonsense verses. But one must see the entire volumes—with all the delightful original illustrations by Sir Basil Blackwood—to appreciate fully Belloc's charming and witty verses that play so subacidly on the platitudes of life and morals that beset his day—and ours. A great humor classic. Three books in one. Total of 157pp. 5⅜ x 8.
T749 Paperbound **$1.00**

THE DEVIL'S DICTIONARY, Ambrose Bierce. Sardonic and irreverent barbs puncturing the pomposities and absurdities of American politics, business, religion, literature, and arts, by the country's greatest satirist in the classic tradition. Epigrammatic as Shaw, piercing as Swift, American as Mark Twain, Will Rogers, and Fred Allen. Bierce will always remain the favorite of a small coterie of enthusiasts, and of writers and speakers whom he supplies with "some of the most gorgeous witticisms of the English language." (H. L. Mencken) Over 1000 entries in alphabetical order. 144pp. 5⅜ x 8.
T487 Paperbound **$1.00**

THE COMPLETE NONSENSE OF EDWARD LEAR. This is the only complete edition of this master of gentle madness available at a popular price. A BOOK OF NONSENSE, NONSENSE SONGS, MORE NONSENSE SONGS AND STORIES in their entirety with all the old favorites that have delighted children and adults for years. The Dong With A Luminous Nose, The Jumblies, The Owl and the Pussycat, and hundreds of other bits of wonderful nonsense. 214 limericks, 3 sets of Nonsense Botany, 5 Nonsense Alphabets. 546 drawings by Lear himself, and much more. 320pp. 5⅜ x 8.
T167 Paperbound **$1.00**

SINGULAR TRAVELS, CAMPAIGNS, AND ADVENTURES OF BARON MUNCHAUSEN, R. E. Raspe, with 90 illustrations by Gustave Doré. The first edition in over 150 years to reestablish the deeds of the Prince of Liars exactly as Raspe first recorded them in 1785—the genuine Baron Munchausen, one of the most popular personalities in English literature. Included also are the best of the many sequels, written by other hands. Introduction on Raspe by J. Carswell. Bibliography of early editions. xliv + 192pp. 5⅜ x 8. T698 Paperbound **$1.00**

HOW TO TELL THE BIRDS FROM THE FLOWERS, R. W. Wood. How not to confuse a carrot with a parrot, a grape with an ape, a puffin with nuffin. Delightful drawings, clever puns, absurd little poems point out farfetched resemblances in nature. The author was a leading physicist. Introduction by Margaret Wood White. 106 illus. 60pp. 5⅜ x 8.
T523 Paperbound **75¢**

JOE MILLER'S JESTS OR, THE WITS VADE-MECUM. The original Joe Miller jest book. Gives a keen and pungent impression of life in 18th-century England. Many are somewhat on the bawdy side and they are still capable of provoking amusement and good fun. This volume is a facsimile of the original "Joe Miller" first published in 1739. It remains the most popular and influential humor book of all time. New introduction by Robert Hutchinson. xxi + 70pp. 5⅜ x 8½.
T423 Paperbound **$1.00**

Prices subject to change without notice.

Dover publishes books on art, music, philosophy, literature, languages, history, social sciences, psychology, handcrafts, orientalia, puzzles and entertainments, chess, pets and gardens, books explaining science, intermediate and higher mathematics, mathematical physics, engineering, biological sciences, earth sciences, classics of science, etc. Write to:

Dept. catrr.
Dover Publications, Inc.
180 Varick Street, N.Y. 14, N.Y.